Crop Productivity—Research Imperatives Revisited

An International Conference
Held at Boyne Highlands Inn, Harbor Springs, Michigan
October 13–18, 1985
and
Airlie House, Airlie, Virginia
December 11–13, 1985

Organizing Committee

Charles J. Arntzen   Stanley K. Ries
Marvin R. Lamborg   Sylvan H. Wittwer

Editors

Martin Gibbs   Carla Carlson

Citation for this book is;
Gibbs M., C. Carlson, editors, Crop Productivity—Research Impera-
tives Revisited, an international conference held at Boyne Highlands
Inn, October 13–18, 1985 and Airlie House, December 11–13, 1985

Organizers' Preface

The period 1970–1975 was one of food shortage and minimum to nonexistent world grain reserves. Agricultural decision makers, in the United States and elsewhere, recognized that greater inputs of fundamental biological science were required to increase crop productivity to keep pace with increasing food demands.

The first Crop Productivity—Research Imperatives International Conference was held in 1975. Six major areas affecting crop productivity were identified. These were: nitrogen input, carbon input, water soil and mineral input, plant protection from pests, environmental stress and plant development processes. Chairpersons and rapporteurs were selected for each group and participants were identified and invited from home and abroad. Each working group was staffed with a multidisciplinary team of agricultural and biological scientists, social scientists, and research administrators. The participants of each group received a preconference position paper written by their chairpersons which was modified and finalized during the conference. From the position paper and discussions during the conference research imperatives were derived for each group. The imperatives formed the basis of a conference proceedings which was distributed worldwide at conference expense. These imperatives, along with the National Research Council Reports, were used by the Office of Technology Assessment and the Office of Science and Technology of the White House, in recommending the establishment of the Competitive Research Grants Office (CRGO) in the U.S. Department of Agriculture. CRGO was created in 1978. Since its inception, the CRGO program office has contributed significantly to the sorely needed body of fundamental knowledge related to crop productivity.

A decade after "Crop Productivity—Research Imperatives" seemed appropriate for a reassessment of the 1975 imperatives in charting a new course for the next decade. The potential for biotechnology to provide agriculture with new products and new plant cultivars has changed the emphasis, the number and kinds of institutions engaged in agricultural research. These changes demand a reevaluation of social, political, and policy issues which govern the nature and intensity of research.

Identifying agriculture research imperatives and policies relating to their implementation constituted the major focus of the 1985 conference "Crop Productivity—Research Imperatives Revisited." A two stage conference was designed. The format followed the 1975 conference. Stage I was held October 14–18, 1985, at Boyne Highlands Inn, Harbor Springs, Michigan, the site of the meeting in 1975. Six working groups were identified and each was composed of a multidisciplinary team of agricul-

iii

tural and biological scientists, economists, administrators and research policy leaders. Plant scientists predominated.

Group 1. Genetic Improvement. Crop breeding strategies, germplasm preservation, molecular genetics, tissue culture, and gene transfer.

Group 2. Plant and Cell Physiology. Carbon and nitrogen metabolism, translocation, developmental physiology, and growth regulation.

Group 3. Rhizosphere Dynamics. Symbiotic associations, physiology of all soil microbes, biological nitrogen fixation, nutrient uptake, efficiency of soil nutrient utilization, and root structure.

Group 4. Biological Constraints. Pest control, pesticides, pesticide resistance, biotype adaptation, allelopathy, host plant resistance, and biological control agents.

Group 5. Environmental Constraints. Climate, water quality, temperature, problem soils and atmospheric pollutants.

Group 6. Production Systems. Integrated farming systems, cropping and grazing systems, tillage alternatives, short rotation forestry, and crop modeling.

Stage II was held December 11–13, 1985 at Airlie House, Airlie, Virginia. The conference format was the same as Stage I, each work group was composed of multidisciplinary teams as previously described. For Stage II administrators and social scientists were in the majority. Topics assigned for the three working groups were as follows:

Group 7. Public Policies and Institutions to Enhance Crop Productivity. The role of policy in development, transfer, and adoption of technology.

Group 8. Development of Scientific Capabilities: Human Resources and Institutions. Development of human resources and institutions for obtaining research and development goals.

Group 9. Government/Industry/University Interactions. The role of public and private institutions in development, transfer, and adoption of technology to enhance productivity.

These proceedings constitute the documents produced by both Stage I and Stage II conferences held at Boyne Highlands Inn and at Airlie House, respectively. It is hoped that they will prove useful for all who have responsibility for conducting and administrating plant science research in the decades ahead.

The organizers of the Conference express appreciation to all participants and especially the untiring efforts of those who led the discussion groups (Kenneth J. Frey, Carole P. Meredith, Lawrence E. Schrader, Gary H. Heichel, Eldor A. Paul, P. Bernard Tinker, R. James Cook, Brian A. Croft, Donald R. Nielson, James M. Davidson, Richard R. Harwood, Bernard D. Knezek, Roger L. Mitchell, Vernon W. Ruttan, Ralph W. F. Hardy, Kenneth R. Farrell, Charles M. Benbrook, and William L. Brown); the rapporteurs (Sharon R. Long, Deborah Delmer, W. Dietz Bauer, David R. MacKenzie, Andrew D. Hanson, James L. Davidson, Reah J. Battenfield, James T. Bonnen, Lawrence Busch and Richard Krasnow); the support staff (Debra Lecato, Marie Ross, Gloria

Blake, Angela Fraser, Deirdre O'Leary and Shelly Hamelink) of Michigan State University; (Dorothy McNeil) of the Battelle-Kettering Laboratory; (Mary Lou Sutton, Aida Neel, Roma DeCoteau) of the National Research Council; the Spartan Travel Agency (Jane Everson, Lawrence Legouge); Boyne Highlands Inn (Winston Findlayson); Airlie House (Viola Westlake) and the editors of the proceedings (Martin Gibbs and Carla Carlson).

The Organizing Committee

Charles J. Arntzen   Stanley K. Ries
Marvin R. Lamborg   Sylvan H. Wittwer

Editors' Preface

We willingly took on the responsibility of editing the many individual contributions and bringing them together into a cohesive publication, *Crop Productivity—Research Imperatives Revisited*. In many ways, it is similar to its predecessor of 10 years ago, *Crop Productivity—Research Imperatives*. This book, however, presents research needs in the context of newer demands on agriculture—and newer opportunities—and expands the discussion to science policy.

Crop Productivity—Research Imperatives Revisited contains the complete proceedings of the two-part conference. The smaller companion volume is a selected summary. The complete book includes: prefaces by the organizing committee and the editors; Crop Productivity—Research Imperatives: A Decade of Change, by S. H. Wittwer; conference imperatives prepared by the organizing committee; the imperatives generated by each of the nine working groups; salient statements taken by the organizing committee from the presentation of the six featured speakers; an interpretative summary written by the organizing committee; a statement bridging the two stages of the conference by Charles M. Benbrook and William L. Brown; texts of the six featured speakers; reports of the nine working groups; solicited comments from participants and concerns of the non-U.S. participants selected by the organizing committee; and the names and addresses of the participants. The summary book consists of the first six items.

We have benefited from the immeasurable help and advice of the organizing committee. We extend deep appreciation to the cochairs and rapporteurs of the working groups who remained at the conference sites to complete their papers. We are indebted to Deirdre O'Leary for dedicated assistance during the conference that formal acknowledgment cannot repay. Special thanks are due to Andrea Clemente, William Vinck, and Robert Och of Waverly Press. Additionally, we acknowledge the contributions of Nancy Robie, Brandeis University, and members of the support staffs of Michigan State University and the Board on Agriculture.

Assembling this information into book form has been a rewarding experience, and truly a joint undertaking.

The Editors

MARTIN GIBBS, Brandeis University
CARLA CARLSON, Board on Agriculture,
National Research Council

Contents

Crop Productivity—Research Imperatives: A Decade of Change

SYLVAN H. WITTWER

Today the world is awash in both grain and oil (2). Prices for each are expected to drop even lower than they are now. A decade ago both were considered in short supply and prices were going ever higher. Who, 10 years ago, would have predicted the present state of affairs? In the United States, corn, wheat, and soybeans have run the full cycle of shortages, high prices, and low reserves to overproduction, surplus stocks, and low prices. Near all-time food production records were achieved in 1984 by the United States, China, India, Indonesia, and many western European countries. In Japan and Taiwan surplus rice is posing serious problems of land diversion to other crops. China and Indonesia are witnessing some of the most impressive gains in food production in history. For the first time in several decades, China is concerned with marketing, handling, and storing of food surpluses. Within 4 years Indonesia has moved from the world's largest importer of rice to a country not only self-sufficient but with the world's largest rice reserves. Many countries in the European Economic Community are moving in as strong exporters. All are in an overproduction trap (3). The only areas of endemic food insufficiency are the Soviet bloc countries and some elements of the Middle East and South Saharan Africa.

Global food production problems have shifted from Asia to Africa, where the need for food is now most critical. Concurrent with the major improvements in food production is the continued existence of extensive malnutrition, poverty, and starvation, especially in Africa (7). There is more famine in 1985 than in 1975. Hundreds of millions of people suffer from a shortage of food and from malnutrition in a world that has, in total, more than enough to feed everyone. At no time in history has the fate of hundreds of millions of starving and malnourished people, particularly in Africa and especially in Ethiopia, been more vividly portrayed to the western world via the media. This spectacle of world impotence toward too much food in some places and too little in others is especially shocking since it is manmade (13).

A decade ago, at the time of the first Boyne Highlands Conference (1) experts predicted food shortages would remain commonplace and all-out production would be required, henceforth, to meet diminishing reserves, a rising population, and increased purchasing power. Some are now predicting that we face an age of a food glut and widespread instability.

In the face of the above dilemmas of uncertainty and instability, increased production capacity—whether that capacity is actually used—

1

must be called for. All projections indicate that, because of international competition in commodity markets, coupled with increasing competition for limited energy, water, and land resources; rising costs of labor; and demands for improved diets and population growth; more science and technology must be put into agriculture to double crop production in the next half century. This must be accompanied by improved institutions and policies, an expanded capital base, and greater entrepreneurial and managerial skills. The capacity to produce and the use of such capacity are two different things, but the capacity must be at hand. New technologies may or may not expand production in periods of shortages and their use should not be suppressed in periods of surpluses (4).

In the United States much effort has been directed toward the management of agricultural research and establishing research policies, priorities, programs, and funding. The fledgling competitive grants program of the U.S. Department of Agriculture (USDA), now in its eighth year, supports basic research in the plant sciences. It originated with the White House and was based essentially on recommendations of the first Boyne Highlands Conference of 1975, supplemented by several reports issued by the National Research Council and the Office of Technology Assessment of the U.S. Congress. Congress has, meanwhile, reacted by funding applied or problem-solving research through a "special grants" system it can control. Scientists from universities, foundations, the federal agencies, and the private sector must continue to speak with one voice because we must compete with lobbying efforts of groups to fund applied research, commodity by commodity.

During the past decade international research networks called Cooperative Research Support Programs (CRSP), with some increase in funding through Title 12, have been initiated by the U.S. Agency for International Development (AID) for field beans, cowpeas, sorghum, and millet. Current annual funding by the AID for agricultural development stands at $650 to $660 million. Similarly to the United Nations Development Program (UNDP), AID has kept pace with rising costs. Meanwhile, funding for International Agricultural Research Centers (IARCs) has jumped from $50 million to its present level of about $200 million. This increase in funding of the IARCs is one of the few cases in which support for agricultural research has exceeded the rate of inflation. Basic research has not enjoyed significant support in the mandates for the IARCs. Both in-house and external reviews have been conducted during the last 5 years at each of the IARCs to assist in establishing appropriate research priorities.

In the United States we have a Joint Council on Food and Agricultural Sciences mandated by the Food and Agricultural Act of 1977. Each year it reports priorities for research, assesses needs in the agricultural sciences, and summarizes accomplishments for the Secretary of Agriculture (5, 12). Resources for the Future, under a contract with the USDA, prepared, with the assistance of an agricultural economist and an agricultural research administrator at Michigan State University, a long-term assessment of the needs in science and technology (4). The Office of Technology Assessment has conducted numerous studies of research needs for U.S. agriculture. Meanwhile, the prominence of agriculture and agricultural research needs reached a new height with the creation of the Board on Agriculture by the National Research Council in 1983. This group responds directly to the governing board of the National Research Council. Several prestigious reports have originated from the Board on Agriculture during the past 2 years relating specifically to bioscience research in agriculture, genetic engineering in plants, and biotechnology (8–10).

One may well ask at this point, why was a second Boyne Highlands Conference to establish research imperatives required? Reflecting back to Krogmann and Key (6), concerning the conference of 1975: "It is an unfortunately rare but certainly a happy day when a broadly represent-ative group of research practitioners can identify priorities for research emphasis and see these priorities implemented in a new grants program."

Again, in 1985, as in 1975, the organization, financial support, and planning of this conference is an alliance of the USDA, state-supported agricultural units, and a private foundation engaged in both basic and problem-solving research. Further, building on the program of a decade ago, we have significant inputs from the private sector, the National Research Council, the National Science Foundation, the U.S. Depart-ment of Energy, AID, IARC, the Global Programs of UNDP, and the social sciences. Following stage I was a stage II follow-up after 7 weeks at Airlie House in the Washington, D.C., area. The second stage of the conference was an innovation to delineate policy and strategy for imple-mentation of research imperatives identified in stage I. Stage II involved key representatives of those groups responsible for federally supported plant science research that have an increased awareness of the impor-tance of policy inputs. About one-third of stage II participants partici-pated in stage I and were involved in formulating the research imperatives at this conference. It is a novel and healthy sign to have planners, research scientists, and critics working together to establish guidelines for research implementation.

The agenda for agricultural research has changed greatly during the past decade. Biotechnology has added a new dimension to the plant sciences (12). The procedures and potentials for the use of recombinant DNA and restriction enzymes to add genes to plasmids were just emerging 10 years ago. The rise and fall of biotechnology corporations and centers is an event of the past 5 years in both agriculturally developed and developing countries.

National agricultural research centers have taken on a new prominence in China with an Academy of Agricultural Science in every province, and in India with 36 agricultural research institutes in addition to 22 agri-cultural universities (11), and in the Soviet Union where Academies of

Agricultural Sciences in the various republics include not only research but advanced training responsibilities. Indonesia, Brazil, Mexico, Japan, and Thailand, to name a few others, have greatly improved their national agricultural research capabilities.

Accompanied by the drive for profit, there have been significant increases in private sector investments in biological research with the expectation that the results of basic research will find immediate application. There have also been major shifts from public to privately supported programs. These changes are occurring not only in the United States but in a host of other nations.

Crop productivity may be defined as the ratio of the value of all the outputs divided by the total of all the inputs. The concept of crop productivity implies arriving at the greatest efficiency in the use and management of resource inputs. These include land, water, energy, climate, fertilizers, pesticides, labor, and machinery. Marginal factor productivity would be the value of output from an increase of one unit of a single input assuming all other inputs remain constant. Emphasis in this conference was designed, as was the one of a decade ago, to focus on the basic biological processes that control, limit, or regulate crop productivity. A production systems working group examined alternative use of resource inputs.

Alternative production systems have surfaced from many sources and interest groups concerned with resource-sparing technologies, environmental constraints, regenerative agriculture, ecologically sustainable production systems, human health and food safety, improved nutrition, and the preservation of land, water, mineral, energy, and genetic resources. Globally it is estimated that we are annually losing 8 million hectares of land from nonagricultural conversions, 3 million hectares to soil erosion, and 2 million hectares each from desertification and toxification. The rate of extinction of genetic resources is estimated at 1000 per year and rising. In a world beset with inequities in food supplies the distributional benefits of agricultural technologies—who benefits and who loses—must be examined along with the equitability of agricultural production and consumption. Reducing operating costs and halting or even reversing losses of natural resources must be addressed.

Major shifts in farm size have occurred during the past decade in the United States, Western Europe, Japan, and China with part-time farming now predominating. This says something about the kind of research we ought to be doing. The conference provides an opportunity for scientists close to agricultural application to interact with those engaged in plant science research.

Portents of a changing climate, which may inadvertently occur from currently rising levels of atmospheric carbon dioxide coupled with the potential yield enhancement from carbon assimilation by plants on a global scale, demand some attention. These concerns were considered by working groups on environmental and biological constraints and plant and cell physiology. Progressively more cultivated land for crop production is being irrigated, and water is projected to be the most critically limiting natural resource input for future agricultural productivity. There is great potential for increasing productivity by better use of land and water resources on land currently in cultivation.

New problems and opportunities have become apparent in plant protection with greater emphasis on integrated control systems. Improving pest management without overreliance on chemicals, and minimizing off-farm environmental degradation were among the priorities addressed. The precipitous rise in numbers of biotypes resistant to pesticides makes the management of this resistance an imperative. We are also on the threshold of a new generation of plant growth regulators that have not only the potential for intensive crop management but also the dual properties of being either fungistatic or herbicidal.

Automation, sensors, new computer technologies, and innovations in communications and management, while not addressed as specific working groups, were reviewed by each working group to develop appropriate research imperatives.

Why was it necessary to revisit "Crop Productivity—Research Imperatives"? In the last decade a whole array of inputs, new and old, is changing the equation that dictates what research we do, who does it, and how it is to be carried out. In 1985 we drew together a widely based representative group of able, concerned, and knowledgeable participants from the United States and abroad to place weight and value judgment on what to do and how to direct effectively crop productivity research thrusts in the next decades.

A golden age of agricultural science is at hand. We now have a confluence of major achievements in microbiology, genetics, biochemistry, plant physiology, plant growth regulation, microbiological transformations, plant protection, environmental stresses, and intensive crop management. Achievements in these areas make progress over a wide front possible for increasing the productive capacity of crops and the stability of their output, and do it with a sustainability of natural resources. How to, first, convert all these developments into a set of research imperatives for the future and, second, get them implemented was the challenge before the participants of this International Conference on "Crop Productivity—Research Imperatives Revisited."

LITERATURE CITED

1. BROWN AWA, TC BYERLY, M GIBBS, A SAN PIETRO 1975 Crop Productivity—Research Imperatives, An International Conference Sponsored by Michigan State University, Agricultural Experiment Station and the Charles F. Kettering Foundation, Boyne Highlands, MI, October 20–24
2. INSEL B 1985 A world awash in grain. Foreign Affairs 63: 892–911
3. JOHNSON GL, CL QUANCE, eds 1972 The Overproduction Trap in US Agriculture. Johns Hopkins University Press, Baltimore

4. JOHNSON GL, SH WITTWER 1984 Agricultural technology until 2030: prospects, priorities, and policies. Michigan State University Agricultural Experiment Station, Special Report 12
5. JOINT COUNCIL ON THE FOOD AND AGRICULTURE SCIENCES 1984 Five-year plan for the food and agriculture sciences. United States Department of Agriculture, Washington, DC
6. KROGMANN DW, JL KEY 1981 The agricultural grants program. Science 213: 178–182
7. MELLOR JW 1985 The changing world food situation. International Food Policy Research Institute, Washington, DC
8. NATIONAL ACADEMY OF SCIENCES 1984 Genetic engineering of plants, agricultural research opportunities and policy concerns. Board on Agriculture/ National Research Council. National Academy Press, Washington, DC
9. NATIONAL ACADEMY OF SCIENCES 1985 New directions for bioscience research in agriculture, high-reward opportunities. Board on Agriculture/ National Research Council. National Academy Press, Washington, DC
10. NATIONAL ACADEMY OF SCIENCES 1985 Research briefings. Report of the research briefing panel on biotechnology in agriculture. Board on Agriculture/National Research Council. National Academy Press, Washington, DC
11. RAO JS 1985 Science and technology in India. Science 229: 130–134
12. SKELSEY AF 1984 Biotechnology in Agriculture—New Tools for the Oldest Science. Joint Council on Food and Agriculture Sciences. United States Department of Agriculture, Washington, DC
13. THE HUNGER PROJECT BOOK 1985 Ending Hunger: An Idea Whose Time has Come. PO Box 2000, Sparks, NV

Conference Imperatives

Issues of common concern in the discussions of the nine working groups, and other issues that transcend the bounds of any single group, emerged during the conference. These issues were identified as conference imperatives. This listing is not a priority ranking.

Interaction of Research Scientists with Innovators of Public Policy

This conference demonstrated that it is possible to bring scientists engaged in basic and applied research together with those involved with agricultural policy and jointly derive research imperatives for improving crop productivity.

Interaction between Public and Private Sectors

In the United States, both the public and private sectors are involved in agricultural research. The private sector is now much more actively engaged than in 1975. Public and private sector research activities are complementary rather than competitive. Therefore, it is obvious that much can be accomplished by greater interaction between these two groups.

Increased Collaboration of Research between Developing and Developed Countries

Although there is now appreciable collaboration between developed and developing countries in agriculture research, it is apparent that we must increase this interaction especially where major food production needs exist.

Remove Constraints for Multidisciplinary Research Both within and between Institutions in the Private and Public Sectors

The agricultural research problems of today are so complex that multidisciplinary teams are required for their solution. More effort should be made to encourage, assist, and reward such activities.

Crop Utilization Research Must Parallel That of Production Research during the Coming Decades

The many problems of overproduction may be partially ameliorated by utilization of excess production as feedstock or fine chemicals. Improved handling, storage, and processing technologies should be encouraged in developing countries. These efforts will provide alternative markets for farmers and be sparing of nonrenewable resources.

7

Sharing and Protecting Genetic Resources

There should be an international program to share genetic resources and protect these resources from being lost to future generations.

Research on Crop Plant Processes

Recent reports using the molecular and recombinant DNA technologies have provided powerful new opportunities for studying the processes of plant growth and suggested ways in which new knowledge may be utilized to increase plant productivity and nutritional quality. Therefore, research on the fundamental processes of plant growth must be supported and intensified to provide a foundation for improving crop productivity both in developed and developing countries.

Greater Private Sector Involvement Is Called for in Support of Research, Education, and Agricultural Leadership Programs Both Nationally and Internationally

Traditionally, advanced degree programs in agriculture at land grant universities have been supported primarily by state agricultural experiment stations. Advanced degree programs in the agriculturally related plant science disciplines at non-land grant universities have been supported primarily from a number of diverse sources including the federal agencies. In the past, these resources have been adequate to meet the needs of the educational institutions. The increased demand by the private sector for such personnel dictates that other mechanisms must be found to encourage greater support of the educational/training infrastructure by the private sector. There has been far less support by the private sector of educational programs in developing countries than in developed countries.

An Appropriate National Forum Is Needed for Effecting Change in Agricultural Research Planning

Based on these Crop Productivity conferences, change is most rapidly effected when dialogue occurs with all interested parties. Interested parties include natural scientists, social scientists, administrators, economists, farmers, environmentalists, and the lay public.

Professional Societies Should Play a More Effective Role in Establishing Research Priorities in Crop Productivity

Historically, individual societies have been most concerned with their parochial interests. Professional societies should interact and support national and international organizations concerned with planning research.

RESEARCH IMPERATIVES
OF
THE NINE WORKING GROUPS

Genetic Improvement

E. T. Bingham
L. Bogorad
W. L. Brown
L. Busch
R. S. Chaleff
E. H. Cobb
J. H. Cock
S. Dumford
D. N. Duvick
K. J. Frey (cochair)
S. K. Hahn
R. W. Herdt
C. E. Hess
L. R. House
C. S. Khush
C.-Y. Kuo

P. J. Larkin
A. Läuchli
C. S. Levings III
S. R. Long (rapporteur)
C. P. Meredith (cochair)
J. P. Miksche
N. Murai
K. Okuno
S. Price
W. H. Riley
V. W. Ruttan
Q.-q. Shao
K. C. Sink
M. Strauss
G. Tolla
O. C. Yoder

1. Analyze the adequacy of accessions, descriptive data, and preservation technology for existing germ plasm collections.
   a. Establish efficient sampling strategies for collecting germ plasm in natural habitats.
   b. Formulate appropriate storage methods for seeds and clonal materials.
   c. Study the seed physiology of recalcitrant species.
2. Enhance and refine strategies for assembling genes into optimal combinations by sexual methods.
   a. Develop alternative methods for economical and large-scale propagation of hybrid cultivars in crops for which this is not currently feasible.
   b. Elucidate the fundamental nature of heterosis.
   c. Investigate fundamental aspects of plant reproductive biology.
   d. Establish the nature and frequency of coadapted gene complexes.
   e. Determine numbers of genes affecting multigenic traits.
3. Analyze the organization, stability, and instability of plant genomes.
   a. Pursue molecular analysis to facilitate gene mapping at the chromosomal and individual gene levels.
   b. Characterize chromosome organization and behavior.
   c. Analyze the molecular processes underlying genome replication, repair, and recombination.
   d. Characterize genome variability at the molecular level.
   e. Understand the molecular and cellular bases for somaclonal variation.

  f. Analyze and use transposable elements to study and manipulate plant genomes.
4. Develop, for all crops, workable and efficient technologies for the introduction of novel genetic material and regeneration of functional transformed plants.
  a. Identify structural and regulatory genes that govern unique and superior genetic traits.
  b. Develop efficient transformation methods for all major crops.
  c. Develop methods for the regeneration of plants from protoplasts in all major crops.
  d. Develop knowledge necessary for manipulation of organellar genomes.
5. Develop the fundamental knowledge necessary for the effective genetic manipulation of desirable crop phenotypes.
  a. Investigate the molecular basis of the interaction between crop plants and their pests, pathogens, and symbionts.
  b. Investigate the fundamental basis of plant response to abiotic stresses.
  c. Establish rapid and simple evaluation and diagnostic tests for detecting resistance and tolerance to biotic and abiotic stresses and for evaluating plant composition.
  d. Investigate the genetic control of assimilate production and partitioning.

Plant and Cell Physiology

W. A. BRUN
P. J. DAVIES
D. DELMER (rapporteur)
D. R. DILLEY
R. F. EVERT
J. A. FLORE
V. R. FRANCESCHI
M. GIBBS
R. HANGARTER
G. H. HEICHEL (cochair)
H. W. HELDT
A. N. LAKSO
A. LÄUCHLI
C. J. NELSON
D. O'LEARY

D. R. ORT
J. W. PATRICK
M. M. PEET
R. RABSON
J. RAWSON
M. REPORTER
S. K. RIES
L. E. SCHRADER (cochair)
T. L. SETTER
J. E. TAVARES
J. THOMAS
R. J. THOMAS
N. E. TOLBERT
V. WALBOT
R. WYSE

1. Strengthen support for fundamental research on metabolism, enzymology, protein chemistry, and plant structure, function, and development.
2. Reduce energetically wasteful processes.
3. Determine the regulatory factors (*e.g.* hormones) that activate the genome to direct DNA replication, cell division, and differentiation.
4. Analyze the changes in gene expression controlling floral induction and development.
5. Identify the metabolic processes and essential gene products controlling plant senescence, and the development of function of sinks.
6. Enhance the partitioning of desired organic assimilates and plant nutrients into harvestable components.
   a. Determine the pathway and mechanisms of assimilate transfer between cells to identify key regulatory sites.
   b. Identify the gene products that determine the quantity and composition of desired assimilates accumulated in economic yield.
   c. Determine physical (*e.g.* turgor) and chemical (*e.g.* hormone) mechanisms of interorgan communication and competition for scarce assimilates.
7. Improve plant performance in unfavorable environments.
   a. Identify multigene traits controlling susceptibility, tolerance, and adaptation to environmental stress.
   b. Determine the cellular and molecular mechanisms by which plants transduce environmental stimuli to regulate metabolism and development.
8. Modify enzymatic activities and intermediary metabolism to control

12

the synthesis of desirable and undesirable plant products and to maximize detoxification of xenobiotics.

9. Exploit plant-microbe interactions to enhance nitrogen fixation.
10. Identify the physiological and biochemical determinants of metabolism, growth, and development essential to the genetic improvement of crop productivity and quality.
    a. Exploit existing genetic variations as a tool to investigate the genetic bases of physiological traits.
    b. Create genetic variation for the physiological and biochemical analysis of traits essential to crop productivity and quality.
    c. Determine the importance of genome fluidity in plant metabolism, growth, and development.

Rhizosphere Dynamics

W. D. BAUER (rapporteur)
G. J. BETHLENFALVAY
B. B. BOHLOOL
A. CLARKE
W. R. EVANS
A. D. M. GLASS
T. L. GRAHAM
P. M. GRESSHOFF
R. D. HAUCK
C. W. HENDRICKS
D. L. KEISTER
M. R. LAMBORG

I. F. MARTIN
J. A. MENGE
E. A. PAUL (cochair)
D. A. PHILLIPS
R. RENNIE
S. E. SMITH
S. M. SMITH
A. J. M. SMUCKER
G. STACEY
J. TIEDJE
P. B. TINKER (cochair)
J. F. WITTY

1. Improve crop productivity through understanding the basic processes of root growth
   a. Characterize plant factors that govern root growth and development and influence the rhizosphere.
   b. Resolve uncertainties regarding root anatomy and function.
   c. Define the mechanism of organic and inorganic nutrient allocation in the plant and thereby enhance efficiency of nutrient utilization.
   d. Characterize microbe-root interactions that result in the modification of root development and function.
2. Increase the efficiency of utilization of nutrients in the soil and plant.
   a. Understand plant regulation of inorganic nutrient uptake as it affects tissue composition and crop nutritional quality.
   b. Exploit genetic diversity in ion acquisition to optimize utilization of soil resources.
   c. Develop effective biological and chemical regulators to manage specific nutrient transformations.
   d. Develop methods for controlled mineralization of soil organic nutrients, to ensure their availability at peak plant growth periods.
   e. Use rhizosphere processes to improve soil structure and prevent erosion.
3. Enhance symbiotic function and control root diseases through a better understanding of plant-microbe interactions.
   a. Take advantage of plant and microbial genetic diversity to make more efficient use of soil resources.
   b. Characterize the nature and effects of chemical signals exchanged between plant roots and microorganisms.
   c. Define the essential components for cell-cell interactions and specificity in pathogenic and symbiotic processes.
   d. Study the physiology and biochemistry of plant-microbe interactions to improve symbiotic function.

4. Improve plant productivity by altering the soil and rhizosphere population through (i) introduction of novel organisms, and (ii) crop and soil management.
   a. Define the genetic, biochemical, and environmental factors contributing to the competitive success of desired organisms in the root environment.
   b. Define factors important to the growth, function, and decline of microorganisms in soil.
   c. Develop methods for *in situ* examination of processes and population interactions in the root environment.
   d. Improve techniques for the culture, introduction, and establishment of desired populations in soil.
   e. Understand genetic exchange among engineered and native microbial populations, and their stability.

Biological Constraints

C. J. ARNTZEN
A. C. BELLOTTI
O. C. BURNSIDE
R. J. COOK (cochair)
B. A. CROFT (cochair)
E. C. CRUZE
C. R. CURTIS
C. J. DELP
M. J. DOVER
A. H. ELLINGBOE
D. W. FRECKMAN
R. E. FRISBIE
R. L. HOUTZ
M. A. HOY

M. KOGAN
H. M. LeBARON
P. J. McCALL
D. R. MacKENZIE
 (rapporteur)
J. R. MILLER
Z. M. NYIIRA
S. R. RADOSEVICH
R. T. ROUSH
A. D. ROVIRA
K. N. SAXENA
A. H. SCHAUER
M. N. SCHROTH
B. S. VINSON
R. L. WAMPLE

1. Improve crop health through better understanding and management of crop patterns, mixtures and rotations, plant residues, and soil.
   a. Investigate the effects of conservation tillage on soil properties and pest population dynamics.
   b. Determine the influence and mechanisms of crop patterns, mixtures, and rotations on the population dynamics and genetic diversity of pests, and their natural enemies.
   c. Determine the mechanisms by which environmental stresses predispose crops to pest damage and disease initiation.
   d. Elucidate mechanism(s) of crop-weed competition and allelopathy.
2. Maximize the capacity of plants to resist pest attack through acquisition and application of knowledge of biochemical and physical processes and genetic determinants.
   a. Determine the genes and gene products of both plants and their pests that confer resistance.
   b. Identify the molecular signals in host-pathogen interactions.
   c. Elucidate arthropod/plant communication systems and metabolic interactions involved in plant resistance.
   d. Investigate the biosynthesis and mobilization of secondary plant products and metabolic costs of plant defense mechanisms.
   e. Design gene deployment schemes to manage genetic diversity for cultivated crops and to ameliorate pest problems.
   f. Identify the effects of plant defense mechanisms on biological control agents.
3. Develop new or more effective biological controls of pests using classical methods and new biotechnologies.
   a. Determine the chemical basis of physiological and behavioral interactions between plant pests and their natural enemies and use this information to improve biological control.

   b. Improve biological control agents by selection and molecular genetic techniques to enhance their efficiency in cropping systems.

   c. Identify key factors regulating the colonization of plant surfaces by microorganisms capable of biological control of plant pests.

   d. Develop methods for identification of biological control agents and their associated target pests.

   e. Develop an information base to predict the fate and effect of genetically engineered organisms in the environment.

   f. Develop technology for culturing, rearing, delivering, and evaluating biocontrol agents under field conditions.

   g. Develop methods to integrate biological control agents and pesticides in agricultural systems.

4. Develop new chemicals (pesticides) for pest control, along with improved and safer methods for their sustained use compatible with crop production strategies.

   a. Develop pesticides that control all or most components of the pest complex of a crop with minimal effects on beneficial species.

   b. Develop pesticide-resistant crop plants and beneficial species to minimize nontarget effects.

   c. Identify mechanisms of chemical control in pests and develop novel chemicals from natural or synthetic sources to exploit these mechanisms.

   d. Quantify the dynamics of pesticide interaction with crops, pests, natural enemies and other nontarget species to achieve increased effectiveness and selectivity.

   e. Develop diagnostic monitoring tools for resistant organisms and strategies to manage resistance to prolong pesticide effectiveness.

   f. Develop improved pesticide application techniques and delivery systems.

   g. Improve the quantification and management of the fate of pesticides in the environment, including processes for avoiding, reducing, or detoxifying them.

5. Improve integrated pest management (IPM) programs by enhancing data collection and assessment, decision supports, and system design.

   a. Develop improved techniques to diagnose and quantify pest incidence and severity.

   b. Define dynamic pest control thresholds for individual species and multiple-pest complexes.

   c. Develop methodologies based on artificial intelligence to improve linkages between pest management strategies and other crop production practices for more efficient and effective pest control.

   d. Conduct research to allow IPM programs to adapt to shifts in crop production factors, in order to avoid loss of effective pest control.

   e. Determine the attainable yields of crops and quantify the factors that limit those yields.

   f. Incorporate concepts of community ecology into IPM systems through modeling and experimentation.

Environmental Constraints

L. H. ALLEN, JR.
J. M. DAVIDSON (cochair)
K. T. ERH
E. H. EVERSON
A. D. HANSON (rapporteur)
R. L. HEATH
W. W. HECK
E. T. KANEMASU
M. M. LUDLOW
T. MAKI
D. R. NIELSON (cochair)
J. T. RITCHIE

T. ROSSWALL
V. W. RUTTAN
M. C. SHANNON
D. A. SLEPER
B. A. STEWART
K. K. TANJI
N. C. TURNER
G. UEHARA
R. L. WAMPLE
F. P. W. WINTERINGHAM
S. H. WITTWER

1. Develop a thorough understanding of the physiological effects of and responses to environmental stress on plants in order to manipulate genetically crops for greater adaptation to environmental constraints.
   a. Understand the mechanisms underlying stress resistance, stress injury, and the efficiency with which environmental resources are used in growth.
   b. Determine for particular environments the physiological characteristics that help the plant avoid or tolerate stress.
   c. Demonstrate the importance of physiological characteristics considered to be adaptive before recommending them as select criteria.
   d. Manipulate the genetic composition of plants to incorporate desired traits, using appropriate technology.
2. Develop a thorough understanding of how environmental modifications can minimize constraints on crop productivity.
   a. Determination of the way plants respond to environmental constraints and how these affect crop growth in the field.
   b. Evaluate the effect of modifying the root and aerial environment to mitigate the impact of stresses.
   c. Develop cultural practices and crop management systems which mitigate responses to stress.
3. Determine the impacts of agricultural practices on the environment.
   a. Quantify the rates of erosion and depletion of soil organic matter as a function of agricultural management practices.
   b. Determine the extent of depletion and contamination of surface water and ground water by nutrients, salinity, pesticide residues, and trace elements.
   c. Quantify gaseous compounds from agroecosystems that cause deleterious impacts on the atmosphere and climate.

4. Understand the impacts of anthropogenic chemicals on agroecosystems.
   a. Determine direct and indirect effects of increasing atmospheric carbon dioxide on agroecosystems.
   b. Assess the effects of photochemically produced ozone on agroecosystems.
   c. Determine the effects of acidic deposition (acid rain), heavy metals, and other atmospheric deposits on agroecosystems.
   d. Determine the effects of chemicals in surface water, ground water used as irrigation water for agroecosystems.
5. Develop alternative cropping and resource management strategies to minimize environmental constraints.

Production Systems

C. E. ALLEN
R. J. BATTENFIELD
  (corapporteur)
C. M. BENBROOK
D. F. BEZDICEK
J. R. BLACK
J. L. BREWBAKER
V. R. CARANGAL
J. L. DAVIDSON (corapporteur)
S. EFFENDI
J. R. FISCHER
R. G. GAST
J. HALLIDAY
R. R. HARWOOD (cochair)
O. B. HESTERMAN

G. L. JOHNSON
J. F. KELLY
B. D. KNEZEK (cochair)
W. LIEBHARDT
R. E. McDOWELL
R. S. RAUSCHKOLB
C. B. RUMBURG
S. SADJAD
S. SRIWATANAPONGSE
J. A. STEWART
E. H. VAUSE
R. D. VOSS
I. E. WIDDERS
S. C. WIGGANS
J. WILLARD

The greatest need in agricultural research is to know the relationship between the biological parts of the production system.

1. Design cropping pattern alternatives which increase productivity and optimize nutrient cycling and use, minimize soil loss, and reduce pressure from insect pests, weeds, and pathogens.
   a. Research alternative rotations to use more completely the growing season.
   b. Define and measure efficiencies of rotation.
   c. Develop nontraditional methods, such as overseeding, to increase cropping intensity.
   d. Study the efficiencies of tropical intercrop production systems.
   e. Identify and genetically improve plant species that are rarely cultivated but which can be usefully incorporated into cropping systems.
   f. Base genetic improvement programs on the criteria that "fit" crops into their intended production systems.
2. Investigate and promote techniques (ranging from cropping practices and cultivars to postharvest handling and storage methods) for farms, especially in developing countries, to provide a year-round supply of nutritious feed for livestock.
   a. Identify and develop varieties of leguminous, dual-purpose crops that can produce high quality food and fodder.
   b. Improve the quality of crop residues as well as grain yield in breeding programs.

3. Promote the use of multipurpose trees in production systems.
   a. Identify agroforestry systems with nitrogen-fixing perennial species that optimize the provision of nitrogen and other nutrients to permit sustainable, high level, crop production.
   b. Identify tree and crop species suitable for alley-cropping and agroforestry combinations, and optimize their production in such systems.
   c. Establish agroforestry systems that maximize the production of high quality animal feeds.
   d. Identify productive cultivars of food trees that are specifically adapted to small-farm cropping systems.
   e. Develop crop production and harvest systems that maximize fuelwood production as well as food and fodder.
4. Investigate the effects of cropping practices on changes in the physical, chemical, and biological properties of soils.
   a. Determine the nutrient requirements of new crops and cultivars.
   b. Develop more effective methods for determining the levels of available nutrients in soil.
   c. Develop management strategies that will increase the efficiency of water and nutrient use and avoid water pollution.
   d. Select crops and management practices to move nutrients upward in the soil profile.
   e. Develop reliable methods for estimating rates of nitrogen fixation in cropping systems.
   f. Assess quantitatively the different ways by which legumes increase productivity in cropping systems.
   g. Study the interactions of soil fauna and tillage in nutrient cycling.
   h. Examine how cropping systems affect rhizosphere activities.
   i. Determine whether alternative cropping patterns influence the proportion of soil organic matter in the labile phase.
   j. Investigate tillage effects on soil properties.
   k. Develop crop genotypes and cultural practices to counter and improve unfavorable soil acidity and salinity.
5. Evaluate and devise innovative methods for processing and handling the biological products of the cropping systems.
6. Adapt emerging engineering technologies and tools that will help in measuring and understanding production systems.
   a. Develop sensors to improve the scientist's ability to understand and the producer's ability to manage crucial biological and physical processes.
   b. Develop "intelligent" machines to perform repetitive, hazardous, or precision tasks for scientists and producers.
7. Develop microcomputer-based models to improve the design and management of production systems.
   a. Develop management models to assist farmers in agronomic decision making.

b. Develop management models that integrate crop and animal production.
c. Develop models that use environmental and biological data to predict the suitability of any crop or cropping system in a given environment.
d. Develop and incorporate crop growth models into management models.
e. Develop and maintain appropriate data bases to provide the information necessary for the development of accurate models.

Public Policies and Institutions to Enhance Crop Productivity

G. W. ANDREWS
R. BAHADUR
C. M. BENBROOK (cochair)
A. R. BERTRAND
T. BEZUNEH
W. L. BROWN (cochair)
A. R. COOKE
B. A. CROFT
P. R. DAY
J. R. FISCHER
T. H. FOSTER
G. H. HEICHEL
H. H. LEPKOWSKI
W. LEPKOWSKI

C. P. MEREDITH
J. P. MIKSCHE
Z. M. NYIIRA
R. RABSON
J. RIFKIN
D. STANSBURY
D. G. STRAUSS
M. SUN
L. TANGLEY
P. B. TINKER
E. H. VAUSE
R. D. WEAVER
S. H. WITTWER
J. ZINN

1. International cooperation.
   a. Develop mechanisms to assure the continued conservation of genetic resources, and the free exchange of germ plasm resources among countries, national and international organizations, and the public and private sectors.
   b. Encourage support of international agricultural research by the United States, and encourage scientific collaboration in breeding and germ plasm conservation programs.
   c. Encourage developed countries in their continued collaborations with the World Bank, United Nations' agencies, and other multinational organizations and countries in fostering the safe and economical use of pesticides around the world.
   d. Improve the use of routinely collected information regarding global agricultural production accomplishments and trends.
   e. Facilitate scientific interchange, including sharing of genetic resources, with the Soviet Union, China, and other centrally planned economies.
2. Adjusting priorities.
   a. Identify and support higher priority work, even in a climate of fiscal austerity (lower priority work should receive less funding, even when budgets are growing).
   b. Continuously evaluate public sector research priorities to assure that public dollars are meeting needs.
   c. Promote competitively funded activities as the primary vehicle for drawing new scientific talent into basic agricultural research. Define scientific research needs broadly; narrow or specific definitions should be avoided.

   d. Authorize special grants when mission-oriented research programs
      can be pursued most efficiently on a regional and multidisciplinary
      basis.
   e. Encourage a higher degree of flexibility for administrators of pub-
      licly funded agricultural research in carrying out cost-saving ad-
      ministrative initiatives.
   f. Establish an improved mechanism to:
      (i) Advise U.S. Department of Agriculture (USDA) and other
          agencies on agricultural research priorities.
      (ii) Facilitate the exchange of information throughout federal
           programs and state agricultural experiment stations.
      (iii) Compile and monitor information on federal and state agri-
            cultural research expenditures, research in the private sector,
            and other indicators of the health of agricultural research in
            the United States. (Such a mechanism could be a new council
            or committee, a consolidation of existing committees, or it
            could evolve from existing informal channels of communica-
            tion.)
3. Multidisciplinary research.
   a. Encourage scientist-initiated multidisciplinary programs by:
      (i) Identifying research problems according to time frame and
          funding sources.
      (ii) Administrative recognition of key researchers who can cata-
           lyze and focus the activities of multidisciplinary groups.
      (iii) Encouraging individuals in departments to participate in mul-
            tidisciplinary projects while retaining affiliation with discipli-
            nary units.
   b. Analyze past and present multidisciplinary research efforts to
      discover the administrative factors that contribute—positively and
      negatively—to multidisciplinary research.
   c. Initiate a special effort, with leadership from the National Associ-
      ation of State Universities and Land Grant Colleges, to overcome
      impediments to multidisciplinary research within academia.
   d. Make available new sources of funds for multidisciplinary research
      in USDA's competitive and special grants programs, particularly
      in areas where no support has been available—several stage I
      imperatives should be included.
   e. Fund new mission-oriented research centers or institutes—both
      with and without walls—through competitive grants for periods of
      several years.
   f. Facilitate the integration of agricultural objectives with health,
      environmental, and conservation goals and encourage further re-
      search on water resources, efficient use of agrichemicals, alterna-
      tive farming, and the environmental impacts of genetically engi-
      neered organisms.

Development of Scientific Capabilities: Human Resources and Institutions

J. T. BONNEN (rapporteur)
M. E. CARTER
D. N. DUVICK
J. P. ECKEBIL
R. J. HILDRETH
W. E. HUFFMAN
G. L. JOHNSON
J. F. KELLY
D. T. KINGSBURY
M. R. LAMBORG

D. R. MACKENZIE
I. F. MARTIN
R. L. MITCHELL (cochair)
N. PERLAS
R. RABSON
V. W. RUTTAN (cochair)
D. STANSBURY
N. D. STROMMEN
D. A. SUTER
J. W. TANNER

Research Imperatives

1. Complementarity between graduate education and agricultural research.
   a. Analyze alternative structures that would promote multidisciplinary research and strengthen complementarity between agricultural research and graduate education.
2. Research on human capital development.
   a. Conduct research on the demographic characteristics of the labor force in order to adjust educational, training, recreational promotion and retention policies.
3. Institutions and policy.
   a. Analyze the implications of major changes in technology for the institutions of agriculture.
   b. Analyze the effectiveness of the articulation and coordination of research and education functions and institutions that have in the past, or might in the future, contribute to the productivity and social performance of agriculture.
   c. Analyze the complementarities between different types of research and sources of productivity that need to be understood for effective research and development (R&D) resource allocation and for social investments in agriculture. An inadequate understanding of these relationships continues to bias social priorities and R&D policy for agriculture.
4. Policy and ethics.
   a. Research the performance of public decision making institutions to improve their structures and the decision rules used in regulating input use, environmental pollution, and food chain contamination involved in crop production.
   b. Research acquisition, storage and retrieval systems for furnishing both value-free and value-knowledge to use to improve public decisions bearing on crop productivity.

25

    c. Expand basic research in the social sciences and humanities to improve the measurement of nonmonetary and monetary values involved in assessing crop production technologies.

    d. Research on optimal public policies involving such crop production issues as (i) ground water pollution, (ii) surface water pollution, (iii) food chain contamination, (iv) redistributive aspects of improved crop production activities, and (v) the employment impacts of labor saving crop production technologies.

    e. Do basic research on alternative decision rules for dealing with the gains and losses which may be encountered in (i) releasing genetically engineered organisms into the environment, (ii) controlling pollutants, (iii) controlling food chain contaminants, particularly carcinogenic, (iv) destabilization of food supplies, and (v) establishing crop production systems for climatically unstable environments.

    f. Research alternative nonmarket programs and policies for controlling short-term overcommitment of resources to crop production while assuming the substantial increases in crop production capacity needed in the long run.

    g. Research private and public institutional and physical infrastructure changes needed to adjust to changing crop production technologies.

    h. Develop skills in using iterative/interactive processes to clarify value and value free knowledge and decision rules in making policy and other decisions.

    i. Research the animal rights issue as it affects the demand for crops.

    j. Research the ethical issues involved in alternative ways of organizing the relationship between public sector crop productivity research organizations and the private sector agribusinesses.

5. Gains and losses from different rates of technical change.

    a. Research is needed on how changes in the economic and technological environment in which they live and work that motivate farmers, consumers, and governments in the United States and elsewhere in the world. A much better understanding of how the world agricultural economy operates and how individual farmers, processors, and consumers behave within it is required.

6. Procedure management of new technologies.

    a. Development of expert systems, use of artificial intelligence and natural language is needed and will be a natural analog to cropping systems research.

    b. Design cropping pattern alternatives which increase productivity and optimize nutrient cycling and use, minimize soil loss, and reduce pressure from insect pests, weeds, and pathogens.

    c. Adapt emerging engineering technologies and tools that will help in measuring and understanding production systems and new-generation instruments that will enable producers to monitor and measure accurately essential dynamic activities related to crop production, providing instantaneous and reliable information to be used in decision support systems.

d. Develop microcomputer-based models to improve the design and management of production systems.

Policy Imperatives

1. Professional and financial incentives.
    a. The Congress should establish a federal scientific research classification system in which salary schedules would not be constrained by the level of congressional salaries. An adjustment upward of 20 to 30% at the upper grade would be necessary to bring federal salary levels to a competitive level.
    b. Ways should be sought to give more adequate recognition, both within the university and within the science community, for outstanding professional achievement. This includes endowed chairs, endowed programs, and professional achievement awards.
    c. The private sector should explore, with the universities and the Agricultural Research Service (ARS), means of institutional methods of strengthening staff development and provide a more effective communication between public and private sector scientists.
2. Complementarity between graduate education and agricultural research.
    a. Reduction in agricultural research funding may have unforeseen impacts on graduate programs in agriculture vis-à-vis recruiting and placement. There are, however, reforms in graduate training that should be considered. Graduate student projects within a college might be intentionally clustered to promote multidisciplinary research and greater educational benefit. Such efforts are within the control of the departmental administration and cooperating faculty.
3. Multidisciplinary and interdisciplinary training.
    a. It is important that professional, financial and administrative incentives be restructured to facilitate the implementation of those multidisciplinary and interdisciplinary research activities that can contribute to the advancement of science and of technology development.
4. Training and retraining of established scientists and administrators.
    a. Establish opportunities for 3- to 6-month visiting investigatorships.
    b. Senior investigator fellowships for 1 to 2 years of study in an established laboratory for the purpose of making major adjustments in scientific activities.
    c. A class of awards modeled on the Presidential Young Investigator awards but directed to the established investigators would assist in linking university and industry scientists for the purpose of cross fertilization.

    d. Universities and research institutes should be more active in open-
ing their facilities to visiting industrial scientists who return for
new training or research facilities.

5. Institutions and policy.

    a. The rules for allocation of federal agricultural research and edu-
cation expenditures should be redesigned to compensate states for
the losses of benefits from their R&D and education investments
that spill over to other states.

    b. Reform the agricultural commodity, credit and tax policies, pro-
grams, and institutions that create incentives for periodic overinvestment of resources in crop production.

6. Policy and ethics.

    a. Systematically teach agricultural ethics for agriculturists whose
work affects crop productivity. This should be taught as applicable
to both private and public decision making.

    b. Systematically expose biological and physical scientists working
on crop productivity to at least the rudiments of public choice
procedures and methods so that they may better deal with the
public choices important for crop productivity.

    c. Arrest the deterioration of public information systems supplying
information on crop yields, acreages, input uses, expenditures
incomes, quality, processing marketing, exports, and utilization.

7. The United States in the global agricultural research system.

    a. It is essential that effective agricultural research capacity be estab-
lished for each commodity and each resource of economic significance in each agroclimate region of the world by the first decade
of the next century.

    b. The United States needs to develop an improved capacity to screen
the world for the knowledge and technology that can contribute to
U.S. crop productivity.

8. The physical infrastructure and support facilities for agricultural
research.

    a. It is essential that centralized research-support functions be given
a high priority for current or future funding.

    b. Maintain a strong federal/state research partnership.

    c. Support and encourage industry/state/federal research initiatives.

    d. Foster and support programs developed by individual states, coun-
tries, or institutions which have applications on an international
scale.

    e. The independent maintenance of centralized data bases is essential
to the long-range productivity of a wide range of research programs.
Existing bases should not be eliminated without in-depth evaluation.

9. Producer management of new technologies.

    a. Curricula at the high school and college level need to be developed
and courses offered to prepare production managers for use of

computers and management science toward a systems approach to decision making.

b. Current production managers will need training and retraining for the utilization of such systems decision making. The rapidly expanding information technology of artificial intelligence (expert systems and natural language) approaches are just beginning to be available. We have a unique opportunity to plan together the ways in which these new approaches can be most effectively delivered to production managers.

c. The selection and provision of the hardware to support these more complex decision approaches will call for expanded comparative information from unbiased, nonproprietary sources. The development of software can very possibly be a joint effort between industry and universities, with appropriate understandings developed through copyright. A key dimension will be the capacity to update rapidly this material in what promises to be a very fast changing information environment.

d. Decisions on how the user will pay, either for stand-alone systems or those provided by input suppliers as part of a total supply package, will very probably be decisions that are best made in the market place. University extension and research can play a role in developing model systems and education production managers on the range of decision assisting systems and their characteristics that are available.

Government/Industry/University Interactions

G. W. ANDREWS
R. BARKER
J. E. BURRIS
L. BUSCH (rapporteur)
L. J. BUTLER
F. BUTTEL
E. H. COBB
J. M. DAVIDSON
C. J. DELP
S. DUMFORD
K. R. FARRELL (cochair)
K. J. FREY
R. W. F. HARDY (cochair)

R. D. HAUCK
G. H. HEICHEL
R. KRASNOW (rapporteur)
P. F. O'CONNELL
R. PATTERSON
E. A. PAUL
J. RAWSON
S. K. RIES
L. E. SCHRADER
W. A. STILES, JR.
M. SUN
G. TOLLA
A. TONJES
H. VON AMSBERG

1. University, industry, and government collaboration.
   a. Clarify and establish *ab initio* the roles of each actor regarding the division of responsibilities concerning the generation of new science and technology and their transfer from the research institutions to ultimate use.
   b. Examine past and existing efforts at collaborative work with a view toward ascertaining factors that contribute to success or failure.
   c. Allow for and encourage experimentation with a range of new and novel organizational and institutional arrangement, recognizing that some of these experiences will be unsuccessful.
   d. Develop acceptable guidelines for collaboration among the parties carrying out joint activities.
   e. State explicitly and openly the rules under which collaborative enterprises are undertaken, so as to allay public fears of collusion, conflicts of interest, or other activities not in the public interest.
   f. Determine existing constraints to collaborative efforts among the three parties, and take steps toward their removal.
   g. Make a sustained, broad reaching effort at removing barriers and devising new means for personnel exchanges among the three parties.
2. An integrative approach.
   a. Integrate biological, environmental, social, and economic factors and dimensions into decision-making systems that guide crop productivity research and technology transfer.
3. Technology transfer: constraints and initiatives.
   a. Establish new means and refine existing means for the transfer of

30

technology among all components of the agricultural community with due concern for the public interest.

   (i) Establish guidelines for government/industry/university relations.

   (ii) Establish the mechanisms that will promote multidisciplinary research in the plant sciences for the purpose of facilitating technology transfer.

   (iii) Develop further incentives for industry participation in the technology transfer process.

   (iv) Recognize the different needs of large and small farmers in the technology transfer process.

   (v) Recognize the different needs of large and small input supply and output processing firms.

   (vi) Improve the mechanisms for farmer and general public input into research and policy decision making.

   (vii) Establish publicly owned, professionally managed, "contained" sites for field evaluation of biotechnology products.

4. International considerations.

   a. Promote activities and policies to foster collaboration between universities, governments, and especially private industry to meet long-term security needs for food, fiber, and fuel in developing countries.

Interpretative Summary

In a two-stage effort, conferees at this international conference focused first on the basic biological processes responsible for the magnitude and dependability of crop productivity and on the identification of research imperatives holding the greatest promise for increased stability and productivity. Those attending the second stage focused on the derivation of policy for implementing these imperatives. Stage I was patterned after a conference, of similar initiatives, title, objectives, organizers, editor, and sponsors, that occurred one decade earlier. Added dimensions in 1985 were support from and participation of representatives of the private sector and greater international involvement. An innovation in conference programming for 1985 was a second stage designed to bring imperatives derived by biological scientists at stage I to stage II, made up of social scientists from academia, the government, and the private sectors, along with research administrators and those knowledgeable of policy issues and channels for implementation.

Economic conditions and crop productivity challenges in 1975 were dramatically different from those in 1985. In 1975 there were food shortages, high prices, low reserves, and goals for all-out production, whereas in 1985 there were in developed countries mountains of surplus food, low prices, large reserves, global gluts, and efforts in production controls. Globally, there was more than enough food for everyone except for purchasing power and distribution. Within this setting there was a political environment (passing of the Gramm-Rudman-Hollings bill December 12 during the stage II conference) that potentially could mandate significant cuts or reallocation of financial support for research. This was a political reality not anticipated by the participants and proved to be a challenge and opportunity for developing an agenda of research policy with appropriate biological and social science inputs along with institutional structures and policies for implementation. Thus the conference became a timely source for guidance in maintaining essential national and international programs and at the same time building high priority new ones during a period of unprecedented budget cutbacks and financial retrenchment.

Specific research imperatives for crop productivity originated from each of six working groups in stage I, from the three working groups in stage II, from solicited comments, and from major issues which became apparent to the organizers and which are designated as conference imperatives. Additional insights relative to research priorities and future directions for agricultural research were provided by speakers at both stages of the conference from which salient statements have been assembled. Contrasts in research agendas within a decade are summarized in the introductory document "Crop Productivity—Research Imperatives

Revisited: A Decade of Change." Current concepts of productivity are discussed which now focus on resource sparing technologies resulting in reductions in inputs, costs, and enhancements of outputs, with an emphasis on developing technologies which will increase capacities to produce and which are within the managerial skills and financial resources of the producers (farmers). Biotechnology, a communication revolution, and automation are new dimensions of crop productivity characteristic of the 1980s.

The Resource Base

Global problems relate to the sustainability and productivity of agriculture, along with the adequacy and dependability of our food supplies. They are associated with changes in the nature of land surfaces; the abundance, availability, distribution, and quality of water resources; fossil fuel resources; and changes in the gaseous and particulate composition of the atmosphere. There are also limitations for the collection, conservation, storage and international exchange of germ plasm. This is especially true for plants that are clonally propagated, coupled with an increasing rate of extinction of wild species.

Land

Never has such a total set of competitive forces been unleashed on global land resources essential for future crop productivity. Yet, this is coupled with a marvelous opportunity to take corrective measures to conserve and improve our soil. With a surplus of almost all crops and declining public support for farm subsidies, there is increasing support for the improvement and conservation of natural resources. We must designate highly erosive, fragile, and shallow cropland for soil-improving crops and practices, grazing, wood fuel production, reserves for wildlife, and for recreation. Such measures and land diversions would simultaneously conserve and improve soil, land, and water resources, and bring agricultural production down to a level where food prices may again be profitable to the farmer and acceptable to the consumer. Problem soils (salinity, alkalinity, aluminum toxicity) constitute a significant impediment to current crop productivity, especially for many developing countries in the arid, semiarid, and humid tropics. Reclaiming these now barren lands as breadbaskets poses challenges for both cultural practices and the breeding of genetically tolerant crops. While it is important to conserve what we have, it is even more important to recognize that land is a capital good in which we have been investing (improving) for decades. Good examples of soil improvement are on the Eastern Seaboard of the United States and in much of Western Europe. For the United States provisions are endorsed for the 1985 Farm Bill creating a conservation reserve program that will remove from crop production highly erosive and other fragile lands with an opportunity for improvement. For the humid tropics, further development of technologies of soil and crop management (conservation tillage, alley cropping) is encouraged so that continuous cropping can be a viable alternative to the slash and burn, shifting cultivation systems which now exist.

Water

Water is currently the limiting resource for crop production in each of the five most populous countries on earth—China, India, the USSR, the United States, and Indonesia. It is recognized as the most critical natural resource for future agricultural development in all of the Middle East, Southern Europe, Egypt, the Sudan, all of sub-Saharan Africa, Taiwan, Pakistan, Australia, Argentina, Brazil, most all of Canada, and most countries in Central and South America. Intelligent management of water resources and investments for their improvement, both as to availability and quality, will be particularly critical for the sustainability, productivity, and dependability of crop production in the decades ahead. It is estimated that agriculture, the world's largest user, consumes, mostly through crop irrigation, 80 to 85% of the fresh water resources in the United States. Greater efficiency in water use for crop production is imperative. One-third of the world's food is now grown on the 18% of the cropland that is irrigated.

Air

An increasingly important environmental constraint, subtle in nature and impacting crop productivity, is air pollution. Ozone, alone and in combination with sulfur and nitrogen oxides, accounts for about 90% of crop losses in the United States caused by air pollutants. Annual crop losses range from 2 to 4%. Legumes are particularly susceptible. No major food producing area on earth is free from the adverse effects of air pollution. No one can yet accurately predict the effects of acid rain on crop productivity. The major effect of the current buildup of atmospheric CO_2 along with methane, carbon monoxide, and chloro-fluoro carbons may not be on the widely publicized warming of the earth's atmosphere so much as on a disruption of the global weather machine.

Air quality (pollution) may have a positive, as well as a negative, effect on plants. Increasing levels of carbon dioxide may enhance plant growth. Atmospheric gases will also indirectly affect soil fertility, and in some instances the water status of the soil in the rhizosphere of crops. The aerial environment, plants, and soil microorganisms are a highly interactive ecosystem and must be studied as a unit.

Genetic Resources

Germ plasm collections contain the genes for future crop improvement. They provide security for future food, feed, and fiber needed by humankind. They are a major resource for solving the fundamental problems of agriculture and biology. Historically 5,000 plant species have been utilized as food for the human race. Today, about 150 species, with a quarter of a million local races, meet the food needs of the world. Plant products derived from fewer than 30 species provide more than 90% of the human diet. Of the 5 to 10 million plant and animal species on earth, the annual extinction rate is high (perhaps 1,000 per year) and rising. Only 5 to 10% of the 250,000 to 750,000 existing species of higher plants have been surveyed for biologically active compounds. The world's primary germ plasm repositories are found at Fort Collins, Colorado, in the United States; the Vavilov All-Union Scientific Research Institute of Plant Industry in Leningrad of the USSR; and the new Germ Plasm Center in Beijing, China, along with the international agricultural research centers. Limitations in assembling and utilizing germ plasm collections include the rapid erosion of germ plasm resources, worldwide deficiencies in funding, and a lack of trained personnel. International cooperation is necessary to solve these problems. International conflict over property rights to genetic material is growing.

Stability of Food Production

During the past decade great fluctuations have occurred from year to year in crop yields. This lack of dependability has been a result of unpredictable policy action, the weather, and pestilence. Unstable food production has been disruptive to farmers, food prices, government programs, and international trade. It most recently has imposed unprecedented food shortages on nations and people on the one hand and on the other massive outlays for government support programs in the form of commodity payments, land diversion programs, and subsidies which have encouraged even greater disruption. Truly this calls for a restatement of the global imperatives of a decade ago, and greater international agreement on what constitutes acceptable policy for agriculture.

Greater stability of food production can be achieved by manipulating both crops and their environment. Substantial progress toward higher crop yields can be achieved through implementing soil and water resource investments and conservation practices. There must be less dependence on and more rational use of pesticides, and more reliance on integrated pest management systems. There is a need for more stable pest resistance, improved nitrogen self-sufficiency in crops, and a wider use of protected cultivation technologies. For example, the use of plastic soil mulches, covers, windbreaks, and irrigation practices has stabilized production in China and other Asian nations.

Greater resilience to drought, heat waves, drying winds, winter injury, freezing temperatures, frost, and air pollutants is a current goal in plant breeding and genetic engineering of crops. Such advances would not only alleviate the effects of climatic hazards, but would extend the boundaries for crop production and provide a degree of resistance to interannual climatic variations and a possible changing climate.

Weather is still the most determinant factor in the lack of stability in crop productivity. Substantial progress has been made in genetically extending the climatic boundaries for crop production and reducing injuries from environmental stresses. Means for achieving high productivity coupled with sustainability and dependability may require altering physiological processes of plant cells. Significant progress in achieving greater resistance to environmental stresses is anticipated within a decade.

Production Systems

Interest in and reference to alternative production systems were noted in all working groups of stages I and II. A detailed report of one working group on this topic occurs in this volume. The concerns are expressed for resource-sparing and environmentally acceptable technologies, low cost inputs, ecologically sustainable production systems, and a total ecosystem approach. New buzzwords and phrases, such as "sustainable," "regenerative," "alternative," "agroecological," "biological farming," "ecologically healthy systems," "holistic," "closed system agriculture," and "stewardship," are now a part of our vocabulary.

Many areas for improvement were identified, including the lowland tropics and erodible fragile soils. Methods for improvement included agroforestry systems, multipurpose trees (food, forage, fuel), and alley cropping. Mixed cropping and other traditional cropping systems comprise a set of technologies that provide a good substitute for productivity under existing environmental conditions and technology for many developing countries. Such systems reduce failures depending on a single crop; they provide a maximum return from land, water, and labor; they optimize the use of sunlight, moisture, and soil nutrients; they reduce the spread and severity of pests compared to typical monocultures; and they may substantially increase food production compared to single crop programs. Technologies that would increase outputs and reduce inputs in developing countries with traditional production systems might serve as a model also to aid farmers in the western world to cut economic, energetic, and environmental costs. Crop cultivars should be developed that will be productive on marginal soils of low fertility, require minimal pest control, and have low water requirements.

Alternatively, much more sophisticated and highly productive but space limited, are systems with huge resource, capital, and management inputs. Included is controlled environment agriculture and programmed plant growth. The intent is to optimize the output per unit input of land, water, and human labor. Here, the current and future roles of computers, sensors, robots, and artificial intelligence are emphasized. Automation of the entire production system is envisioned.

An immediate problem for the agricultural community—quite different than a decade ago—is to avoid overproduction, with the overcommitment and waste of resources that goes with it. Overproduction has become chronic in industrialized-developed nations—not an aberration. To design a macroinstitutional system, with programs, technologies, and policies to achieve steady long-run production to meet effective market demand, satisfy current, and anticipated nutritional needs and dietary changes and at the same time improve and conserve resources and avoid the short-term overproduction trap remains as the supreme challenge. Policy is needed for control of short-term overcommitment of resources for crop production realizing that a substantial increase in capacity will be needed in the long run.

Crop Quality and Utilization

Society is becoming increasingly aware and concerned with human health, food, and crop interrelationships. There is a rising interest in physical fitness and increasing expenditures for "health," "natural," and "organic" foods. Populations are aging and households are becoming smaller. We have a new audience of consumers concerned with human health, food safety, and pesticide residues. These concerns will affect food purchases and crop productivity. Nutritional policies are impacting food policies and food policies in turn are affecting agricultural policies. Consumers are demonstrating an increasing awareness of nutritional values, storage quality, and natural and artificial ingredients in the processed and packaged product. Quality will increasingly become an aspect of plant breeding for genetic improvement in both food and fiber crops, in production systems, and for sources of biologically active materials.

Vastly improved food utilization programs constitute a future challenge for crop productivity. The capacity to produce enough food, and some to spare, has been demonstrated. The problem is utilization. Densely populated countries now encounter enormous pre- and postharvest wastes and losses in nutritional values of what is produced because of poor keeping quality, inadequate storage, failures of packaging and distribution systems, and because the surpluses are not stored or processed. Food problems on a global scale cannot be solved without establishing protocols for efficient and effective storage and improved utilization.

Biotechnology and Plant Breeding

Historically the primary genetic contributions to increased crop productivity have been hybrid vigor, increased harvest index, semidwarfness, pest resistance, and time to maturity. Factors that have developed somewhat independently with current great potential impacts on genetic crop improvement are germ plasm collections, international agricultural research centers, computers, and now biotechnology. Classical plant breeding will be essential to incorporate the results of new technologies into usable cultivars to maintain and improve crop productivity, retain and add to knowledge for development of new cultivars, for advanced degree programs in universities, and to effectively utilize the products of biotechnology. Crop improvement is being actively pursued on three fronts: conventional plant breeding, cellular manipulation, and recombinant DNA technology. These approaches will continue to be used.

Genetic engineering techniques include the use of recombinant DNA, construction of plasmid vectors, cloned DNA fragments, and transposable elements. The crown gall (*Agrobacterium*) T_I plasmid system enables the incorporation of useful germ plasm into crop cells. It is already clear that other approaches to plant cell transformations are likely. This suggests that all crop systems will be amenadable to one or more methods of modification.

Areas of biotechnology that will, in the near term, play important roles in crop productivity include greater efficiency in producing genetically improved disease resistant crops through the tissue culture cycle; anther culture in cereal grains (rice, wheat) to reduce the time to produce a new cultivar; the development of crops resistant to herbicides; that are salt tolerant and heat and drought resistant; creation of plants which synthesize their own pesticides; and genetically engineered microorganism for soil treatments that will control pests or can be sprayed on plants to achieve greater resistance to environmental stresses.

Future challenges which may be accessable to research in biotechnology will be a greater understanding of growth and development processes and interorgan communication where knowledge in crops lags far behind that for similar processes in animals. Knowledge to bridge these gaps is crucial for controlling growth and development, root, tuber, seed and fruit production, water requirements, stress resistance, crop maturity, and senescence. The problems of control and regulation of nitrogen fixation and photosynthesis, the nature of hybrid vigor, and the induction of flowering, while of great potential for improved crop productivity, have thus far not been solved and require renewed efforts.

International Concerns

There is an ill conceived notion that technical assistance to agriculturally developing countries has given rise to the present food glut and unfair competition in international trade. The conclusion has been that this is a result of utilizing the latest U.S. and other developed country technologies and their cheap labor. The conclusion from the conference was that the future well-being of U.S. agriculture will become increasingly dependent, on interaction between U.S. scientists and institutions and those in other nations. Particularly noteworthy is that those nations receiving technical aid from the United States are not our chief competitors and often the primary source of food products imported from the United States. These countries are rich in germ plasm resources essential for future agricultural development.

Where there is no growth there is no purchasing power. Growth in demand for U.S. exports must come from increased income of developing countries. Without assistance for more rapid development, they will lack income to buy food exports. Even the developing nations that are self-sufficient in food at low per capita income levels have a propensity to spend increased income on food that always outruns their agricultural output capacity.

Strong support was expressed for the activities and accomplishments of international agricultural research centers and recognition given to the rapid development and accomplishments of many national agricultural research centers. Serious consideration should, however, in the future be given to broadening the mission of the international agricultural research centers to food crop utilization as well as production. U.S. biotechnology and that originating from other developed countries may be neither suitable nor appropriate for developing nations. While the approaches may be comparable, both the strategies for use and many of the crops will be different. Further, the food crisis of today and that projected for the future is in Africa, and the effort there does not yet begin to match the crisis. Agricultural research imperatives for the developing world will become similar to those for the developed world; and the nations of the developed world will increasingly draw upon the traditional or modified technologies of what are now agriculturally developing countries. Thus, "scientific exchange" rather than "technology transfer" may characterize future scientific interactions of nations. There should be a two-way rather than one-way flow of information.

Non-U.S. participants did not predominate but were well represented at both stages of the conference of which there were 37 from a total of 205 participants. Interests of foreign participants were expressed as a need for improved food and crop utilization; retention of conventional methods for crop improvement including the development of F_1 hybrids; improvement of local crop cultivars having minimal resource inputs; management of the fragile easily erodible tropical soils for crop production; integrated pest management; and the enhancement of crop productivity under subsistence farming conditions and with mixed cropping and other locally traditional methods.

Human Capital

It was evident from the conference that there is now a treasure trove of human resources consisting of a large worldwide body of trained agricultural scientists, and that considerable progress has been made during the past decade. (The most crucial deficiencies are now in Africa.) Here the United States has made a significant contribution but cannot continue as the lead nation in agriculture without new efforts for development. Most of the post-World War II veterans who are now plant scientists will be retiring within a decade and there now appears few to be taking their places. During the past decade, with the rise of biotechnology, there has also been a move out of the public into the private sector. State Agricultural Experiment Station support of advanced degree programs, because of budgetary constraints, has fallen off from its traditional subsidization of 9 out of 10 receiving advanced degrees (M.S., Ph.D.) in the agricultural sciences in the United States.

Several factors were identified as constraints for availability and quality of human capital and development of their scientific capabilities. Salary schedules are not attractive or commensurate with other scientific fields. There is a lack of recognition and an awards program for achievement, and failure to provide opportunities for scientific exchanges among young investigators. There has been a deterioration of public information systems, a serious lack of knowledgeable and articulate agricultural spokesmen, and a failure to recognize the economic, social, environmental, and human health impacts of new crop productivity technologies. There are inaffective incentives and strategies for stimulating interactions, partnerships, and personnel exchanges between the public and private sectors conducive to greater cooperation and financial support. New directions in curricula offerings should take greater notice of agricultural ethics, computer sciences, biotechnologies, new communication arts for information transfer, and monitoring changes in natural resources. New sets of private consultants independent of public sector personnel have emerged during the past decade to assist farmers in the adoption of relevant technologies because such services were not provided by either the existent public or private sectors.

At the international level tens of thousands of foreign alumni of U.S. land grant and other universities are now abroad. They consist of agricultural leaders throughout the world with a loyalty to their home institutions and former thesis advisors. These alumni provide a great opportunity to act as a linkage for encouraging scientific exchanges and cooperative research efforts. The world, until now, has been highly dependent for its agricultural development and leadership upon the land grant university system of the United States. With the current and projected constraints in funding, the recent movement of trained biologists from the public to private sector, the pending retirement of a large cadre of post-World War II trained agricultural scientists, and the failure of young scientists to enter the field of agriculture, the question of where the agricultural development scientists for the next decade will come from is paramount.

Institutions

Investments must be made in institutional arrangements to match and sustain those in human capital and new technologies. The solution for every problem in crop productivity involves an institutional dimension. New institutions (national and international) will need to be created, linkages extended, and complimentary interests brought together. Especially important will be linkages between the traditional and the newer nontraditional participants (or potential participants) in agricultural research and development. Policy, policy institutions, and processes all call for modification if research imperatives are to take advantage of opportunities to create a greater productive capacity, develop resource sparing technologies, assure dependability of production, establish food security, and meet the increased purchasing powers of people and their desires for dietary improvement and human health. With changing patterns of emphasis the complimentary roles of the public and private sectors must be under continuing surveillance as to their respective roles and contributions. There is little likelihood, for example, of substitutability by the private sector for adaptive and maintenance research which has been and will likely remain as the domain of the publicly supported institutions. A specific opportunity for cooperation between the private and public sectors, within nations and consortia among them, would be the establishment of field evaluation sites (reserves) for the release, evaluation, and containment of genetically engineered organisms and other biotechnology products.

Institutional arrangements, organizational prerequisites, operational strategies, and human resources must exist to deliver technology packages to farmers who are within their differing managerial skills, intellectual capacities, and financial resources. Heretofore, the land grant university system with its research, teaching, and extension components coupled with the federal partnership of the U.S. Department of Agriculture (USDA) and local feedback mechanisms, has been singularly successful. The current technological revolution, coupled with the social and political changes of the past decade, is now stressing the system. New operational strategies and institutional arrangements will be needed to ensure a free flow of information among disciplines, scientists, and their constituencies. To date, most collaborative efforts internationally in research have been with the public sector, yet the private sector has unique expertise for development of technologies and their delivery. To encourage the private sector to collaborate in agriculture research and development will require both innovation and changes in attitudes of all concerned.

Salient Statements from the Conference

JAMES H. ANDERSON

" ... we should prepare for much closer scrutiny of our [research] programs and stiffer standards by which our programs are judged."

"Though it may come as a surprise to some deeply involved in agricultural research, many others consider our programs bloated sacred cows and deserving of cuts."

" ... our priority setting process is being influenced by groups we might formerly have considered outside traditional agricultural circles."

"We must be willing to become politically involved, and must also be willing to strike up new alliances in the legislative process."

"We have to gear our presentations to the questions congressmen will ask of all programs: is this in the public interest? Will the people in my district be better or worse off as a result? Is the long-term gain worth short-term expenditures?"

"We must be willing to present our cause at every available opportunity in a responsible manner if we expect to convince the Congress and other key decision makers that our work is important for the nation's well being."

"The agricultural research community must present a unified front. In the past we have not done a very effective job in this arena .... "

GLENN L. JOHNSON

"The trap which agricultural scientists must avoid is that of either saying or permitting others to say that technology automatically expands production in periods of shortages."

"Today, agricultural economists are again focusing on unstable international trading arrangements and the monetary/fiscal operations of government as the cause of the current farm crises."

" ... in all but 8 of the last 65 years we have suffered the consequences of producing more than the market would absorb at acceptable prices."

" ... creating a capacity to double production in the next 50 years does not mean that we will actually have to utilize this knowledge to double production."

"Production cannot be readily controlled by disposing of technology. Technology, once created, is available and cannot be easily eliminated."

"It makes little sense to think that the tendency to outproduce effective demand and create adverse pressure on farm prices can be cured by eliminating government programs. It makes even less sense to expect that failing to support technological research for agriculture will affect production enough in the short run to offset the long-term disadvantages of failing to provide support."

ABDELMUHSIN ALSUDERY

"For individual governments and the world community at large, the magnitude of malnutrition, hunger, starvation and famine has become a matter of embarrassment."

"Many regions suffering from food deficit today were either self-sufficient or food exporters not so long ago."

" ... in Africa the population is growing at about 3% per annum, whereas food production is barely half of that rate."

"Undue reliance on the market mechanism for food distribution does not take into account the fact that, in most developing countries, a large section of the rural population is too poor to buy the minimum required food."

"There is inadequate emphasis of traditional crops (broadly identified as millet, sorghum, cassava, yams, pulses, bananas, and plantain). ... "

"In Africa, in particular lack of human resources has been identified as a serious bottleneck to output growth and improved food security. In most of the countries, there is a lack of supply of skilled manpower."

"I conclude that the real problem in tackling hunger and poverty is the lack of political will."

CHARLES E. HESS

" ... benefits of the new technologies affect all of us, because Americans spend a smaller percentage of their income on food than almost everyone else in the world."

"Today approximately 3% of our population is directly involved in on-farm production of food and fiber compared with 13% in Western Europe, 32% in Russia, 40% in Latin America, 50% in Asia, and 73% in Africa."

"While it is true that science and technology have made larger farming operations possible, it is incorrect to place most of the blame for the decline of farm numbers and the growth of farm size on science."

"We must be careful that the misguided view, that the solution to surplus problems is to stop research, does not jeopardize the long-term competitive and environmental health of our agriculture and nation."

' ... we must provide assurance that the work [research] we do is for the benefit of the greater society and not for specific interest groups."

" ... the excitement and opportunity in the biological sciences is taking place when enrollment in the land grant colleges of agriculture is declining, particularly in the plant sciences ... it is essential that the interaction between basic research and application be fostered and maintained."

"We must encourage the interaction of basic and mission oriented research and avoid the creation of elitist groups of faculty."

" ... with the changing structure of agriculture, the changing nature of agricultural research, and the changing backgrounds of the participants in the agricultural research system, we need to make adjustments if we are to continue serving agriculture and the larger society. ... "

Peter R. Day

"No one would deny that plant genetics and plant breeding are entering an exciting period of change and development which is in large part due to the accelerating pace of discovery in plant molecular biology."

"Government funding for plant breeding has declined at an alarming rate both in the United States and United Kingdom."

"It is unreasonable to expect that by simply asking plant breeders and molecular biologists to collaborate they will easily produce crop plant improvements."

"The large conceptual gap between molecular biology and plant breeding must therefore be overcome by special efforts."

"For politicians struggling to devise support systems to maintain agriculture and the communities dependent on it, overproduction that is sustained by taxing the rest of the community is wholly unacceptable."

" . . . while we recognize that yield is of overriding importance, we must also stress that improved efficiency, lower costs, better quality and protecting the environment through reducing applications of agrochemicals are increasingly important goals."

"It is clear that the translation of a laboratory product into a new crop plant that farmers will want to grow and which can survive the harsh realities of agriculture is quite outside the responsibilities of the plant molecular biologist."

"We have to put the new ideas to work carefully and responsibly and above all to make the impact a successful one."

Robert Barker

" . . .agricultural research [is] people rich and resource poor with a coefficient of elasticity approaching zero."

"The biological problem of how to achieve high productivity has been solved, the socioeconomic problems of how to manage that production remain as do the economic incentives to continue to strive for increased efficiency."

"Not all of the world needs us [the U.S.] and the parts that do cannot all afford us."

"In my view it is the potential for the development of ecosystems science which will greatly expand our capacity to manage increasingly complex systems. . . . "

"Most of our organizations are segmented by disciplines despite the fact that almost all of the world's problems are multidisciplinary in character."

"Basic *versus* applied [research] is more a matter of term than intent. Neither of these divisions has served us well."

"I do not recommend doing away with traditional disciplines, at least not the major ones. I do recommend the creation of flexible groupings and more stable centers to focus on major research areas. And I urge those who provide research funds to use them to that end."

"The involvement of industry scientists in campus-based research can ensure technology transfer and enrich the teaching and research programs of the campus."

"Agriculture [products] for chemical feed-stocks will eventually be important."

"The research mission of agricultural institutions should increasingly encompass the food industry and other industries, present or potential. . . . "

"We need new configurations and new players on the team, but I'm fairly sure that at best we will only find the resources to start the ball rolling. It will be up to us to restructure what we have to win the game."

INVITED LECTURES

The Politics of Agricultural Research[1]

James H. Anderson

Ancient Greek mythology told of Hydra, a monster with many heads. When one of its heads was cut off, two more would spring up to take its place. In many ways I believe agricultural research has also faced its own Hydra.

The Traditional Challenge

Since time began, man has been faced with a single, inescapable, important problem: to provide enough food for each generation to bring its children to maturity. Through countless centuries the demands for food production were so pressing and regular that man's life and society's order were molded by it. Throughout man's existence we have been chained to the soil and the omnipresent concern of getting enough to eat. Agricultural research was born of that concern and although we have moved from crude experiments to the most amazing high technology, production has remained our main target, our Hydra. The record shows that research has given the farmers the weapons to meet the nation's production needs, to cut off the Hydra's head.

"Total agricultural production is more than twice the levels of 1930, even though the agricultural resource base has not substantially changed. The growth in farm output has come as much from the higher productivity of agricultural resources as from greater input use" (13).

The New Challenges

Funding at the state and federal level is probably a familiar topic for most agricultural researchers; consequently, I would like to limit my comments today to a brief review of the 1985 federal appropriations for research and extension programs in agriculture and the potential impact of the federal deficits on future appropriations. The 1985 federal appropriation (11) for areas within the U.S. Department of Agriculture (USDA) included $296,106,000 for the Agricultural Research Service; $285,776,000 for the Cooperative State Research Service; $76,996,000 for Animal Health and Disease Research; $343,727,000 for the Extension Service; and $46,000,000 for Competitive Grants. We appreciate these funds; they represent considerable efforts to persuade policymakers of our work's merits. However, it will be especially important in the immediate future that we recognize our position within the larger budget picture. Our country faces a budget deficit of approximately $200 billion in this year

---

[1] Introduction by Charles J. Arntzen.

(4). The debt subject to limit is projected by some to increase to as much as $2.5 trillion in 1988 (12).

The collected requests, pleadings, and demands of countless interest groups bent the congressional ears and raided the public coffers. Efforts to trim appropriations have uncovered few programs that were actually considered expendable. Taxes levied to address deficits have instead fueled program expansion. The short-term outlook is not bright, and recent congressional action gives little cause for cheer.

Former Director of the Office of Management and Budget David Stockman (8): ". . . dismisses the budget resolution adopted by Congress on August 2 as a limp rag that comes nowhere near the austerity needed to tame the federal deficit."

He leaves office ". . . with a sense of futility, convinced that the government had just squandered the last opportunity to get control of the deficit. Basically . . . the window of opportunity has closed. By his analysis, the administration's lack of leadership, Congress's refusal to sacrifice pork-barrel programs, and his own tactical errors figured in the failure" (8).

Obviously, many parties share the blame for such a large problem. Alan Greenspan, chairman of the Council of Economic Advisors in the Ford administration, is quoted as saying "The deficit had been building into a great difficulty for 15 years" (8). The deficit poses such a serious problem that 32 states have called for a constitutional convention to balance the budget. Approval by only two more states is needed for such a convention, and legislative leaders including Senator Robert Dole (Republican, Kansas) are strongly lobbying for it. Dole says "The interest payment on the debt is $140 billion a year and it's not going to get any better" (4). My purpose is not to point fingers but to point out the implications of the deficit for agricultural research. Much has been written about how the deficit has affected farmers, but we researchers must also realize how it will affect us.

My premise is simple: the deficit will eventually demand an assessment of our governmental activities—including agricultural research. Even if new taxes are passed, I do not believe we can or should look forward to regular funding increases or program expansions at the federal level. Instead, we should prepare for much closer scrutiny of our programs and stiffer standards by which they are judged. We will be one of many, many worthy programs that must compete to maintain steady levels of funding, inflation or no inflation. Allies of these other programs will be quick to question our programs. Although it may come as a surprise to some deeply involved in agricultural research, many others consider our programs bloated sacred cows and deserving of cuts. There is a tendency to take selected "success stories," usually focusing on surpluses, and imply or argue that extensive research is no longer warranted. Obviously, this reasoning reveals more about the writer's knowledge of research than that research's merits. Nonetheless, right or wrong, this kind of criticism is read by a public and legislature eager to slash government waste. We can no longer stick our heads in the sand, routinely asking for increases while pretending the deficit will take care of itself. In the absence of new revenue, any increases for one program will likely mean cuts elsewhere. Even if new revenues are available, the competition for them will be equally fierce. Stockman says, "Raising taxes is going to be tough—cutting spending is going to be tough—the political resistance will be strong. But on the other hand, doing nothing at all and borrowing $200 billion is not an economic free lunch. We have to realize we're in a period of national sacrifice" (9). Our research activities will be under continuing scrutiny by many groups, most of whom will not be familiar or sympathetic with agricultural research.

Prioritizing

This brings me to the second challenge for agricultural research, which I term prioritizing. In the context of today's discussion, I would like to focus on the way our priority setting process is being influenced by groups we might formerly have considered outside traditional agricultural circles. We are hearing from concerned citizens or groups who want to exert more influence on the kinds of research we do in a number of areas. What distinguishes these groups is that many of their most vocal spokesmen are not in the traditional land grant/USDA research establishment. As Charles Hess (7) so aptly put it: "The public and/or special interest groups are no longer content to let scientists alone make decisions about how or what technology will be introduced into society and are increasingly using litigation to make their case. The great concern that I have is that special interest groups are taking advantage of this litigious environment and, in the absence of equally articulate and vigorous opposition, may lead to the establishment of legislation and laws that in the long term will be detrimental to the freedom of inquiry, to the United States' competitive advantage, and to society in general."

Fifteen or 20 years ago concern over the safety of laboratory animals was very much the province of the researchers. Animal rights activists, though respected, were also seen as a quaint minority, a step or two above those trying to make Esperanto the world language. In the last year or two there has been a marked change in that status. Now their cause has caught the public's attention. I would imagine every experiment station director has faced more serious questions on this matter than we might have predicted a few years ago. Time will tell just how strong sentiments on animal rights are. It may be that this is a passing political fad, but we must also be prepared to respond constructively to lengthy inquiries. Obviously, our house must be in order to do so. While there are some valid considerations raised by the animal rights people as well as some opportunities for constructive dialogue, in many other instances their arguments can be distilled to equal parts of emotion and stubbornness. We must not respond in kind, but we must respond with fact, or grant them the policymaking in this area by default.

Environmental groups have been seeking a voice in agricultural research for a longer period of time. Although there remain hard-line ideologues in the environmental camp, I believe our relationship with them is maturing into one of cooperation rather than confrontation. I think we can be proud of the efforts we have made to take environmental concerns into consideration. However, the discussion of environmental issues should foretell a future when these formerly outside interests will be integrated more regularly into the policy forum.

In Michigan, the state House of Representatives just concluded a series of public hearings on pesticide use. The hearings included agriculturalists, but also public health officials and other participants. Such a hearing represents a departure from the past when topics such as pesticide use were of interest only to farmers and researchers. Now, we must "go public" on many issues. As Orville G. Bentley, Assistant Secretary of USDA's Science and Education Administration, notes (private communication, 1985), land use, including erosion, water rights, particularly out west, and use of chemicals are a few topics facing agriculture that have some implications for agricultural research.

Currently, Jeremy Rifkin is receiving a great deal of notoriety through his lawsuits against genetic engineering experiments. An article in *Fortune* magazine (3) summarized the situation:

"Arguing that possible hazards hadn't been properly assessed, Rifkin got an injunction preventing researchers with the University of California at Berkeley from testing in an open field bacteria that had been genetically altered to retard the formation of frost on plants. As a result, no microbe or plant genetically altered by recombinant DNA had been field tested in this country."

There have been some interesting reactions to Rifkin's actions. Although the injunction technically applied only to institutions receiving federal grants, private companies have chosen to abide by it rather than face possible lawsuits or bad press (3). The Rifkin case demonstrates how an outsider can present a challenge to priority setting in agricultural research by marshaling such forces as the courts and public opinion to such a degree that these nonscientific and actually nonpolitical considerations are seriously taken into account. Finally, the Rifkin case demonstrates the absolute necessity of presenting the scientific side to complex, often emotional issues so that policymakers have a balanced base of knowledge upon which to make their decisions.

Elizabeth Wehr (14) said: "The level of public education about both scientific and nonscientific issues raised by genetic engineering—and biotechnology in general—will determine the sensitivity of regulation, or patent law, and of other policies with which (we) will have to live. Representative George Brown (Democrat, California) has warned, rightly, that misinformation can be enacted into law."

Given the new, largely unchartered territory so much of our research is taking, it doesn't take much imagination to see cases like Rifkin's taking on extreme importance. It also does not take much foresight to see that we in agricultural research must do a very good job of explaining our activities—in advance of such confrontational settings—to policymakers and the general public. If we do not, outside groups will set the research agenda. That brings us to my third and final important challenge: communicating.

Communicating

The examples I have just mentioned, along with the budget sessions that are likely to come as the deficit is addressed, make communication of our goals and activities paramount. There are three main issues we will need to keep in mind, our audience, our strategy, and our attitude.

In considering our audience, we must include the interest groups that I have mentioned above. We must also consider the general public and we must especially consider the Congress and executive branch offices. Each of these has undergone many changes in the last decade. The interest groups are more vocal; the layman is beginning to take a look at agriculture. But it is the change in government that I want to confine my remarks this morning.

Congress is reflecting changes in our country's demographics. There is a declining rural/farm population in real terms. Along with the population decline is a declining identification with farming and a declining understanding of it. I think laymen today are generally surprised to hear the extent to which farming relies on scientific innovations, and how developments such as computers on farms are becoming relatively commonplace. There has been a shift to urban areas, and a corresponding shift to urban interests. There is nothing wrong with that, but we should be aware of these shifts and what they portend for agricultural research.

Congressional membership has shifted to urban areas. This is in response to the population shift, as well as the one-man/one-vote legislation of the early 1960s. I should add, as one of Michigan's congressmen, William D. Schuette (private communication, 1985), does, that this does not automatically mean these congressmen will be less sympathetic to our needs. Our presentations will be more effective if we do keep this factor in mind.

Another major consideration in Congress is the breakdown in party discipline and the implications that has for us. Not long ago it was necessary to convince only a few key legislators of a program's merits. Generally, when a committee chairman was convinced, you could be reasonably certain a specific action would or would not take place. Lobbying was fairly straightforward and much easier than it is today. Now, we are in the post-Watergate political age with a host of changes altering the political landscape. The concept of party authority as well as the old seniority systems of committee assignment were victims of reforms, particularly among Democrats, and an influx of new members. Both 1974 and, to a lesser degree, 1984 brought new congressmen to the Hill, congressmen eager to take on positions of real authority and willing to break with senior members to seat their new colleagues. With a few notable exceptions, the committee chairmen are not as powerful as they once were, which opens up the process, but also means many more members must be convinced of a program's merits.

There has also been a dramatic growth in the number of committees and subcommittees. The budget committees created in 1974 are one example (15). Agriculture cuts across many lines; therefore, many members of Congress are involved in the deliberative process and must not be convinced of a program's merit:

"The number of subcommittees increased to 157 in the House and to 124 in the Senate to allow new members to run something. Including full committees, there were 326 committees in Congress. . . ."

The "outside interests," the new committees and subcommittees, the greater number of people to be persuaded have all in turn sought a voice in agricultural policy. When added together they create quite a force in policy discussions, a force seen with concern by some (6).

"In the late 1960s Don Paarlberg, now professor emeritus at Purdue University, concluded that agriculture had lost control of its policy agenda. He was referring to the many diverse groups other than traditional farm interests involved in the policy process . . ." (6).

We should also note that this same basic trend of new actors in the policy process is also seen in the executive branch. Bonnen (2) writes: "The USDA, in collaboration with Congress, used to develop executive branch agricultural policy positions in the 1950s and early 1960s with periodic pressure and criticism from the Council of Economic Advisors and the Bureau of the Budget. Now the USDA finds itself faced with the additional participation not only of White House special assistants but the Office of the Special Trade Representative, the State Department, and the Treasury Department as well as the Department of Defense and the National Security Council. . . ." Again, I should point out that these additional voices will not necessarily be negative, but we must take note of their role in policymaking.

Obviously, our strategy should be to tailor our efforts in contacting congressmen to reflect the changes I have mentioned. Anita Brown, Staff Assistant to the U.S. House Committee on Agriculture, described the information needs of congressmen in a series of questions (private communication, 1985): "What is the program? what are its benefits? how do our requests change the current program or organization? and what effect do we foresee down the road as a result of the proposed action?" She adds that land grant universities must explain clearly their research program's problems, successes, and intended direction. This is particularly important with nonscientific or nonagriculture members.

Our strategy, therefore, must be a simple one. We have to gear our presentations to the questions congressmen will ask of all programs: Is this in the public interest? Will the people in my district be better or worse off as a result? Is the long-term gain worth short-term expenditures? We must make sure that we do not present such technical documents or such narrow topics that it is hard to see where our programs fit in the overall picture.

The last issue in communication is our attitude. In the past, I have come across researchers and administrators who had little use or praise for "politics." In some settings it has even been fashionable to adopt a cynical attitude toward the political process and to show little patience for elected officials who are slow to appreciate what we are doing. These attitudes must be discarded. In the first place, my experience convinces me that our political overseers are neither shameless wheeler-dealers nor disinterested bystanders. More often, I have found congressmen to be receptive and responsible, but also pressed in by every imaginable interest clamoring for their attention.

The burden to deal with agricultural research rests initially with us. We must be willing to present our cause at every available opportunity in a responsible manner if we expect to convince the Congress and other key decision makers that our work is important for the nation's well being. Howard Diesslin, National Association of State Universities and Land Grant Colleges, estimates that as late as the 1960s and early 1970s, 90% of the experiment station directors were not politically involved (private communication, 1985). We literally cannot afford such inaction today because the stakes are too high. A recent article by Armstrong (1) in the *Christian Science Monitor* said, "Like a rusting scythe, the nation's university laboratories—at the cutting edge of U.S. scientific research—are becoming old and obsolete."

At the same time, long-range food production needs and the need to more effectively protect the soil and water resource base necessitate improvements in production efficiency and resource conservation. To neglect research, facilities and staff will slowly and silently stack the deck against future generations dependent on new innovations today. Alternatives to research are not promising. "With no increase in per acre yields of major crops, an additional 95 million harvested acres would be needed to meet projected requirements in 2000; clearly demand for cropland of this magnitude would place enormous pressure on the cropland base ... Soil erosion and water pollution would surely worsen as production expanded to more and more ecologically fragile croplands" (5). Balanced against those concerns is the budget deficit I mentioned earlier. In keeping the deficit in perspective, I find it useful to refer to two quotes from R. Emmet Tyrrell (10): "The present deficit is practically equal to the entire 1974 budget" and, "... to get federal spending back to 20% of GNP (its level a decade ago) Congress would have to cut more than $120 billion over and above its present promised cuts."

Smoke and mirrors will not cut the deficit; neither will half-hearted or overly technical narrow arguments win agricultural research a favorable hearing. We must be willing to become politically involved, and must also be willing to strike up new alliances in the legislative process. Obviously, agriculture does not have to go it alone in the legislature, but as the budget tightens we must have something to offer that other groups will be willing to support. For researchers this means we must be able to explain the value of programs to the general public, recognizing the results may be complex or several years down the road. It will be necessary to present a unified front. In the past we have not done a very effective job in this arena and too often we have resorted to political expediency or emotions of the moment to sell our programs.

Now we have an important tool to avoid that. The 1977 Agriculture Adjustment Act established within the USDA the Joint Council on Food and Agricultural Sciences whose "primary responsibility is to foster coordination of the agricultural research, extension, and teaching activities of the federal government, the states, colleges, and universities, and other public and private institutions and persons involved in the food and agricultural sciences."

I believe the Joint Council is doing a very credible job of carrying out its congressional mandate. The Joint Council serves as an effective link with other federal agencies that will be increasingly important to agricultural research in the future. Its few years of existence have seen the Joint Council develop into a strategic player in agricultural research, and I hope the cooperation and support its members have given can be maintained.

Concluding Remarks

The year 1985 has been important for agriculture. The farm crisis in this country and the famine in Africa have brought agriculture a hearing in many important forums. While I am disappointed at some of the misinformation that persists and has unfortunately gained a wider audience, it is a hopeful sign that issues of such great concern are being addressed by the greater population.

Our experience this year confirms what I have thought for some time. The shifts in our political organizations do not by themselves exclude the deserved treatment of agriculture as a national priority of the highest order. However, it does confirm the critical necessity for those of us who have the scientific and technical credentials to make our programs and our needs clearly and widely known. While our policymakers are receptive, they cannot be expected to reward us for our failure to apprise them of the importance and needs of our work.

We must adopt an active communication with them and with the general public if we are to responsibly maintain our research capability for the next generations of scientists.

Mythology tells us Hydra was finally killed altogether by Hercules. While the appearance of these additional concerns that I have discussed may be troubling, we have no choice but to face them. We have a worthy purpose, an urgent need, and we need to muster the resources to get on with the job. Thank you for your attention this morning, and I hope you will join me in working toward that end.

Acknowledgment—Special appreciation is given to Mr. Kelly Bartlett, Legislative Research Analyst, Michigan House of Representatives, for his help in the preparation of this paper. Mr. Bartlett did much of the background work and assisted greatly in the preparation of the manuscript.

LITERATURE CITED

1. ARMSTRONG S 1984 Outmoded university labs may be blunting the United State's high-tech edge. Christian Science Monitor, September 25, p 19
2. BONNEN JT 1984 US agriculture, instability and national political institutions: the shift from representative to participatory democracy. *In* United States Agricultural Policy for 1985 and Beyond. Department of Agricultural Economics, University of Arizona, Tucson, pp 53–83
3. BYLINSKY G 1985 Test-tube plants hit pay-dirt. Fortune, September 2, p 53
4. CAIN C 1985 Dole asks state role on deficit. Detroit News, September 26, p 1A
5. FARRELL KR 1984 Feeding a hungry world. Resources 76: 10 (Spring), 1984
6. FARRELL KR 1985 The 1985 farm bill. Resources 79: 7 (Winter), 1985
7. HESS CE 1984 Freedom of inquiry—an endangered species. Paper read at National Association of State Universities and Land Grant Colleges, Denver, CO, November 13, 1984
8. REILLY A 1985 David Stockman: economic crisis ahead. Fortune, September 2, p 86
9. STOCKMAN D 1985 "This Week with David Brinkley." American Broadcasting Corporation, September 29
10. TYRRELL R 1985 Getting a grip on the budget. Detroit News, August 19
11. US CONGRESS 1985 House Committee on Appropriations, Subcommittee on Agriculture, Rural Development and Related Agencies Appropriations Bill, 1986, 99th Congress, 1st session, Rept 99–211
12. US CONGRESS 1985 House Committee on Appropriations, Hearings before a Subcommittee of the Committee on Appropriations, Agriculture, Rural Development and Related Agencies Appropriations for 1986, 99th Congress, 1st session, p 2
13. US DEPARTMENT OF AGRICULTURE 1982 1983 Fact Book of US Agriculture. USDA Miscellaneous Publication No. 1063, pp 2–3
14. WEHR E 1984 Scientific, ethical and legal questions in university: a press perspective. Paper read at the ACE-NASULGC Joint Meeting, Denver, CO, November 13
15. WILDAVSKY A 1979 Politics of the Budgetary Process. Little, Brown, Boston

Agricultural Surpluses—Research on Agricultural Technologies, Institutions, People, and Capital Growth

Glenn L. Johnson[1]

I believe the best way to indicate the objective of this paper is to describe the situation that led to the invitation to address you.

An early version of the introductory background paper that Sylvan Wittwer prepared for this conference contained the following paragraph:

"A decade ago it was predicted by some that food shortages would remain commonplace and all-out production would be required, henceforth, to meet diminishing reserves, a rising population and increased purchasing power. Conversely, some are predicting now that we face an age of glut."

As Sylvan asked me to read his tentative draft and to give him the benefit of my constructive criticism, I wrote the following memo to him:

"Somehow or another, Sylvan, you have to make the long-run case for increased productive capacity whether or not that capacity is actually used. We made that case in our report (7) and I am making it again in the paper I will present on technology at the American Agricultural Economics Association (AAEA) meeting the first part of next month (4). The trap which the biophysical agricultural scientists must avoid is that of either saying or permitting others to say that technology automatically expands production in periods of shortages. This trap should be avoided because, first of all, it is untrue. In addition to technology, appropriate institutions and infrastructure, technical and entrepreneurial skills must be in place. If this untruth is accepted in periods of food shortages and, hence, unreasonably high prices for food, then it will also be believed in the much more common periods of surpluses and unreasonably low prices for farm products and food. In the latter instance, the obvious conclusion is that production can be controlled by placing constraints on the generation of new technology and the utilization of old technology. In fact, the agricultural research establishment is now encountering such arguments as a result of having oversold in the 1970s the untrue conclusion that production could automatically be expanded by improving technology."

As a result of my memo, Sylvan redrafted the introductory background material for this conference and asked me to do for the conference that which I suggested needs to be done. I am the "somehow or another" I

---

[1] Introduced by Stanley K. Ries.

wanted Sylvan to find for making the long-run case for increased productive capacity whether or not that capacity is actually used.

In what follows, I will indicate why farmers outproduce market demand. I will also present arguments indicating that technological advance
is not the major cause of farm surpluses and low prices. I will devote a
section to the history of agricultural production in the United States and
look 50 years into the future to gain some perspective on our future
production possibilities and needs. I will assess the four main sources of
growth in capacity to produce agricultural products. A balanced agricultural research program must research all four sources of growth in
capacity to produce agricultural products. I will then look at research on
new institutions needed when production so far exceeds levels of effective
market demand to generate adverse prices for farm products. In conclusion, I will address four questions presented from the floor at the Boyne
Highlands conference.

Why Farmers Outproduce Market Demand

In this section, I explain why farmers outproduce effective market
demand in market-controlled economies. This explanation has been
carefully and extensively researched by a number of agricultural economists. I draw it directly from a book entitled *The Overproduction Trap
in U.S. Agriculture* (3) published by Resources for the Future. Explana-
tions of the tendency of market-controlled as opposed to government-
controlled agricultural economies to outproduce effective demand can be
based on several facts about agriculture (3). Outproducing effective
demand is defined as producing so much that the product cannot be sold
in the market at prices that cover the current acquisition costs of the
inputs and investments used to produce the product. Such overproduction
results in unduly depressed prices, if there are no government storage
and price support programs. If, on the other hand, there are government
and prices support programs, such overproduction results in the accumulation of surpluses in the hands of the agencies operating the storage
programs. The basic facts about agriculture needed to explain this
tendency are discussed in each of the following paragraphs.

The first crucial fact is that farmers make substantial long-term
investments in such "long-lived" durables as land, machinery, irrigation
systems, drainage systems, herds, orchards, and improved pastures, as
well as in the production of such important "short-lived" intermediate
inputs as feed grains, roughages, feeder cattle, and in the production of
such long-lived capital items as breeding herds, orchards and even
buildings, and drainage and irrigation systems.

The second crucial fact is that the durables in which farmers invest
tend to have acquisition prices that are much higher than their liquidation
values. The difference between such prices is due, of course, to the costs

of transporting durables to farms (from one farm to another) installing and setting them up, and dismantling them to move them from the farm of a seller to the farm of a buyer. Closely related to this price characteristic of durables is the fact that other durables have acquisition costs and liquidation values which, though near equal, tend to rise and fall directly with the value of the products they are used to produce. An example of such a durable is farmland. Acquisition cost and selling price rarely vary from each other by more than 5 to 10%, yet are so closely correlated with the values of the products they are used to produce that the overall use of land is not very responsive to product prices.

The third basic fact about agriculture is that farmers are not and cannot be perfectly informed about conditions affecting the future value of their long-term investments. The values of a farmer's durable investments are affected by declarations of war, making of peace, changes in the value of the dollar, losses of foreign markets, shifting tastes and habits of consumers, changes in the trading regulations of importers and exporters, evolving tax structures and changes in a substantial number of other variables unknown at any point in time. The importance of these potential sources of investment errors changes continuously and unexpectedly. Consequently, farmers are not and cannot be perfectly informed. In this connection, I point out that the very best economists have not succeeded in predicting many of the important changes that affect the value of farm durables.

Because they are imperfectly informed, the fourth crucial fact is that farmers make investment mistakes. Some of their mistakes involve overinvestment—others, underinvestment.

The fifth fact is that mistakes of underinvestment are easily corrected. If a farmer underinvests, the durable of concern is capable of producing more than it costs and the farmer can simply correct his mistake with additional profitable investment.

The sixth fact is that mistakes of overinvestment in durables are difficult and costly to correct. To correct a mistake of overinvesting in a durable, a farmer has to dispose of the excessive amount he has acquired. Unfortunately, this involves liquidating his excess investment by selling it at a liquidation or salvage price substantially below current acquisition price. The difficulty of disinvesting is further complicated by the possibility that the liquidation value of the durable involved has fallen for all potential buyers because of general overinvestment on the part of farmers in general.

The seventh factual characteristic of agriculture is its chronic tendency to outproduce effective market demand. This characteristic is explained by the much greater difficulty encountered in correcting overproduction rather than underproduction mistakes. Thus, in a market-controlled agricultural economy there is a bias or tendency toward overproduction, even when the initial errors are randomly distributed with respect to over- and underinvestment.

The eighth factual characteristic of agriculture has to do with consequences of this tendency to overinvest and overproduce (2). The consequences are:

1. Low earnings[2] on farm investments and, hence,
2. Capital losses on current as well as historical acquisition prices of investments, and
3. Cash flow problems and bankruptcy for highly leveraged farmers.

I hardly need to tell this audience that these three consequences are characteristic of agriculture in the United States in 1985. While people in this audience know that these consequences are now evident, they may not be aware that the tendency of farmers to outproduce effective demand has been evident in all but about 8 of the years since the end of World War I. In most of these years, farmers have produced so much output that the consequences have been either (a) undue adverse pressure on prices in the absence of government price support and storage programs, or (b) the accumulation of surpluses in agricultural storage programs. The data reviewed in the book cited above are consistent for the past 65 years with the analysis sketched out above.

It is important for our purposes today to note that the mistakes of investments made by farmers are due to imperfect knowledge of future changes in many variables. Of the variables listed, only one is agricultural technology.

Technology Is Not the Major Cause of Surpluses and/or Low Prices

When we examine market-controlled agricultures around the world at any point in time, or when we examine the history of individual market-controlled economies through time, it becomes clear that imperfect knowledge of technological advance is not necessary for the development of agricultural surpluses and/or adverse prices and that technological advance is seldom the major important cause. In the paragraphs to follow, I examine the situation for Nigerian yam and cassava production in eastern Nigeria during the 1960s. I will also look at the situation in U.S. agriculture from 1918 to 1929 as well as in the first 4 years or so of the Great Depression.

In the 1960s, technologies employed by eastern Nigerian farmers in growing yams and cassava could be described only as primitive. While I was director of the Economic Development Institute at the University of Nigeria, we researched the profitability of yam and rice production in the Abakaliki region (10). In doing this, we also learned quite a bit about cassava prices and resource earnings in cassava production. The eastern Nigerian farmers readily outproduced effective demand with very primitive technologies for yam and cassava production. According to our calculations, yams sold at a price that returned yam farmers about 15

---

[2] In technical economic terms, shadow prices or within-firm opportunity values bounded upwardly by acquisition costs and downward by liquidation or salvage values.

cents per day of labor devoted to yam production. The minimum wage in industry and government was about a dollar a day. If labor earned as much as 15 cents per day, returns to the primitive capital used to produce yams had to be around 5% in an economy where interest rates were far higher than that. The yam farmers produced enough product to keep the yam prices so low they suffered from low prices. Primitive low-tech production methods did not spare them. At the time these studies were made, the situation for cassava production was less favorable than for yam production. Advanced technology was not used for cassava production either. It is also interesting to note that there were no governmental price support and storage programs to cause overproduction of yams and cassava. There was only a market operating in the presence of a primitive technology with farmers imperfectly informed about the extent of local markets and partially isolated from larger national markets by high transport costs. In the United States the end of World War I to the onset of the Great Depression was a period of relatively low level technology compared to the technologies employed since World War II (9). Government programs did not exist to cause overproduction relative to effective demand. It was a period in which farmers experienced the consequences of having overinvested in durable factors of production, especially land. The causes of these investment errors by farmers were primarily the unduly high price expectations generated by World War I combined with their inadequate knowledge of the loss of markets that would take place with the reestablishment of peace in Europe. Overproduction and adverse prices developed despite the then relatively low level of technology and in the absence of governmental price support, production control and storage programs. Clearly, neither technological advance nor government programs could have caused the adverse pressure on agricultural prices and the capital losses imposed on farmers in the 1920s.

My memory of agricultural economic problems starts along about 1924 or 1925 when my overleveraged farmer father was in the process of going broke. After that traumatic experience, he worked in a factory and ran a small part-time farm nights and on weekends. He managed to save enough to get back into farming on a full-time basis in 1928. He was, of course, imperfectly informed about the Great Depression, which would soon strike the country, leaving him so leveraged that his creditors did not even bother to close him out or to drive him into bankruptcy. Throughout the depression years from 1929 to 1933, he continued to feed the farm surpluses that generated adverse pressure on farm product prices. Again, neither advance technology nor agricultural programs were the culprits. Like the farmers of 1985, my father suffered the consequences of his own imperfect knowledge as well as the imperfect knowledge of economists concerning the consequences of the monetary/fiscal and trade policies followed by the United States and her trading partners first at the end of World War I and then in the later 1920s and 1930s.

Today, agricultural economists are again focusing on unstable international trading arrangements and the monetary/fiscal operations of

62   JOHNSON

government as the cause of the current farm crises. In 1984 there were
three sessions on this topic at the annual meeting of the AAEA. There
were more such sessions at this year's AAEA annual meeting and at this
year's triennial meeting of the International Association of Agricultural
Economists whose theme was "Agriculture in a Turbulent World Economy." Unstable monetary and trading arrangements are assigned substantial responsibility for turbulence (8). It is mainly general economists
and politically motivated people who are so naive as to regard our current
problems as stemming from government programs. A large group of
equally naive persons place the blame on high technology.

I believe it is important for us to keep in mind the parallel between
the mid-1980s and the 1920s. Farmers were in trouble in both periods
because of earlier mistakes of overinvestment and overproduction. Their
mistakes were not caused primarily by imperfect knowledge of new
technology or by the existence of high technology or government price
support, or production control and storage programs for agriculture.
Rather, their mistakes arose mainly out of imperfect knowledge of
international trade and national and international monetary and fiscal
policies and programs of the United States and her trading partners.

Some Agricultural Production History and the Future

Figure 1 displays data on the history of agricultural production over
the last century from 1880 to 1982. In this period, the U.S. agricultural
economy increased its output about sevenfold (7). This was, of course, a
remarkable achievement. For the most part, we have needed the increase
in production. However, as indicated above, in all but 8 of the last 65
years we have suffered the consequences of producing more than the
market would absorb at acceptable prices. Those consequences have
appeared either in the form of adverse prices in absence of storage

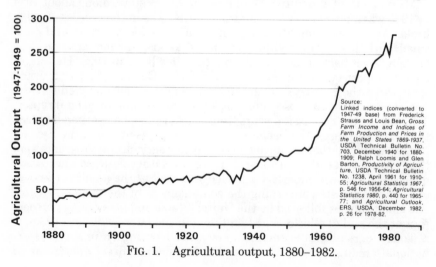

FIG. 1.   Agricultural output, 1880–1982.

programs or in the form of accumulating surplus stocks in government hands when price support programs have prevented prices from falling to the low levels required to equate effective demand with production.

Before looking into the future, I want to draw what I regard as an important distinction between *actual future production* and *capacity to produce* what may be needed in the future. When we think about the capacity we should have to produce in the future, we should not necessarily think in terms of producing all we would be capable of producing.

In the report that Sylvan Wittwer and I published last year, we reached the conclusion that world producers should double their capacity to produce in the next 50 years. To repeat, that is not the same as concluding that we should double the amount actually produced by 2030. What we should actually produce will depend, in substantial part, on changes in demands and needs we cannot fully foresee at this time. We believe we should have capacity to double production, if needed because of:

1. Anticipated growth in world population,
2. The continued existence of hunger and famine around the world,
3. Anticipated increases in incomes in many parts of the world,
4. Strong foreign competition in the export markets for our crops,
5. National security considerations,
6. The foreign exchange we will need to buy fossil fuels and other primary commodities, and
7. Possible industrial needs for biomass from agriculture to use as a source of energy, and chemical feedstocks.

Sylvan and I spent some time estimating what would be required if we were to actually double output in the next 50 years. In our judgments, a doubling of actual output production would require (7):

1. Seventy percent higher yields than in 1980,
2. Use of 16% more acres than were used in 1980, many of which would be more ecologically fragile than acres now farmed,
3. A one-fourth increase in the intensity with which our land is cropped,
4. Improved institutions to serve agriculture, and
5. Fewer unskilled laborers but many more skilled agricultural workers on farms, in agribusiness, in farm organizations, and in governmental agencies serving agriculture.

We also noted that all of the above would probably have to be done without using much more energy than was used by U.S. agriculture in 1980.

Clearly, to double our capacity to produce agricultural products in the next 50 years will require major improvements in technology, institutions, and people. In turn, these will require substantial increases in funding for agricultural research (7). Much research will be required to increase yields 75%. Still more research will be needed to expand our acres cropped by 16% without running into intolerable erosion, pollution, and food chain contamination problems. The one-fourth increase in cropping intensity will also require substantial investments in biological and technological research. Improving the institutions that serve agriculture so agriculture is capable of obtaining the inputs and marketing twice the present levels of production will also require both basic and applied research in the rural social sciences and humanities. Research will also be needed to train and develop the skilled women and men required to handle advanced technologies and to operate the new public and private institutions required to serve agriculture.

In closing this discussion of the history of U.S. agricultural production and its future, I point out again that creating a capacity to double production in the next 50 years does not mean that we will actually double production. What Sylvan and I have asserted is that we need to develop this much capacity. We should let effective demand indicate whether to actually convert such capacity into production.

Four Sources of Growth in Capacity

Study of agricultural development processes around the world indicates that growth in capacity to produce agricultural products depends on four important variables:
1. Improved technology,
2. Better institutions to serve agriculture,
3. Improved human skills and capacity (T. W. Schultz, University of Chicago, calls this human capital), and
4. An increase in the biological and physical capital base of agriculture.

Africa contains many countries where the greatest constraint on agricultural production is inadequate institutions, including poor agricultural policies and governmental programs. Improving technology and educating people will do little good in many African countries, unless institutions and policies are improved (1). Two outstanding examples in world agriculture that illustrate the importance of removing institutional and policy constraints when human skills and technologies are already available can be found in the Peoples Republic of China and in Hungary. In both countries, production was adversely affected by poor policies and institutions. When policies and agricultural institutions were reformed, dramatic increases in agricultural production took place. India and Pakistan clearly demonstrated the advantages of overcoming technological constraints in rice and wheat production when policies and institutions were also moderately improved.

When examining the history of agricultural development around the world, one concludes that these four sources of growth are individually necessary but individually insufficient. I have become so convinced of this that I am now distrustful of estimates made by my fellow agricultural economists concerning the contributions of technological advances independent of the presence of adequate institutions, human capital, and in stocks of biological and physical capital. It is important to advance simultaneously on all four fronts or, if one or more of the four individually necessary sources of growth is inadequate, to concentrate attention on the inadequate or limiting source. If I am correct on this, it makes little sense for us to debate here about which of the four sources is more important or which has the highest payoff or to attempt to promote one at the expense of the others. What is needed is a balanced research program—a program balanced with respect to research on the four sources of agricultural growth of a program concentrating on the constraining source or sources, whether the constraints be in the form of inadequate technologies; institutions, policies, and programs; human capital; or the base of biological and physical capital.

When I look 50 years into the future either at U.S. agriculture or world agriculture, I find technological advance to be essential. I believe I should supplement the defense and advocacy of biological and physical science researchers with those of a social scientist. I am convinced that arguments I have presented above are useful in promoting essential technological research for agriculture over the long pull.

In return for my defense of the essentiality of both basic disciplinary and applied research in the biological and physical agricultural sciences, I, in turn, ask you to defend the essentiality of both disciplinary and applied social science to improve:

1. The institutions that serve agriculture,
2. The human skills and capacities used in agriculture, and
3. Agriculture's base of biological and physical capital.

In addition, I ask you to defend the essentiality of both basic disciplinary and applied social science research to help increase the incomes of the poor and hungry so they may be able to convert their needs for food into effective demand.

New Institutions Are Required when Short-Run Cuts Are Needed in Production

In market-controlled economies, production almost inevitably exceeds effective demand to create either adverse pressure on farm product prices or, in the presence of price support and storage programs, the accumulation of expensive governmentally held agricultural surpluses. Production cannot be readily controlled by disposing of technology. Technology, once created, is available and cannot be easily eliminated. It is also extremely difficult to control production by disposing of human capital once we have generated human skills and capacities specialized to agriculture. Production cannot even be controlled effectively by letting the market lower prices, impose capital losses on farmers, and drive leveraged farmers into bankruptcy. As farm production does not respond significantly in the short run to lower prices, prohibitive costs must be imposed on farmers and society at large to cut production.

Since the mid-1930s, government programs have provided a great deal of short-term relief to farmers from the consequences of outproducing effective demand. At the same time, these programs have permitted substantial growth in farm production in the long run. Figure 1 indicates that the record is not such a bad one. The drawback is that these programs have been expensive to government and, hence, to taxpayers. If the explanaton I advanced above of the tendency of agriculture to outproduce effective demand is true, simply getting rid of production control, price supports, and storage programs will not eliminate the problem. Just as in the 1920s and in the early 1930s there will continue to be a need to protect farmers from adversely low prices, the imposition of capital losses and bankruptcy. It makes little sense to think that the tendency to outproduce effective demand and create adverse pressure on farm prices can be cured by eliminating government programs. It makes even less sense to expect that failing to support technological research for agriculture will affect production enough in the short run to offset the long-term disadvantages of failing to generate yield-increasing, land-conserving and enhancing, intensive-cropping, and energy-efficient technologies.

We will continue to need, in the future as in the past, institutions, policies, and programs to control production in the short run. As the programs, policies, and institutions we have developed to date for this purpose are far from satisfactory, our agricultural research programs should include basic disciplinary research in the social sciences relevant to the applied design of new institutions, policies, and programs. New institutions must provide and permit long-term growth while, at the same time, providing short-term control over production. In some senses we have not done so badly. We have had a growing productive agriculture based on improved technology, rather effective institutions, and an adequate supply of increasingly well-trained people (human capital), not to mention a growing base of biological and physical capital of improving quality. In many of the years we have been able to protect farmers in significant ways from the adverse consequence of outproducing effective demand. The main complaint is that our short-term production control price support and subsidy programs have been too expensive. An important challenge ahead for agriculturalists, including especially the rural social scientists, is to design more effective institutions, policies, and programs for the short-run control of production.

Questions from the Floor

(After the above was presented, questions came from the floor. In this section, each of these four questions will be considered in turn.)

Support for Agricultural Research. A conference participant asked whether adequate support for the research program I indicated was needed would be forthcoming, particularly from state legislatures. In responding to this question, I drew on an argument I recently presented in a paper at the University of Bonn (5). In that paper, I noted that agricultural researchers in universities and agricultural research administrators are increasingly oriented toward fundamental or basic research in such disciplines as biochemistry, molecular biology, physics, economics, and chemistry—to the neglect of the practical problems of farmers. I also noted that, at the same time, the agricultures of the western democracies are becoming increasingly industrialized and specialized. A consequence of this specialization is political pressure from producers of specialized commodities concentrated in areas of high comparative advantage for more problem solving and subject matter research to serve the special interests of agricultural producers. The danger is that the disciplinary interests of university and institutional agricultural researchers and the specialized problem solving and subject matter interests of agricultural producers will "pass in the night" without being aware of the other's presence. If this happens, it will be difficult to mobilize political and social support from agricultural producers for either state or federal appropriations to finance needed agricultural research. Obviously, disciplinary biological, physical, and social science research is becoming relatively more important as we move to high technologies, more sophisticated institutions, and the need for more skilled agricultural workers, managers, and administrators. At the same time, the demand for problem solving and subject matter research of immediate practicality is also increasing. It should not be forgotten that basic disciplinary research and problem solving and subject matter research are complementary. The agricultural research institutions of this country must earn their support by serving specialized industrial producers in addition to doing the needed disciplinary research. This will also enable them to exploit the complementarities between the two kinds of research. In addition to support from state and federal legislatures, it should prove possible to expand direct support from the commercial, specialized industrial agricultural producers and their associations and agribusinesses for more practical problem-solving and subject matter research. In more direct response to the question, I believe it will be difficult to finance the needed agricultural research in the decades ahead. But we can do a better job if we in the universities' research and extension agencies serve the needs of agriculture for problem-solving and subject matter research as well as basic disciplinary research.

The Dangers of Specialized Industrial Agriculture. The question was raised as to whether the specialized industrial agricultures I had just discussed are inherently and inevitably damaging to the environment and to the structure of agriculture. My response is rather noncommittal. I know of highly specialized industrial agriculture systems that are much more protective of the environment than are diversified, less industrial, systems. I also know of miserable diversified subsistence farming areas. The farm my wife and I have in western Illinois, for example, is wholly specialized in the commercial production of corn. I believe that erosion is now less of a threat than it has ever been in the history of that farm. The land is now better preserved and in the highest level of productivity it has ever attained. Further, we know of no more profitable way of operating the farm than the way it is now being operated, where profits are defined to account for long-run environmental issues. If we did, we would change to the more profitable method. In any event, our earnings maintain property values and the ability to pay taxes on a desirable rural infrastructure in a nice western Illinois community.

Role of the Extension Service. In response to a question concerning the role of the Cooperative Extension Service, I indicated that the "investigations" carried out by extension service workers differ very little from the problem-solving research often demanded from experiment stations. These two types of work serve the same end and help meet the needs of agriculture. Both are to be encouraged and recognized as important. I indicated that I saw advantages in dropping the distinction between extension investigations and problem-solving research in the experiment stations. I hope that we can support, recognize and award problem-solving expertise, whether done by extension workers or researchers.

I should also point out that problem-solving research on agriculture policy problems is seldom extended by extension service workers. "Extension" of problem-solving policy research tends to be done by researchers when they testify before state and federal governmental agencies or serve as consultants to the action agencies of state, federal, and local governments. Much of the future success of Land Grant Agricultural Experiment Stations and Cooperative Extension Services depends, in my opinion, on our ability to deliver the results of problem-solving research and investigations to our clientele on farms, in agribusinesses, in farm organizations, and in government.

Kinds of Research and Institutions Needed to Maintain Short-Term Control Over Production while Encouraging Long-Term Growth in Productive Capacity. In responding to this question, I drew on materials presented in a previously cited book edited by myself and Leroy Quance (6). In that book, it was suggested that the tendency of agriculture to overproduce in the short run could be controlled in four ways, each of which is discussed briefly in the following paragraphs. Readers wanting more detail on these arguments are referred to pages 180–185 of the cited reference.

It is believed that research can much better monitor the investments of farmers' productive assets. Researchers can keep track of such investments and can estimate when the output generated by such investments is likely to create adverse pressure on farm product prices. On the basis of such research, extension programs can be designed to help "blow the whistle" as farmer investments begin to be excessive. While this is a promising area in which more can be done by research and extension workers than is now being done, there is little basis for hoping such research and extension can be so effective as to handle the whole problem.

Farmers are atomistic competitors and in seeking their own gain, often collectively overinvest and overproduce for the reasons explained in the first part of this paper. It seems necessary, therefore, that the suggested research and educational efforts of the Agricultural Experiment Stations and Cooperative Extension Services be supplemented with legislation to enable associations of producers to exert greater collective short-term control over the use of land, new technologies, and human skills to produce agricultural products. Such controls are needed to restrain the inherent tendency of market-controlled agricultural economies to out-produce effective demand. Currently, we place less reliance on organizations of producers to control production than we do on governmental programs for that purpose. Our governmental programs have been too expensive and have been less effective than they should be. Legislation enabling producers to exercise such control would not require governmental appropriations to subsidize storage and to finance price support programs. Instead, prices would be maintained by short-term restrictions on production. Such restrictions would make it less necessary for the government to operate expensive storage programs to keep surpluses already produced off the market.

Grower and producer associations granted power to control production would also have monopolistic power to exploit consumers. For this reason, legislation enabling associations and organizations of producers to control production should be accompanied by legislation to police such organizations. The effect of this proposal would be to reduce the price support, production control, and storage programs of the government and transfer production control activities to associations of growers. The reduced role of government in operating such programs would be offset by a need for increased control of activities to associations of growers. The reduced role of government in operating such programs would be offset by a need for increased control of the growers' associations by government. Legislation enabling the exercise of such controls should be passed at the same time legislation is passed to enable producer associations and organizations to function in the manner suggested above. It should not be forgotten that legislation to control large-scale, nonfarm corporations was not passed until many years after the enabling legislation needed to establish such organizations was put in place. Similarly, it should not be forgotten that control legislation to regulate the activities of labor unions was not passed for several years after the legislation enabling such unions to affect wage rates by controlling delivery of labor services was passed.

For major commodities, such as corn and wheat produced over wide areas in the United States, it seems unreasonable to expect that producer associations will be able to agree on and effectively administer production control programs over such widely dispersed areas. If this is true, a residual need will remain for government to operate price support, production control, and storage programs for such commodities. Thus the government would need to continue in a reduced way some of its present price support, production control, and storage programs.

LITERATURE CITED

1. AVERY D 1985 U.S. farm dilemma: the global bad news is wrong. Science 230: 408–12
2. JOHNSON GL 1958 Supply functions—some facts and notions. *In* EO Heady

et al, eds, Agricultural Adjustment Problems in a Growing Economy. Iowa State College Press, Ames, IA, pp 74–93

3. JOHNSON GL 1972 Characteristics of US agricultural economy. *In* GL Johnson, CL Quance, eds, The Overproduction Trap In U.S. Agriculture. Johns Hopkins University Press, Baltimore, pp 5–21

4. JOHNSON GL 1985 Technological innovation with implications for agricultural economics *In* Agriculture and Rural Areas Approaching the Twenty-first Century: Challenges for Agricultural Economics, Iowa State University Press, Ames, IA In press

5. JOHNSON GL 1985 Agricultural Economics—Dwindling Support and Expanding Opportunities, Theodor Brinkmann Lecture presented at the University of Bonn, West Germany, October 9, 1985. Lecture to be published by the University of Bonn

6. JOHNSON GL, CL QUANCE, eds 1972 The Overproduction Trap in US Agriculture. Johns Hopkins University Press, Baltimore

7. JOHNSON GL, SH WITTWER 1984 Agriculture Technology Until 2030: Prospects, Priorities, and Policies, Special Report 12. Agricultural Experiment Station, Michigan State University, East Lansing, MI

8. RENBORG U, A MAUNDER, eds 1985 Agriculture in a Turbulent World (Proceedings of the 19th Conference of the International Association of Agricultural Economists). Gower Publishing Company, Ltd, Westmead, England. In press

9. VANGIGCH FL, CL QUANCE 1972 The overall pattern of production, disappearance, income, and resource use. *In* GL Johnson, CL Quance, eds, The Overproduction Trap in U.S. Agriculture. Johns Hopkins University Press, Baltimore, pp 67–87

10. WELSCH DE 1965 Response to economic incentive by Abakaliki rice farmers in Eastern Nigeria. Farm Econ 47: 900–914

The World Food Problems: Assessment and Solutions[1]

ABDELMUHSIN ALSUDERY[2]

Malnutrition, hunger, starvation, and famine are concerns of many today. Academics, political leaders, administrators, and other professionals have been paying more attention to these problems in recent years than they did in the past. For individual governments and the world community at large, the magnitude (as measured by the proportion of population affected) of these problems has become a matter of embarrassment. Despite advances made by science and technology in different spheres of life, little progress seems to have been made in eradicating signs of malnutrition and starvation from the face of the earth. On the contrary, in many areas of the world the number of people suffering from starvation is increasing every year. What is a matter of grave concern is that the burden of suffering is unevenly distributed among different regions of the world, different classes of people, and different age groups within each region.

Many regions suffering from food deficit today were either self-sufficient or food exporters not so long ago. It is interesting to note that, before World War II, Western Europe was the only importing region in the world. All other regions were grain exporters, the largest being Latin America, which exported twice as much as North America. This pattern of trade changed only gradually between 1960 and 1970, but after 1970 the change was very drastic. Today even Latin America as a region has become a net importer, along with Western Europe, Eastern Europe, the USSR, Africa, and Asia. Over the years it seems that the food production systems of the developing world have been disturbed by five major factors:

1. Introduction of cash crop production, which has taken over good lands in many areas and pushed the poor into marginal areas;
2. Penetration of the market as reflected in the increasing proportion of population obtaining basic required food through the market, thereby making purchasing power a key element of the food availability;
3. Changes in the land tenure system;
4. Environmental degradation leading to the loss of productivity of the land. According to United Nations Environmental Program, 26

---

[1] Introduced by Sylvan H. Wittwer.
[2] Former President of the International Fund for Agricultural Development, Rome, Italy.

billion tons of top soil are lost annually and 26 million hectares are reduced to zero productivity annually as a result of desertification and

5. The population growth beyond the carrying capacity of the land. Imbalance between population growth and food production growth has been a major factor in Africa's food dilemma. The population is growing at about 3% per annum, whereas food production growth is barely half of that rate. In addition, rapid population growth has contributed directly to high rates of urbanization, which in turn has accentuated Africa's deteriorating food situation.

The Trend and the Current World Food Situation

According to the Food and Agricultural Organization (FAO), world food production during the first half of the 1980s grew at an annual average rate of 2.4%, the same as that of the 1970s. The growth of production in China has contributed mostly to this trend. As for the developing market economies, growth of food production during 1980 to 1984 was 2.7% per annum, while the corresponding figure for 1971 to 1980 was 3.3%. Thus, food production growth has barely kept pace with the population growth in the 1980s with the exception of the Far East. Particularly alarming was the situation in Africa and in least developing countries where food production growth rates of 1.3 and 1.2%, respectively, are well below the respective population growth rates.

Although imports of food by developing countries constitute a big financial burden, increased volume of food imports had been an important factor in improving the nutritional standards for many countries during the 1970s. In all regions, the share of imports of food in total calorie supplies increased, for example, from 6 to 13% in Africa between the early 1970s and the early 1980s; 8 to 15% in Latin America; 12 to 23% in the Near East; and 5 to 7% in the Far East during the same period. However, developing countries had to curtail their imports in the 1980s due to the world economic crisis, which reduced the demand for their exports and, hence, their capacity to pay for imports.

The latest available data suggest that the world output of cereals will be a record in 1985 to 1986, at 863 million tons, some 34 million tons above the previous year. Improvement in weather is likely to contribute to improve harvests in many African countries and also in the USSR. The cereal stock of the world would represent 20% of the consumption in 1986 to 1987, which is considered adequate.

Multiple Dimensions of the World Food Problem

To seek durable solutions to the world food problem one needs to analyze carefully its multiple dimensions.

Seasonal Dimensions

Seasonality in availability and price movements affects intake and has implications for storage, transport, marketing, income, and employment generation. This is of course more of a regional and local problem.

Cyclical Dimensions

Cyclical problems manifest themselves in the form of natural disaster, market swings, wars and civil disorders, and the like. The consequences of the two African droughts of 1972 to 1974 and 1982 to 1984 are well-known. The unprecedented price rise, caused by a supply shortage in the international market of the early 1970s, seriously eroded the ability of food-deficit countries to obtain the necessary food imports. During that period the Ethiopian famine cost 500,000 lives; the Bangladesh famine claimed close to 1 million. Bangladesh was unable to buy food in the international market and emergency food shipments arrived too late. On the other hand, during 1982 to 1984 the African countries suffered from drought-related shortages. In addition, along with other food-deficit countries they found themselves in a disadvantaged situation, because with a sharp decline in their commodity export prices and high cost of energy, they were unable to import food commercially, although supply was abundant in the international market. The problems created by war and civil disorders are also very well-known.

Populations are dislocated and unlinked from the production base. Emergency food supplies have to be delivered under very unfriendly conditions. Productivity capacity use remains very low. And resumption of production requires financial and physical assistance and strategic forward planning. Examples of such populations included the 10 million Bangladeshi refugees who fled to India in 1971 during the Pakistan civil war, the Afghan refugees in Pakistan, the Cambodian population, and the Ethiopian population in the civil war-torn area.

Geographical Dimensions

The geographical dimensions of the problem arise from the fact that regions differ in terms of their intrinsic capacity to produce food. This, combined with differences in the state of agricultural technology, has created wide diversity in the availability of food between regions within the same country and between countries. There is sharp contrast between the recent crisis when the European Economic Communities (EEC) "suffered" from unprecedented surplus while at the same time thousands died from starvation in sub-Saharan Africa and over 100 million remained exposed to the threat of starvation for a prolonged period.

Another example is that of geographical diversity in food production. The United States, Canada, and EEC have a cereal stock of about 125 million tons out of a total world stock of about 290 million tons (as of February 1985). On the other hand, the bulk of the 125 million tons of developing country cereal stocks was concentrated in China, India, and a few Far Eastern countries.

Marketing and purchasing power dimensions are important factors when considering solutions to the world food problems. Marketing has been hampered by inadequate transport, storage, and pricing policies. Insufficient price incentives have often led farmers to produce only for self-consumption. Additionally, undue reliance on the market mechanism for food distribution does not take into account the fact that, in most developing developing countries, a large section of the rural population is too poor to buy the minimum required food. Hence, the creation of employment and purchasing power must go hand-in-hand with reliance on the market for food distribution. The lack of effective demand for food may aggravate a food-deficit situation by inducing outflow of market surplus to other regions. Some of the past famines occurred at a time when there was not an overall significant decline in food availability compared with the previous period. The problem was one of distribution through market and lack of purchasing power of consumers. The market mechanisms failed in many instances to move supplies from surplus to deficit areas in time of crisis. The free hand of the market does not always work the way it should. Sometimes, market flows may have to be supplemented by deliberate actions of the government and local authorities to avert human suffering.

Related to a reliance on the market mechanism for food distribution is the seasonal market price swings, which often find the small producers selling cheap after harvest and being forced to buy back a part of their requirement later at a much higher price. Undue government intervention in the market often creates additional problems, especially when the government is the monopoly buyer, and domestically procured and imported food grains are cheaply distributed to urban areas, thereby depressing market prices and discouraging domestic production.

International markets present four specific problems:

1. The international market supply comes from a few sources while demand is generated by many;
2. Countries with greater purchasing power can preempt supply. In 1972, large grain purchase by the Soviet Union was one of the factors precipitating the 1973 to 1974 world food crisis. Lack of foreign exchange may affect the purchase by poorer, deficit countries. This year alone low-income developing countries will require about $2 billion (U.S. dollars) in food aid and loans to finance required food imports. In this context one must take note of the International Monetary Fund's (IMF) cereal facility. Although only four countries have so far been able to take advantage of this facility, the recent 4-year extension of the facility is a move in the right direction;
3. Insulation (protection) of domestic markets by country groups from external shocks creates large supply and price variations in the

international market. This affects countries, both producing and consuming, exposed to such swings in market conditions; and

4. Since international market supply comes from a few countries, supply and prices are very sensitive to the domestic production, stock and pricing policies, and performance in those countries. The 1974 world food crisis was preceded by a slight shortfall in U.S. production below the trend, the first time in 25 years that such an occurrence took place.

Policy and Planning Dimensions

Policy and planning problems have plagued the food and agricultural sector at national, regional, and international levels. The food sector by and large has been neglected in public sector resource allocation. The average share of agriculture in central government public expenditure in developing countries has varied between 5 and 10%, although the sector accounts for a very large share of gross development product, employment, and export. Total public expenditure in agriculture in constant prices has either grown very slowly or declined over the 1978 to 1982 period in all regions except the Far East and Asia. There has actually been a decline of 5.3% per annum for the least-developed countries over this period. Within agriculture the food sector has lagged behind in public support related to the cash crop sector, which earned foreign exchange. There has been a general lack of balance in the development of the agricultural *versus* nonagricultural sector, on the one hand and food crops *versus* export crops on the other hand. Many countries failed to recognize that it was not easy to industrialize by neglecting agriculture, which was a source of raw material, food, cheap labor supply, and last but not least, investible surplus. Similarly, the food sector cannot be improved if the export sector fails to grow, since the latter is the source of foreign exchange necessary to import inputs and equipment for the food sector. Export crop producers will suffer in the absence of marketed food supply at reasonable prices, which is possible only if the food producers are able and willing to produce in excess of their own consumption requirement. Alternatively, export crop producers will be forced to neglect those crops and, to the extent feasible, will try to satisfy their own food consumption needs. This will essentially lead to inefficient allocation of land, labor, and capital, with its consequent cumulative adverse effect on both food and cash crop production.

Emphasis on Traditional Crops

Another policy aspect is the inadequate emphasis on traditional crops (broadly identified as millet, sorghum, cassava, yams, pulses, bananas, and plantains), which hold a considerable promise for sub-Saharan Africa, among other regions, where subsistence households have been cultivating them for a long time. These crops account for a significant share of the daily calorie intake in many countries. They are also important in terms of land use, labor absorption, family and community food security, national self-sufficiency in food, and the involvement of women. Their importance as food security crops arises from the fact that they are more drought resistant and relatively easy to store compared with imported cereals, which have imposed an undue burden on foreign exchange resources and the storage and transport capacity of the developing countries. Despite these well-recognized advantages, they have been considered as a "poor man's" crops and have suffered from lack of improved technology. Very little resources have been devoted to research on development of improved varieties, better pest and disease control, on improved processing, for example.

Research, Extension, Training, and Credit

Agricultural research and extension have been poorly funded. Whatever resources were allocated went to research on cash crops. Regional and international research centers under the auspices of the Consultative Group on International Agriculture Research are making good efforts; however, there is a need to do more, particularly in terms of improving capacities of national institutions, promoting farming systems-based research, expanding field trials under normal farming conditions, and strengthening linkages between research, extension, and training.

Extension services are virtually nonexistent in many countries. Where they exist, they have little to offer to the farmers. The extension agents are usually poorly trained, poorly paid, and poorly equipped. Above all, the extension service is very poorly managed. Restructuring of the extension services has been attempted in many countries with varying results.

According to many experts, training of agricultural officials as well as of farmers is crucial if the battle against hunger is to be won once and for all. In Africa, in particular, lack of human resources has been identified as a serious bottleneck to output growth and improved food security. In most of the countries, there is a lack of supply of skilled manpower. Integration of manpower into a sound institutional structure would provide a basis for efficient program design and implementation. Regional and national training institutions have been unable to respond to the increased demand for trained manpower. Typical problems are shortage of trainers, poor curricula, and lack of training equipment. The problem is confronted at all levels—national, regional, and project. The situation has been further aggravated by a lack of incentives for the trained manpower who often find a way out of the system to the parastatal sector, the private sector, or abroad.

An important aspect that deserves special emphasis is credit, the source of innovation and investment by farmers. Unfortunately, they have received little support from institutional sources, which have shied away from the agricultural sector in general and food production in particular.

Farmers had to rely primarily on the high cost, informal sector. In some cases, the informal sources of credit have played a very important role by filling the void, but they have often been exploitative, and their actions have militated against investment in new technology and other risk-taking activities by the small farmers.

An important event in the history of international cooperation took place in 1974. The World Food Conference of 1974 not only marked the first occasion of a global understanding of the need to focus on the longer-term investment in food production but also recognized the link between the food and poverty issues. This led to the creation of the World Food Council and International Fund for Agricultural Development (IFAD). In this connection the efforts of John Hannah are widely acknowledged. Being the first executive director of the World Food Council, his effective role in assisting member governments during the establishment of IFAD has been highly appreciated. The creation of IFAD—with its objectives of assisting developing countries in increasing food production, reducing malnutrition, and alleviating rural poverty—is a landmark in the history of development financing.

For IFAD, the emphasis on low-income developing countries is not a matter of choice, it is built into the institution's charter. As of September 1985, the Fund has provided loans to 55 countries that total $2 billion (U.S. dollars).

A major area of IFAD's concern is the generation of productive employment for the landless in rural areas. The major strategy to achieve this has been to devise innovative means for extending credit to this group without collateral so they could purchase productive assets that would give them employment and income. This has been successfully accomplished in several countries in Asia to the point that it is now generally acknowledged that the landless, if the proper institutional set-up is promoted, are as creditworthy, or even more so, in comparison with other groups of rural population.

Finally, IFAD has responded to the critical situation in Africa by formulating a Special Program for sub-Saharan Africa to address the longer-term problems of rural development and food production. The Fund has been very careful to avoid duplication of efforts with other multilateral and bilateral agencies working in this region.

Which Way to Move in the Future

The background and the dimensions of the world food problem suggest a wide range of short-, medium-, and long-term measures to overcome the basic impediments to the elimination of hunger within a reasonable period of time. The resolutions of the 1974 World Food Conference laid out a comprehensive list of such measures. What was true then is also true today—concerted multifaceted actions must be undertaken at the local, regional, national, and international level.

As for emergency assistance at the country level, it is necessary to develop national preparedness plans to tackle potential food shortages. Some of the elements of these plans include early warning systems, food relief contingency schemes, backup arrangements for mobilizing supplies, and detailed plans for distributing emergency food supplies, which in turn call for strengthening logistical capacities. By prepositioning food stocks in disaster-prone areas, the lead time necessary for providing food to the famine-affected populations can be cut down. At the international level, required measures may include: stand-by resources for the International Emergency Food Reserve, strengthening the emerging provisions of the Food Aid Convention, and establishing a system of interim food reserves. Because of its precarious situation, Africa deserves special emphasis.

To tackle the African predicament, future measures should take into account the following lessons drawn from recent developments:

1. Famine-stricken populations require emergency food assistance, but their long-term well-being lies in employment-creating investment in the sustained development of local food production;

2. Populations who do not have access to productive resources must be provided with opportunities for self-employment or wage employment so as to have the purchasing power to obtain the necessary food. Therefore, both agricultural and nonagricultural rural activities must be supported to assist the rural poor to improve their condition;

3. The objective of durable employment creation and poverty alleviation must not be forgotten in the pursuit of economic efficiency and growth of output;

4. In the search for a lasting solution to the hunger problem, steps must be taken to ensure that international aid flows actually reach the rural poor—the small farmers and the landless workers. The former are efficient producers, responsive to market and institutional incentives. The latter must be aided through investment in employment-generating activities in rural areas, which boosts total rural production and reduces pressure on rural-urban migration; and

5. In most developing countries, sustained growth of output and employment is not possible without substantial investment in rural development. In the long run, underinvestment in rural areas will undermine the overall objectives of development and equity.

It is recognized by all concerned that once emergencies have passed, the critical issues of rehabilitation and the long-term development in Africa must be addressed simultaneously. The rehabilitation support must be in the form of: Assuring adequate supplies of food production inputs for the coming season, particularly seeds and fertilizers; assuring logistical capacity and incentives to make these inputs locally available at the time needed; affording access to these inputs by all, through credit or other means; and provide technical guidance for the best use of these inputs.

The long-term challenges confronting Africa have been summarized by FAO in a succinct way with which there can be little disagreement. The major areas of emphasis are:

1. Careful utilization of natural and financial resources;
2. Protection and enhancement of the environment;
3. Development of human resources and institutions;
4. Finding an answer to the demographic problem;
5. Slowing down the rapid urbanization trends;
6. Striking a balance between food crop and export crop production;
7. Evolving an appropriate production incentive framework without necessarily sacrificing consumer interests;
8. Increasing the flow of domestic and external resources to agriculture;
9. Allocating a larger share of resources to agricultural research;
10. Developing where appropriate a combined regional approach to food issues; and
11. Putting appropriate emphasis on traditional crop production through technology adaptation and/or diffusion, technology development, infrastructure and draft power development; and policy and institutional support.

While the above have been mentioned specifically in the context of Africa, many of these elements are also applicable to other situations. It is very clear that, to avert a deteriorating food situation, timely formulation and implementation of national food strategies is important. It must be accompanied by training of policy analysts, improvement of statistical data, close monitoring and evaluation of programs, recognition and promotion of the role of women, and development of technical and economic cooperation at all levels.

As the World Food Council pointed out at its 11th session, increased emphasis must be placed on policies and reforms that provide for more balanced food crop and export crop policies, that intensify investment in small-scale irrigation, and adjust national priorities to deal more broadly with rural poverty.

On the question of external assistance to agriculture, there can be little controversy—the volume must increase substantially and the share of concessional assistance in total assistance to agriculture must increase. For Africa alone, the executive director of the World Food Council has estimated that at least $1 billion (U.S. dollars) more than what has so far been committed must be made available in concessionary aid. In this context, one must reiterate the case for concluding the second replenishment negotiations of IFAD's resources without any further delay. The Fund is one of the most important sources of concessional resources for investment in the development of food production in low-income developing countries. Donors must reassert their faith in this institution and come to an understanding about its future long-term financial level. This is a must for IFAD to operate effectively at an appropriate level, as it has in the past.

The question of effectiveness of aid in support of the food sector must receive proper attention from all concerned. Improving the quality of aid will require adjustments in domestic policies and also in the policies of the donors. Aid agencies need to orient their policies and programs to support the policy adjustments of recipient countries. A more focused approach to food and agricultural development should be the central policy focus of both donors and recipient countries alike. Furthermore, there should be an improvement in programming of food aid to support developmental activities.

Finally, there are a few issues involving the external environment that must be addressed in the context of seeking to resolve the world food problems. These issues relate to the following:

1 Resolution of the debt problems in a manner that will not overlook the special needs of the small-scale food producers;
2. Adjustment of the developed country economies to accommodate agricultural exports of developing countries;
3. Greater emphasis on agricultural commodities in future multilateral trade negotiations under the auspices of the General Agreement on Tariffs and Trade (GATT);
4. Raising the food aid conventions minimum overall commitment to 10 million tons; and
5. Engaging the International Wheat Council to explore the possibility of including new elements in an agreement that will facilitate development country imports taking full account of the interest of all parties concerned.

I conclude that the real problem in tackling hunger and poverty is the lack of political will.

Past, Present, and Future of Agricultural Research[1]

Charles E. Hess

Productivity in American agriculture has been hailed as one of the success stories of our nation, a prime example of American ingenuity. A look into the early history of our country, however, shows that productivity had a rather slow start. Documentation for this conclusion is shown in Figure 1 (4). The Office of Technology Assessment report divides the history of agricultural productivity into four major periods—hand power, horse power, mechanical power, and finally, science power. The transitions from one form of power to another were marked by the Civil War, World War I, and World War II.

From Figure 1, it is clear that during the period called "science power," or more correctly, the period of science and technology, is when dramatic gains in productivity were achieved. Several indices to measure productivity from the 1950s to 1978 are provided by Evenson *et al.* (1). As shown in Figure 2 from Evenson *et al.*, land productivity increased at a rate of nearly 2% per year. There was a dip in productivity in the early 1970s, when, in part, less productive land was removed from the soil bank in response to world grain shortages. The index of labor productivity is widely used in agriculture and industry and, as shown in Figure 2, since 1950, labor productivity has grown far more rapidly in agriculture than in the non-farm sector. Total productivity, which is calculated by dividing the index of farm output by the index of total farm input, has also grown rapidly since the 1950s. According to Evenson *et al.*, in the 30-year period from 1949 to 1979, scientific and technological innovation increased agricultural output by 85% with no change in the aggregate level of agriculture input.

What is the foundation upon which this period of science power is built? According to agricultural historian Morton Rothstein (7), the beginning is found in the formation of a loosely knit and highly diverse network of farmer clubs that evolved into state agricultural societies. The work of these new institutions became particularly significant during the 1840s, when the first major advances in agricultural technology were introduced, including the reaping machines developed by Obed Hussey and Cyrus McCormick, and the steel-tipped plows manufactured by John Deere. Before that, the bottleneck to increased productivity in small grains was the inability of the individual farmer to harvest efficiently the grain. Rasmussen (6) has called the period from 1840 to 1880, the "First

---

[1] Introduced by Sylvan H. Wittwer.

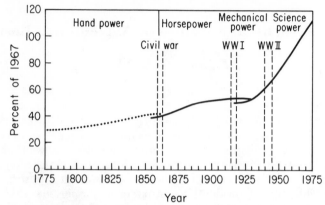

FIG. 1.   U.S. agricultural productivity growth during the past 200 years.

American Agricultural Revolution," when the diffusion of horse-drawn machinery made possible the rapid expansion of wheat output by increasing the yield per man hour rather than per acre.

By the 1850s, the State Agricultural Society and other farm organizations, such as the Grange, had strengthened. The United States Agricultural Society, whose members were primarily from the eastern states and who sought to apply science to the service of farmers, began pushing for congressional action to establish federally endowed universities. Their interest was raised by the discoveries of scientific research that were applicable to agriculture in special institutional settings such as Harvard, Yale, and other private universities, but they wanted "better," practical knowledge about the biological and chemical processes in farming that Justus Liebig's work in soil chemistry had promised.

In 1862, Congress passed the Homestead Act, created a Department of Agriculture, and—most significant to this discussion—approved the Morrill Land Grant Act. There was not, however, full support for the legislation. The southeast was opposed to federal aid and the west considered legislation that gave each congressman 30,000 acres from the public domain to be grossly unfair, since most of the congressmen were in the east and the public lands were in the west. However, the income from the land was to be used to support a university where agricultural and mechanical arts could be taught and the Act created a system of public universities dedicated to the mission of offering practical help for farmers through science and technology. The Act has been called one of America's great social inventions. It has also been described as an act of faith with few immediate results. Political activists were critical of the apparent failure of the newly formed land grant colleges to teach useful courses or to engage in research that addressed the immediate needs of the farmer. These criticisms are not unfamiliar to us more than 100 years later.

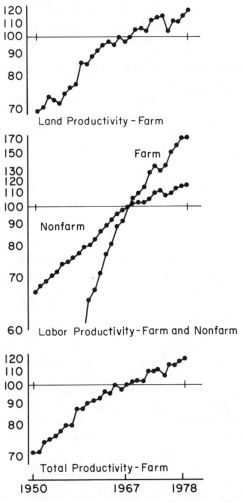

FIG. 2.   Productivity measures (1967 = 100).

Nevertheless, faith in potential progress through science was undiminished and the state agricultural societies, producers' associations, and administrators of the land grant colleges working with elected representatives at the state and national levels, provided the impetus for the Hatch Act of 1887. The Hatch Act established the agricultural experiment stations to serve agriculture with research and testing. When it became obvious, some 20 years later, that the small staffs at the experiment stations were overwhelmed with routine service functions, and major problems lacked attention, the network of agricultural organizations, land grant administrators, and legislators pushed through the

Adams Act of 1906, which increased the appropriations but required that all additional support be devoted solely to research. The specific wording of the legislation obligating additional funding to research is: " ... and the annual amount to be paid thereafter to each state and territory shall be thirty thousand dollars, to be applied only to paying the necessary expenses of conducting original researches or experiments bearing directly on the agricultural industry of the United States having due regard to the varying conditions and needs of the respective states or territories." Thus, the Adams Act of 1906 gave each experiment station the mandate to do original research and endorsed a decentralized strategy that was believed to be the best way to solve each state's unique farm problems.

I shall point out here that Evenson *et al.* (1) have stated that the decentralized strategy is one of the strengths and sources of the success of the American agricultural research system. Still, growth in agricultural productivity in this early period of the 20th century remained relatively slow.

Part of the problem was the lack of communication. Few farmers benefited from the gradual spread of electricity, telephones, paved roads, or better schools, all of which were changing the lives of urban Americans. The limited involvement of farmers in short courses taught at universities did not provide the regular, practical, and immediate help they needed, and most remained in social isolation. It was Henry Ford's "Tin Lizzie" that started breaking into that isolation, bringing to farmers a growing number of young men, newly trained at land grant universities and eager to demonstrate new techniques and varieties of farming and to deliver information that would improve the livelihood of the farmer.

An example of the success of such "extension" efforts was the work of Seaman Knapp, who organized teams to help sharecroppers in Louisiana and Texas in their struggle against the boll weevil. By demonstrating ways to cultivate cotton that would disrupt the weevil's life cycle, the virtue of these pre-extension era workers became evident and the idea quickly spread. In 1914, Congress passed the Smith-Lever Act, which provided federal funding to supplement state and county funds. Thus, the Cooperative Extension Service was established, providing rapid diffusion of scientific and technical knowledge. The birth of cooperative extension is viewed as the second major invention that shaped our agricultural institutions, helping make possible the rapid growth in productivity during the science power era of American agriculture.

World War II helped accelerate the true transformation of agriculture in the United States, just as it ended the Depression. The shortage of labor pulled many of those underemployed on the farm into the factory, service, or other urban jobs, providing parity prices for those who stayed on the farm for the first time since 1920. During the war, farmers received special exemptions for fuel and tires, and by using all available machinery, produced 25% more food and fiber with 25% fewer workers. Also, new

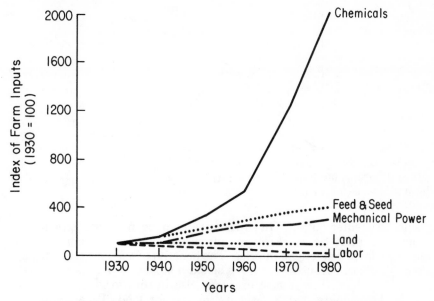

FIG. 3.   Changing inputs in agricultural production, 1930 to 1980.

chemicals such as herbicides and organophosphate pesticides, produced in association with the war effort, became available for agricultural use. A measure of the increased use of science and technology power is shown in Figure 3 (2). Between 1930 and 1980, labor input declined by more than 80%. Meanwhile, the use of mechanical power rose 200%, agricultural chemicals 1900%, and seed almost 300%. Crop land as an input remained almost constant.

In addition to increased efficiency of production from the application of the new tools provided by science, tax laws encouraged expanded production capacity through the substitution of capital for labor and land. Examples of the tax provisions include tax advantages for expanding many capital investments, capital gains treatment of certain livestock returns, investment tax credits, and accelerated depreciation rates. In other words, federal policies provided an incentive to use the new science and technology, and consequently contributed substantially to the rapid increase in productivity.

What have the benefits and costs to society been during this period of rapid increase in productivity due to "science power?" One benefit of increased productivity or increased production efficiency is that costs to the consumer have been reduced. A generalized presentation of the distribution of the benefits of new technology is shown in Figure 4 (3). To be adopted, new technologies usually reduce the unit cost of production, or keep it below what it otherwise might have been. This often

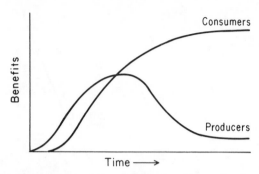

FIG. 4. Generalized nature of the distribution of benefits from a new agricultural technology over time.

results in greater output. Given that the demand for most agricultural products is inelastic, increases in output are generally accompanied by relatively large reductions in price. The benefits of the new technologies affect all of us, because Americans spend a smaller percentage of their incomes on food than almost everyone else in the world. In 1950, the average household spent 22% of its income for food. Today, approximately 15% of household income is spent on food. In other countries, the percentage income spent for food is as follows: Israel, 24.8%; Germany, 27.0%; Japan, 34.0%; Russia, 50.0%; and developing countries, 60 to 70%.

Not only are consumers the ultimate beneficiaries of agricultural research, but it is lower income families who benefit most. In fact, the cost per household for agricultural research is only $1.31 for the lowest income class, that of under $5,000 annual income. But for the highest income families, those earning over $20,000, the research cost is $25.60. Compare these costs to the average benefits per family, which fall between $16.20 and $30.74 in 1979. The cost-benefit ratio ranged from 1.20 for high-income families to an impressive 12.37 for low-income families.

An Office of Technology Assessment report (4) entitled *An Assessment of the United States Food and Agricultural Research System* states: "Both benefits and costs of agricultural research tend to redistribute income from higher to lower income families. However, even those families in the highest income class receive net benefits from research investment on agricultural productivity."

Another benefit of increased productivity, at least initially, was the release of labor from food and fiber production to work in other sectors of our economy. As shown in Figure 5, the greatest decrease in farm workers since 1950 was in the category of farm family labor, often the unpaid or underpaid sons, daughters, and spouses of the average farmer. Today approximately 3% of our population is directly involved in on-farm production of food and fiber compared with 13% in Western Europe, 32% in Russia, 40% in Latin America, 50% in Asia, and 73% in Africa.

FIG. 5.   Decrease in number of farm workers, 1950 to 1980.

The flow of labor from farm to non-farm sectors of our economy has raised the national income because average non-farm income is typically higher than the average farm income. It is estimated that, from the period from 1949 to 1979, the increase in total national income amounted to $111.8 billion.

But, in addition to the release of farm labor for work in other sectors of the economy, there was also a dramatic decrease in the number of farms and an increase in farm size, as shown in Figure 6. In 1930, there were 6.3 million farms, averaging 157 acres in size. In 1983, there were 2.3 million farms averaging 437 acres. Many critics blame science and technology for the decline in farm numbers and the growth of farm size. Farmers in the 1930s were largely self-contained, but now they purchase about three-fourths of their production staples, such as pesticides, machinery, fuel, improved varieties, and fertilizers from outside sources. Extensive purchase of production supplies from non-farm sources requires that farmers maintain adequate cash flow and be able to obtain operating credit. This situation makes the farmer far more vulnerable to economic externalities while still being subjected to the vagaries of weather and the marketplace.

While it is true that science and technology have made larger farming operations possible, it is incorrect to place most of the blame for the decline of farm numbers and the growth of farm size on science. Economic factors such as economies of scale associated with large purchases, and policy issues discussed earlier—such as investment tax credits, accelerated depreciation rates, and government price supports—and other farm programs, all contribute to the decrease in farm numbers. In our current economic climate of depressed farm prices and loans made with high interest rates, the number of farms will continue to decline and the average farm size increase.

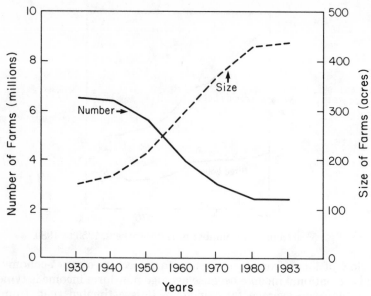

FIG. 6.   Number of farms compared with farm size.

Along with the criticism of the effects of science upon farm size is the current association of science and technology with farm surpluses. Once again, we hear the suggestion that a moratorium be placed on "production" research, or that resources in the plant and animal sciences be reallocated to agricultural economics and marketing programs to solve the "real" problem in agriculture—finding a home for surplus products. In my opinion, agricultural research that leads to a more efficient conversion of the sun's energy into corn, soybean, or strawberry production, does not cause surpluses. It is the farmer's decision—often influenced by federal policy—to increase the acreage of a more efficient new variety, rather than to decrease the acreage, thereby decreasing inputs, producing the same amount at less cost, and enabling him to be more competitive and show a larger return on his investment. If we are to maintain our competitive advantage in the international marketplace when the dollar returns to more realistic values, we had better continue our investments in agricultural research. As Evenson et al. (1) have stated, agricultural research represents one of the best research investments in any sector of our economy, providing an annual rate of return on the research investment of approximately 50%. Equally important, if we are to reduce our dependency on agricultural chemicals through the development of disease and insect-resistant varieties, and increase the efficiency and range of biological nitrogen fixation; provide greater resilience to environmental stress, to develop new crops; and to preserve genetic diversity in plants, we had better continue to invest in agricultural research in general, and plant biology research in particular. Fortunately, Dr. George Keyworth, the President's Science Advisor and Director of the Office of Science and Technology Policy (OSTP), recognizes the value of investing in research to keep America competitive. His special support of the USDA Competitive Grants Program in Biotechnology is an example of putting such policy into action. A proposed initiative for science and technology for the 1986–1987 fiscal year is being explored by Dr. Keyworth and the staff of the OSTP and, if successful, will contain a component for plant biology being jointly developed by the USDA, the National Science Foundation, and the Department of Energy. We must be careful that the misguided view, that the solution to surplus problems is to stop research, does not jeopardize the long-term competitive and environmental health of our agriculture and nation.

We must also recognize that we are working in a society that wishes to play a larger role in setting the research agenda, whether it be farmers plagued with low prices and high debts; farm workers concerned about displacement by labor-saving devices; environmentalists concerned about pesticides, ecologists and others concerned about the release of recombinant DNA modified organisms; or animal rights activists who wish to prohibit the use of animals in research or for food. As I have stated many times before, these concerned individuals have mastered the use of the media and the courts to make their case. We, too, must become involved.

First, we must be sure our own house is in order. Beyond the traditional objective that technology must be profitable for the user, we must continue to apply additional criteria in agricultural research and development. We must also be certain that society is aware of what criteria we are using. Included are: (a) energy efficiency, (b) acceptable long-range physical impact on the environment, (c) the study and minimization of health and safety risks, and (d) awareness of any social consequences, their acceptability to society and potential ways to address expected social costs.

Second, we must be sure the research we do is necessary, and that if there are risks, such as the possible release of a pathogen, all reasonable precautions are taken. When animals are used in research, we must ensure that they are properly cared for and that any pain involved is reduced to a minimum. The fact that the scientific community established its own stringent restrictions at the beginning of recombinant DNA research gave assurance to a majority of the public that we placed a high value on their safety and concerns. In return, there was self-policing rather than overregulation from outside groups. Finally, when doing research supported in a large part by public funds, we must provide assurance that the work we do is for the benefit of the greater society and not for specific interest groups. It is far better that we regulate ourselves than have external agencies do it for us.

Beyond these activities, we have a special responsibility as educational institutions to do all we can to ensure that our graduates, whether from agriculture, engineering, or the liberal arts, have scientific and agricultural literacy. Part of the current problem is due to a lack of background on which to base rational decisions. We are attempting to do research in an environment in which the public is underinformed, misinformed, or wholly ignorant of the issues, but at least a part of that public wants to play a role in the decision-making process. This is perfectly appropriate in a democratic society. However, we must educate the public and the policymakers about our research and the benefits to society and assure them that we are aware of the risks and the costs as well as the benefits. Then their participation in the decision-making process will be based on knowledge rather than fearful ignorance.

What about the future of agricultural research? It is both a tremendous opportunity and an enormous challenge. As Michael Phillips (5) of the Office of Technology Assessment has stated, "American agriculture is now entering a new major technological thrust—the biotechnology and information technology era." Phillips believes that this new era could be more profound than any previous era we have experienced. Accompanying the new era are an expanded involvement by the private sector in applied agricultural research and an increased public sector emphasis on basic research. The new biotechnology is providing new tools to move genetic information from microorganisms to plants, or to move single genes from one plant to another. It is also rapidly expanding our basic knowledge about plant growth and development and how genes are expressed or not expressed during development. Also, the time span from discovery of basic information to its application has grown considerably shorter. Earlier studies indicated that the time between a basic discovery and its application might be as long as 25 years. Now, 25 months would not be unusual. The coupling of molecular biology with computer technology to study active sites on molecules and then design new ones to achieve specific functions has tremendous potential to speed the development of environmentally acceptable new compounds in comparison to the synthesis and screening techniques that have been the primary source of biologically active compounds.

What then are the challenges? First, the excitement and opportunity in the biological sciences is taking place when enrollment in the land grant colleges of agriculture is declining, particularly in the plant sciences.

Second, is the fact that the faculty in land grant colleges expanded substantially after World War II, but they are now retiring and with them is going a wealth of experience. The new faculty members we are hiring come from nonagricultural backgrounds and are trained in disciplines such as genetics, plant physiology, biochemistry, and molecular biology. The rewards system, in the form of extramural support and promotion, favors continued research in discipline specialties and publication in peer reviewed professional journals. The result is a lack of commitment to the missions of the college and university and a lack of communication with the constituencies that formed the land grant college in the first place and continue to be the major source of organized support. The perception of today's farm community is similar to that expressed back in the 1800s: we do not teach useful courses or engage in research that addresses the farmer's immediate problems.

What is the proper course of action to capitalize on the potential of the new technologies; to recognize the changing structure of agriculture and the agricultural research system; to maintain the synergistic inter-action between basic and applied research that has made us so successful; and, finally, to maintain the linkage with the farmer to ensure that new information is rapidly put to use on farms of all sizes to enhance American agriculture's economic viability and competitive advantage?

Let me turn first to the challenge of decreasing student numbers in the plant sciences. We recently conducted a study in a number of California high schools in both urban and suburban areas, the primary source of our undergraduate students. We discovered that students have a negative attitude about agriculture and are uninterested in plant science in general. To them, there appears to be no excitement and no obvious career possibilities, as compared to engineering or computer science. This revelation is certainly dismaying, but it also does not make sense when I think about the excitement generated by stage I of this conference at the Boyne Highlands Inn. We must capture this excitement and instill it in the science classes in our junior and senior high schools where students are first exposed to plant biology, and in my opinion, are for some reason, not excited about it. Developing laboratory experiments in plant cell culture that can be conducted with limited facilities at a high school level should capture the imaginations of many bright young minds. The era of biotechnology can provide us with the format to rebuild the storehouse of intellectual capital in the plant sciences. And we can begin with tomorrow's scientists, who are eighth and ninth graders today.

Now to the larger challenge: how do we perform our role in research and, at the same time, serve our constituencies in agriculture, particularly if the land grant colleges are to play a larger role in basic research and the private sector a larger role in applied research?

First of all, I want to make it clear that I am not suggesting we separate basic and applied research and divide them between the public and private sectors. A number of studies have shown that it is essential that the interaction between basic research and application be fostered and maintained (8). It is a great strength of the land grant colleges. The interaction ensures a relevance of the basic research to state and national needs, and helps ensure high quality applied research using the latest information and techniques. Evenson et al. (1) stated that the greatest impact of "science-oriented" research is realized when it is conducted in association with technology-oriented research. Last year, the National Science Foundation established the first six engineering research centers to foster this same interaction in the field of engineering, a program fully endorsed by Dr. Keyworth. At the same time, however, we must recognize that land grant colleges are not the only actors in the applied research arena, particularly in biotechnology.

Next, we must recognize the fact that our new faculty will come primarily with a discipline background and without agricultural experience, and will work in a rewards system that nurtures basic research. We must also recognize that land grant universities have been, and should continue to be, a source of new knowledge developed through basic research and that such research is an essential component of graduate education.

The result is a widening gulf between the research being conducted in the university laboratory and the application of knowledge in the farmer's field. The gap has to be closed from two directions: one, from the university side, and the other from the outreach component of the land grant university, the Cooperative Extension Service. From the university side, I believe we have to modify our rewards system to recognize quality, mission oriented research as well as basic research published in peer reviewed journals. We must encourage the interaction of basic and mission oriented research and avoid the creation of elitist groups of faculty. For example, in hiring for the new biotechnology, you could create an institute of molecular biology with a staff of molecular biologists. Or, you could place the molecular biologists in mission oriented departments to allow better interaction with breeders, geneticists, and physiologists and to have them work together on problems confronting the agricultural and environmental sciences. We did just that, but we are also providing mechanisms to facilitate interaction among the molecular biologists so they will maintain their disciplinary strengths. A growing knowledge and respect for each other's fields and strengths will result in better appreciation of the other's research when they are involved in peer reviews.

Another approach to motivate productive collaboration is to create an environment that encourages multidisciplinary research. The most effective way to create such an environment is to provide funds to support that research. Some entities, such as the McKnight Foundation, have awarded grants partly on the basis of proven ability to conduct multidisciplinary research. I encourage policymakers in all agencies to set aside some funding specifically for this purpose. These grants have to be larger than grants for individual researchers, and ideally should be provided for a longer period of time, such as 5 years rather than 3 years.

Still another approach to closing the gap between basic research and its application is to modify the historic role of Cooperative Extension. That is to recognize specifically and provide funding for an applied research role for the Cooperative Extension Service. Ideally such research should be jointly planned and conducted by the research faculty and the extension specialists. Such interaction would enhance two-way communication, bringing the real world into the laboratory and making the extension specialist more aware of the research being conducted in the university and how it may be applied to the solution of problems in the field. This approach would reestablish the continuum that has existed in the past between basic research and the application of knowledge on the farm and in the environment. The question is raised, but what will Cooperative Extension give up if it is to become involved in applied research? Two possibilities are suggested. One is to concentrate the scope of Cooperative Extension's mission to agricultural and agriculturally related programs, rather than attempting to be a service to all people. The second possibility is to concentrate on service to small and mid size farms, since the large farm operations may have their own research unit or hire private consultants to provide advice.

I believe that the structure of the land grant college system with its tripartite responsibility of teaching, research, and service is basically sound. However, with the changing structure of agriculture, the changing nature of agricultural research, and the changing backgrounds of the participants in the agricultural research system, we need to make adjustments if we are to continue serving agriculture and the larger society and continue to enjoy their support in return.

LITERATURE CITED

1. EVENSON RE, PE WAGGONER, VW RUTTAN 1979 Economic benefits from research: an example of agricultural science. Science 205: 1101–1107
2. GENERAL ACCOUNTING OFFICE 1985 Briefing Report to Congress (November). U.S. Food: Agriculture in a Volatile World Economy. GAO/RCED-86-3BR
3. NIELSON J 1978 Public support for agricultural research and extension—investing in the future Mississippi Agricultural Experiment Station, Special Publication (December), p 5
4. OFFICE OF TECHNOLOGY ASSESSMENT 1981 An Assessment of the United States Food and Agricultural Research System. OTA-F-155 (December), p 67
5. PHILLIPS MJ 1985 Implications of evolving technology for American agriculture. Unpublished manuscript based on work on an Office of Technology Assessment study of the relationship between technology, farm structure and public policy
6. RASMUSSEN WD 1962 The impact of technological change on American agriculture, 1862–1962. J Econ Hist 22: 578–591
7. ROTHSTEIN M 1985 Technological change and American farm movements (Working Paper Series No. 23). Agricultural History Center, University of California, Davis, CA
8. SHAPLEY D, R RUSTUM 1985 Lost at the Frontier—U.S. Science and Technology Policy Adrift. ISI Press, Philadelphia

The Impact of Biotechnology on Agricultural Research[1]

Peter R. Day

This paper considers current work in plant molecular biology and the effect it is having on breeding agronomic crop plants. Most reviews of this topic discuss the achievements in molecular biology, using them as a basis for speculation about their practical potential. The goals include increasing photosynthesis, introducing genes for nitrogen fixation, resistance to stress or parasites, and improved nutritional quality. The time scales vary. Some are long—of the order of a decade (11) or more—others are unrealistically short. No one would deny that plant genetics and plant breeding are entering an exciting period of change and development, which is in large part due to the accelerating pace of discovery in plant molecular biology (14). However, I have chosen not to discuss findings in any detail but will instead deal with the problem of harnessing and transferring the new technology. All too often the problems associated with transfer receive either lip service or it is taken for granted that they will be solved by advances in the science. I set out below the nature of these problems and some suggestions on how they can be overcome.

Polarization

One unfortunate but not unexpected result of the impact has been polarization. Molecular biologists and plant breeders use different languages and work, on very different time scales, at either end of the spectrum of organization from molecules to populations. They therefore cannot be expected automatically to have a productive interaction. Molecular biology is widely perceived by government and industry as a means of revolutionizing plant and animal improvement. It is attracting substantial funding. Plant breeding, on the other hand, is a well established if inexact discipline, that is continuing to deliver improvements at the end of a long chain of effort extending over many seasons and trials on many sites. Government funding for plant breeding has declined at an alarming rate both in the United States and United Kingdom.

Plant breeders express their cynicism toward the more extravagant claims made for biotechnology. Some believe that it is a passing phase. All of them are concerned that tunnel vision may so distort the balance of effort in agricultural research that conventional skills, tools, and

[1] Introduced by Robert Rabson.

facilities are neglected or discarded. As I will argue presently, all of these resources will be sorely needed for the foreseeable future.

It is unreasonable to expect that by simply asking plant breeders and molecular biologists to collaborate they will easily produce crop plant improvements. Their interaction must be encouraged. It cannot be productively sustained if the two activities are carried on in separate places nor will it work properly if the two communities remain isolated under the same roof. It is most important therefore to develop strong bonds that grow in both directions and to nurture communication and interaction.

At the Plant Breeding Institute in Cambridge a conscious effort has been made to establish a properly balanced strength and excellence in breeding and in the sciences that underpin crop improvement. For example, expertise in cereal cytogenetics, pathology, physiology, chemistry, and statistics has served as a backup and support system for cereal breeders. It has provided genetic variation from alien species in a form breeders can readily use, solutions to problems of instability and sterility, and new tools to speed their work. It has demonstrated how to select and assemble characters in new cultivars through understanding their genetic controls and their linkage relationships. It has led to the exploitation of a range of dwarfing genes, resistance to eyespot disease (*Pseudocercosporella herpotrichoides*) from *Aegilops ventricosa* and the glutenin storage proteins in wheat that contribute to baking quality, to quote but a few examples.

Work in cytogenetics has the advantage that it directly involves whole growing plants, making the link with breeders simpler. Molecular biologists tend to be more remote from crop plants, concentrating instead on model systems, tissue cultures and cloned fragments of plant DNA, and on plants chosen for their experimental convenience rather than their commercial significance. They are consequently much less aware of breeders' problems. Molecular genetics and cytogenetics have much to contribute to each other. Cytogenetics can help to simplify the development of methods by providing materials that are well explored and understood genetically. However, this dialogue may take some time to be of direct help to the breeder unless he joins in or is represented in it.

The large conceptual gap between molecular biology and plant breeding must therefore be overcome by special efforts. One way is to have people who can work with both groups. Their job is to solicit specific pieces of technology and show how they can be put to work in breeding programs, if necessary by producing material for breeders to evaluate. They must be able to recognize the potential of new findings and help in the discussions of how they might be adapted and developed to be useful. Such people are rare. At the moment there are no training programs to produce them. There are some that might be modified for this purpose. In Cambridge, for example, a 1-year master of philosophy program offers training in plant breeding to graduates in agriculture, botany, genetics, and other related subjects. At the present time this program would be very useful to a graduate in biochemistry who is already prepared in genetics and molecular biology. For those not so prepared it would need considerable augmentation to be really useful training for transferring biotechnology. Those who will do this job must understand plant breeding goals and how breeders set about relieving the constraints to progress. They must also understand molecular biology sufficiently to be able to pick out those parts that are useful and influence research planning so that particular relevant areas of science are properly considered. They must also resist the temptation to become molecular biologists themselves and unconcerned with its application.

Realistic Expectations

Crop production depends on a flow of new varieties which, through improvements in yield, quality, and resistance to various stresses, contribute to greater output, reduced production costs, or often to both. Plant breeders can therefore expect that effective work in biotechnology will help them to achieve their objectives. Breeders first identify useful variation and then try to assemble it in new forms from which, with the aid of a wide range of tests and trials in different locations and seasons, they can select those which show general adaptation and improvement in one or more respects. Since plant molecular biology is concerned with the organization of plant genomes, how they are constructed and regulated, and how genotype is expressed as phenotype, it should make major contributions to plant breeding. In fact its contributions so far are modest but not unimportant.

There are several reasons for this. The first and most obvious is our ignorance of the genetic and molecular basis of most of the characters plant breeders must, of necessity, work with. For example, harvestable yield is the result of many component processes that may individually respond to adjustment but which require overall integration. It would be naive therefore to expect, with our present knowledge, that genetic information could be assembled in such a way that a simple transformation step would enable us to introduce it and effect a great increase in this character. Much variation for yield is likely due to differences in regulatory genes that affect development and metabolism (1). We are only at the beginning of work to isolate and manipulate such genes.

Another surprising gap is our ignorance of the molecular basis of pest and disease resistance. Simply inherited resistance is widely used by breeders and is an obvious objective for crop plant improvement by transformation. However, we are still unable to identify the product of a gene for race-specific resistance that recognizes an avirulent pathogen and induces the synthesis of a range of "defense" chemicals whose effects appear to restrict pathogen growth. Until this is fully explored in several different systems, we cannot confidently predict when we will be able to manipulate single-gene resistance by transformation. Even though such resistance may well select new parasite biotypes, there are strategies such as varietal mixtures that can be used to extend the useful life of such resistance in agriculture (5).

Achieving the Right Balance

In his introductory paper to this conference Sylvan Wittwer (19) stressed the importance of doubling crop production in the next half-century. These are brave words at a time of agricultural surplus. For politicians struggling to devise support systems to maintain agriculture and the communities dependent on it, overproduction that is sustained by taxing the rest of the community is wholly unacceptable. In Britain agricultural surpluses are seen as being due in part to the effectiveness of our own research programs. As a consequence, government expenditure on agricultural research and development is being cut and industry has been invited to support programs it considers vital and which would otherwise be closed. In England and Wales the program of cuts we are now embarked upon will involve the loss of some 2000 jobs, many by enforced redundancy, to reduce the Agricultural and Food Research Service (AFRS) from 6000 to 4000 staff over a 3-year period. Ministry of Agriculture support will be reduced by 10 million pounds in 1986–1987 rising to 20 million pounds in 1987–1988, a cut that will be shared by AFRS and the Agricultural Development and Advisory Service (ADAS) and in which AFRS is expected to lose more than 10% of its government support.

The political view that research is responsible for the surplus is of course absurd. Within the European Economic Community the agricultural policy of subsidy has encouraged gross overproduction by farmers. However, while we recognize that yield is of overriding importance, we must also stress that improved efficiency, lower costs, better quality, and protecting the environment through reducing applications of agrochemicals are increasingly important goals. The tremendous interest in plant molecular biology among the major agrochemical companies reflects their concern that in 15 to 20 years from now they may have no market for their products. They know that crops that produce their own protective chemicals, growth regulants, and fix their own nitrogen will bring this about.

However, in the meantime plant breeders must continue to anticipate and respond rapidly to new markets, new market requirements, new pests and diseases, and new methodology. It would be irresponsible therefore to dismantle the facilities and disperse the expertise so carefully assembled to do this job effectively.

There is a danger that in our eagerness to develop and exploit new technology we may expect too much of it. Some of the difficulties ahead are easy to foresee and can be illustrated as follows. At the recent First International Congress of Plant Molecular Biology in Savannah, Georgia, two groups reported engineered expression of resistance to the herbicide glyphosate. The first group selected a Petunia cell line with an elevated level of the target enzyme 5-enolpyruvylshikimic acid 3-phosphate synthase (16). The second, isolated from the bacterium *Salmonella typhimurium*, is a mutant with a resistant form of the enzyme. They introduced the gene, via an *Agrobacterium* transformation vector, into tobacco and tomato (4). Although neither group claimed to have produced lines with agronomically useful levels of resistance, this can certainly be anticipated. Once such levels have been achieved in an agronomic crop, the following steps must be taken to exploit the discovery:

1. *Test stability.* Is the character inherited stably and expressed to the desired extent in those parts of the plant where it is needed?

2. *Field testing.* (i) Permission. Procedures are now being established. They are likely to require submission of data obtained from greenhouse tests designed to assure regulatory authorities that the new forms pose no threat to the environment. The debate on these issues continues (15). It seems likely that the need to follow guidelines or national laws will impose delays and additional costs on the process of harnessing biotechnology for plant breeding.

Field testing of plants derived from the Petunia cell line would not require permission since the line was not generated by recombinant DNA methods. The same is true of mutants directly selected in the presence of herbicide for insensitivity (see Ref. 17).

(ii) Evaluate field performance. Is yield or quality compromised by the new character? Atrazine-resistant brassicas are significantly less productive than susceptible lines that are otherwise identical. Are there other defects? Is the level of herbicide resistance sufficient to withstand the effects of variation in soil type and climate likely to be encountered by the cultivar? Will it tolerate heavy doses caused by errors in application?

(iii) Breeders' evaluation. Will this new character be of sufficient promise that a breeding program will be modified to include this character in the production of new varieties?

3. *Breeding strategy.* Will transformation enable otherwise finished varieties, already released or about to be released, to be "polished" by the addition of this resistance? This is unlikely to be simple since unless the integration sites for transformation can be controlled, each herbicide-resistant product of transformation is likely to be unique and will thus have to be evaluated for stability and performance in all respects, not just herbicide resistance, over a number of sites and seasons.

It is more likely therefore that one or a few stable products of transformation will be used by breeders in the same way that new germ plasm variants are used. This will allow attempts to increase expression of the new character or to ameliorate defects that result from pleiotropy by modifying or changing the genetic background. However, this approach will not accelerate the progress of breeding but will instead enlarge the range of characters that can be incorporated.

4. *File for patent protection.* Existing plant variety rights legislation in

most countries allow protected varieties to be used as parents in breeding programs. The investments being made in biotechnology are very high and the reward of being first in the market place is not likely to be sufficient. There is consequently much interest in patents that will provide protection not only for the new crop variety but for the engineered genes that it carries. There is of course the problem of describing such genes. One option is to use the DNA sequences. Whether it will be possible to describe them in such a way as to cover all possible trivial alterations that would not affect the phenotypes they express, much in the way that blanket patents are sometimes issued for synthetic chemicals, remains to be seen.

5. *Extension to other crops*. Glyphosate resistance will be most profitably deployed in crops grown on a very large scale such as cereals. For the time being there are no satisfactory transformation systems for cereals; however, selection of mutant forms such as maize lines resistant to imidazolinone herbicides (17) provide an alternative route. All of the problems discussed above also apply to the extension of a gene construction to other crops. Of course the experience and data already obtained may well save much time and effort.

It is clear that the translation of a laboratory product into a new crop plant that farmers will want to grow and that can survive the harsh realities of agriculture is quite outside the responsibilities of the plant molecular biologist. It is equally clear that we will remain entirely dependent on the collaboration of plant breeders. To neglect their needs and overlook the vitally important contribution they are making now will imperil the benefits from applying new technology. We must also remember that plant breeding is not standing still. It is making extensive use of developments in other sciences such as electronics (hand-held data loggers, data processing, new analytical methods), mechanical engineering (single seed descent growth chambers for winter wheat, improved items of farm machinery designed especially for breeders) and biochemistry (PAGE, ELISA, HPLC, NMR, monoclonal antibodies and other analytical methods as well as chemical gametocides and a range of other agrochemicals). Some of these are illustrated or discussed further in Refs. 3 and 6–8.

Progress So Far

Plant molecular biology is already making important contributions to plant breeding. Probes are now in use to detect viroid and viral genomic RNA in host plants. Probes for potato virus X and Y and leaf roll virus are helping breeders measure resistance to these viruses or their aphid vectors (2). They are relatively simple to produce and do not require experimental animals. Male sterile maize cytoplasms can be rapidly identified by dot blots that detect specific mitochondrial DNAs by probing with clones prepared from the DNA species S1 or S2 that are present in high concentration in S cytoplasm, in much lower concentration in N and absent in T (9). In many European wheats, chromosome 1B has a short arm from rye. Plants in which chromosome 1B is derived entirely from wheat can be detected by their failure to give a positive dot blot when probed with a highly repeated rye DNA sequence (12).

Breeding bread wheat is very dependent on the high mass endosperm proteins (3). These determine important viscoelastic properties in bread doughs. Some of the genes responsible for individual gliadin and glutenin subunits have now been isolated and sequenced at the Plant Breeding Institute and Rothamsted (see Ref. 8). The new information will provide ways of comparing different endosperm protein genes from wild wheat relatives. At the present time it is impossible to carry out conventional quality tests with their grain because they are so unlike cultivated bread wheat. If those genes likely to confer quality can first be identified they can then be transferred to breeding lines by hybridization.

Knowledge of which protein structural features are critically important will mean that directed changes in the DNA sequences will be introduced to test the effect of altering amino acid sequences in individual protein subunits (10).

In Brassica crops self-incompatibility promotes outbreeding by preventing growth of self-pollen on the stigmas of expanded mature flowers. Compatible pollen tube growth leading to fertilization occurs only if the stigma carries alleles of a locus S, which are different from those carried by the male parent. The control is sporophytic so that individual pollen grains carrying either S1 or S2 alleles behave as though they had the constitution of the male parent S1S2. This breeding system has been successfully exploited by Thompson (18) for the production of outstanding productive double and triple cross hybrids of marrow-stem kale (*Brassica oleracea*). In Cornell University, Nasrallah *et al.* (13) have prepared a cDNA to messenger RNA isolated from *B. oleracea* stigma cells that directs synthesis of an S allele-specific glycoprotein involved in the incompatibility reaction. They used the clone to probe DNA restriction digests prepared from an F2 family of 55 plants segregating for S6 and S14 alleles. The homozygous parents (S6S6 and S14S14) and the F2 population from selfing the F1 were obtained by pollinating flower buds before the stigma glycoproteins are expressed and can interfere with pollen growth. The Southern blots showed S-allele-associated restriction site polymorphisms that correlated exactly with the S allele segregations, heterozygous plants showing a hybrid pattern. This probe can therefore be used to determine the S genotype from DNA digests prepared from approximately 0.25 g of leaf tissue of a seedling without waiting for it to flower. This is likely to be a useful time-saving tool for plant breeding and is an obvious example of technology that can be applied immediately.

Conclusions

Agricultural science is developing rapidly. Its broad concern with microorganisms, plants, and animals means that the range of new opportunities is equally broad. Molecular biology has an alluring appeal as a common denominator. At the same time agricultural science has the awesome responsibility of feeding the world with the least possible damage to the environment. We cannot allow our fascination for what is new and glamorous to distract us from the important job we have to do with our present tools. We have to put the new ideas to work carefully and responsibly and above all to make the impact a successful one. Countless hungry mouths in the years ahead are going to depend on us.

LITERATURE CITED

1. AUSTIN RB 1986 Opportunities for the Application of Molecular Biology to Crop Improvement in the EEC with Particular Reference to Wheat, Oilseed Rape and Faba Beans. Cambridge University Press. In press
2. BAULCOMBE DC, RB FLAVELL, RE BOULTON, GJ JELLIS 1984 The sensitivity and specificity of a rapid nucleic acid hybridization method for the detection of potato virus X in crude sap samples. Plant Pathol 33: 361–370
3. BINGHAM J, JA BLACKMAN, RA NEWMAN 1985 Wheat: A Guide to Varieties from the Plant Breeding Institute, National Seed Development Organisation, Newton, Cambridge
4. COMAI L, D FACCIOTTI, WR HIATT, G THOMPSON, RE ROSE, C MAU, J FILLATTI, J KISER, N MCDONALD, DM STALHER 1985 Genetic engineering of glyphosate tolerance into crop plants. Abstracts First International Congress of Plant Molecular Biology, Georgia, p 53
5. DAY, PR, JA BARRETT, MS WOLFE 1983 The evolution of host-parasite interaction. In T Kosuge, CP Meredith, A Hollaender, eds, Genetic Engineering of Plants: An Agricultural Perspective. Plenum Press, New York, pp 419–430
6. DAY, PR 1985 Crop improvement: breeding and genetic engineering. Phil Trans R Soc Lond B 310: 193–200
7. DAY, PR 1985 Future trends in plant breeding. In LG Copping, P Rodgers, eds, Biotechnology and its Application to Agriculture (Monograph No. 32). British Crop Protection Council, Croydon, pp 25–31
8. DAY, PR, J BINGHAM, PI PAYNE, RD THOMPSON 1986 The way ahead: wheat breeding for quality improvement. In JMV Blanshard, PJ Frazier, T Galliard, eds, Chemistry and Physics of Baking: Materials, Processes and Products. Royal Society of Chemistry, London. In press
9. FLAVELL, RB, RJ KEMBLE, RE GUNN, A ABBOTT, D BAULCOMBE 1983 Applications of molecular biology in plant breeding: the detection of genetic variation and viral pathogens. In J Nugent, M O'Connor, eds, Better Crops for Food (Ciba Foundation Symposium 97). Pitman, London, pp 198–212
10. FLAVELL, RB, PI PAYNE, RD THOMPSON, CN LAW 1985 Strategies for the improvement of wheat grain quality using molecular genetics. Biotech Genet Engr Rev 2: 157–167
11. GENETIC ENGINEERING: A NATURAL SCIENCE 1985 Monsanto Co., St. Louis (1985)
12. HUTCHINSON, J, A ABBOTT, M O'DELL, RB FLAVELL 1985 A rapid screening technique for the detection of repeated DNA sequences in plant tissues. Theoret Appl Genet 69: 329–333
13. NASRALLAH, JB, TH KAO, ML GOLDBERG, ME NASRALLAH 1985 A cDNA

clone encoding an S-locus-specific glycoprotein from *Brassica oleracea.*
Nature 318: 263–267

14. NATIONAL RESEARCH COUNCIL 1985 New Directions for Biosciences—Research in Agriculture: High-Reward Opportunities. National Academy Press, Washington, DC

15. PRAMER D, ED 1986 Engineered Organisms in the Environment: Scientific Issues. American Society for Microbiology, Washington, DC. In press

16. SHAH DM, JW WINTER, PS SANDERS, CM HIRONAHA, HC STEINRUCHEN, N AMRHEIN, RT FRALEY 1985 Gene amplification is the molecular basis for glyphosate resistance in Petunia cells. Abstracts First International Congress of Plant Molecular Biology, Georgia, p 22

17. SHANER D, T MALEFYT 1985 Herbicide resistant maize through cell culture selection. *In* LG Copping, P Rodgers, eds, Biotechnology and Its Application to Agriculture (Monograph No. 32). British Crop Protection Council, Croydon, pp 45–50

18. THOMPSON KF 1967 Breeding problems in kale (*Brassica oleracea*) with particular reference to marrow-stem kale. *In* Plant Breeding Institute; Annual Report 1965–66, pp 7–34

19. WITTWER SH 1986 Crop productivity—research imperatives—a decade of change. *In* M Gibbs, C Carlson, eds, Crop Productivity—Research Imperatives Revisited, an international conference held at Boyne Highlands Inn, October 13–18, 1985, and Airlie House, December 11–13, 1985

The Changing World of Research Opportunities[1]

Robert Barker

It is often the case that the title, decided on in advance, is not quite appropriate by the time a presentation is to be given. That is true with this paper. It would be titled better as "The Changed World of Research Opportunities," for recently, many, and very significant, changes have occurred in the spectrum of research opportunities; what is changing now are the ways in which those opportunities are being used. The research entrepreneurs have just begun their work.

Two quite different meanings can be inferred for the phrase "Research Opportunities." One would lead to a focus in this paper on the changes that have occurred and are occurring in the sciences that nurture agriculture, the other would lead to consideration of the organizational options that the scientific ferment makes possible or desirable. I will focus on the latter, and I will deal more with my own perception of the world of scientific research than with its documented (or documentable) reality. And while I will concentrate on agriculture and the land grant institutions, I will not limit myself because the changes that are occurring make the general scientific environment more and more relevant to agricultural problems.

A reasonable perspective on the changing scene can be obtained by looking back 10 years to the time of the first conference, by looking at present opportunities, and then by extending the trend lines to predict (or imagine) the future.

Research in 1975

The situation with respect to agricultural research in 1975 and which in a significant degree continues today can be described by a series of "one-liners": most research is commodity oriented, most university-based agricultural research is people rich and resource poor, industry-university collaborations generally involve trade associations or commodity groups, research opportunities largely delimited by the missions of traditional federal and state funding sources, most basic biological science separated from its agricultural context, and agriculture in the United States is energy, technologically and chemically intensive. These points warrant consideration in terms of their effect on research opportunities and outcomes.

---

[1] Introduced by Charles J. Arntzen

The strong commodity orientation of research is the inevitable and entirely appropriate consequence of the following factors: the research universities as well as federal laboratories had as their mission the support of state and regional agriculture; agricultural industries are small and are dispersed both geographically and organizationally; land grant university research is organized to support the agricultural extension services; and development as well as research is an essential part of the land grant mission. In many cases, research, development, demonstration, and even delivery of a service is needed to meet the needs of agricultural industries.

Many, if not all, research opportunities can be realized only if funding is provided to begin them. Agricultural industries can only rarely provide funding for basic research. When funds are provided, they tend to be linked to the need for a solution to a particular and often short-term problem. Many research units have become organized by projects oriented to specific crops and commodities, on the ready to respond to short-term industry needs. In many cases, research programs must operate facilities that are typical of those used in the industry so that research and development can be pursued to the practical outcome. As a consequence of these modes of operation, agricultural research in 1975 had become people rich and resource poor with a coefficient of elasticity approaching zero. It was not unusual for more than 90% of the research budget to be committed to fixed expenditures, mainly personnel, many in permanent positions. The principal flexible elements in the system were the graduate students and funds obtainable from agencies with nonagricultural (or perhaps pseudoagricultural) missions.

The system I have described might seem to be frozen. Although some parts were (and are), there was still mobility, driven by the creativity of some of the scientists involved in it.

The "1975" system was formed by traditions and evolutionary processes begun in the 1860s. Very basic research had always been integral to the mission of the agricultural universities. As the knowledge base developed, particularly in the biological areas, research became more resource intensive, more molecular in its focus, less obviously related to the agricultural mission. It was difficult to reallocate resources against the pressures for maintaining the commodity orientation and the facilities and personnel committed to them. Institutions solved the problem of funding in the basic biological sciences by allowing, even encouraging, faculty members to seek funding from agencies with nonagricultural missions. While this approach made sense in terms of "the unanimity of biological phenomena" it had two important negative results. First, many basic science faculty members developed careers with no awareness or interest in their role as members of the agricultural research system. Second, the molecular biology of plants was greatly neglected, at least as compared to the molecular biology of microbes and animal cells.

I will return to these points later, but now I want to list some of the major differences in the present situation.

Research in 1985

1. Molecular biology techniques, particularly in molecular genetics, are applicable to all areas of biology including agriculture and medicine.

2. Biological methods are competing with chemical methods in pest control.

3. Ecosystem science is well developed and its industrial counterpart, operations research, is developing rapidly.

4. Agriculture is facing new realities of overproduction and its economic consequences.

5. High powered computing offers opportunities for analysis and simulation of complex social, biological, and agroecosystems.

6. Analytical systems are becoming increasingly sophisticated in terms of what can be measured and simpler in terms of application. Measurements at 10^{-18} molar are possible in some cases. What can be measured can be regulated.

What do these factors imply for the future of agricultural research? Which is the most important?

I will take a circuitous route to the answer.

Research, even very basic research, can be quite substantially affected by significiant practical breakthroughs. When the polio problem was "solved," another rationale for basic research on viruses had to be found. If it had not, much of the work would have had to be discontinued. In agriculture, the focus of the past has been on enhanced productivity. In a sense this problem has been solved, yet it must remain as the central theme for agricultural research. While the biological problem of how to achieve high productivity may have been solved, the socioeconomic problems of how to manage that production remain. So do the economic incentives to continue to strive for increased efficiency.

The concept that the United States can feed the world, which has motivated much of our drive to increase productivity, is flawed. Not all of the world needs us (yet?) and the parts that do cannot all afford us. It is almost axiomatic that when we are needed, we cannot be afforded. I am sure that most farmers would agree with this, that even in those cases where commodities are sold abroad the price is far from fair.

Yet we cannot deal with the present condition of surplus production by stopping research on methods to increase the efficiencies of our agricultural systems. Research on crop productivity is essential to improve the overall economic health of agriculture, to sustain and improve our competitive position in world markets and to fulfill our responsibilities to developing countries.

Now to answer the question: "Of the factors listed, which is the most important for future research initiatives?"

In my view it is the potential for the development of the ecosystems sciences. I use the term, ecosystems, in a broad sense to imply holistic and integrative approaches to complex systems. Such approaches will greatly expand our capacity to manage increasingly complex systems, to

develop conceptual models of such systems and to fit into them the
myriad basic discoveries that derive from our total research effort. I will
refer to this as a "total ecosystems approach." Its long-term goal would
be similar to that of engineering operations research and integrated
manufacturing programs. We cannot yet operate with a total ecosystems
approach, but we are getting there. In my view, its importance lies in the
effect that trying to think in such terms would have on the planning and
performance of research. Much of what will be derived from biotechnology as well as basic and applied research in the soil, meteorological,
plant, and animal sciences will serve us best if it is managed within a
developing concept of the agricultural-ecosystem. For example, the total
ecosystem approach to a commodity crop would include:

I. The commodity
   A. Biological factors that determine inherent capacities and inter-
      actions with other biological systems (intrinsic and extrinsic
      genetic interactions with other biological systems capacities,
      pests, competitors)
   B. Physical factors that determine the extent to which biological
      capacity is expressed (light, temperature, humidity, substrate)
II. Economic factors—long- and short-term, that determine the value
   of the commodity
   A. Production
   B. Transportation
   C. Processing
   D. Marketing
   E. Competition
   F. Impact on the ecosystem: are there "unpaid bills" associated with
      the commodity?
III. Sociobiological factors that determine the uses made of the com-
   modity
   A. Commodity—acceptability, biological value
   B. Legal and regulatory implications
   C. Competition—customs, alternative commodities, alternative eco-
      system use
   D. Public opinion

Such global thinking may be unrefined at present, but it will develop
more quickly from now on as the computing power necessary to create
some of the models and manipulate some of the variables are developed.
This year has been most significant in this regard with four new university centers created to bring "supercomputer" power to the universities
and to the industries that interct with them. At Cornell the application
for National Science Foundation (NSF) support of the supercomputer
initiative included proposals to apply this new tool to ecosystems, with
specific concern for those that are threatened by toxic chemicals, as well
as proposals dealing with diagnostic strategies and economic systems.

The gap between what we do now, what we can do in the next few
years, and the eventual prospect for simulation science is still large.

What of the next few years? Even without computers, the ecosystem approach to agricultural research can have great benefits. I believe it can help to resolve the dilemma of basic *versus* applied research and can integrate the research activities of participating scientists; greatly reinforcing the mission-orientation of agricultural research organizations while strengthening basic research and improving education.

It is my perception that the potential for significant research in most areas related to agriculture has been well explored in this conference. In what follows, I would like to make a few recommendations based on my perception of the potential for what I have described as the "total ecosystem approach" outlined above.

1. If the potential for (and of) a total ecosystems approach is granted, it follows that agricultural research institutions should begin to build toward that end. Now a total ecosystem is multidimensional, and human organizations tend to be one- or two-dimensional. Most of our organizations are segmented by disciplines despite the fact that almost all of the world's problems are multidisciplinary in character.

A Recommendation. Since the world's problems are the source of our research opportunities, we should do research on the total ecosystem in organizations that foster multidisciplinary, multidimensional approaches and be alert to the interconnectedness of the individual problems we address. As far as I can tell, everyone at this conference concurs in this recommendation.

2. To address properly many of the research problems that face us we need to expand the workforce. The debate on basic *versus* applied research has tended to separate university from industry and, within the university, biologists interested in agricultural systems from those interested in the natural world, the organismal from the molecular. (Basic *versus* applied is more a matter of term than intent.) Neither of these divisions has served us well.

A Recommendation. Campus-based research should be developed so as to include industry scientists and to create multidisciplinary teams to address both short- and long-term research goals. (I do not recommend doing away with traditional disciplines, at least not the major ones. I do recommend the creation of flexible groupings and more stable centers to focus on major research areas. And I urge those who provide research funds to use them to that end. Industry scientists should be able to participate in these research teams *ad libitum* and industries should recognize the great value to be obtained by having their more senior scientists intimately connected to one or more university center[s] dedicated to research in the area[s] of the corporation's greatest interest.) I believe also that corporations will be served best if they encourage these centers to do basic research in the general area of their interest. They should encourage publication and reward their scientific staff for their participation in these centers and for bringing value back to the corporation from them.

3. It seems clear that the development of a total ecosystems approach

to agriculture will fall to the land grant universities. Most are farther down that road than they may recognize but most have not come to grips with how to make the transitions that will facilitate its development.

A Recommendation. A major focus of the university-based Agricultural Experiment Stations should be the development of systems approaches to the major agricultural problems facing their state and region.

This focus should not be to the exclusion of commodity-oriented research nor to direct all of the research carried out by station scientists. The expertise of individual scientists is essential to the success of multi-disciplinary programs; that expertise must be fostered and researchers should be expected to be in the front ranks of their disciplines. The multidisciplinary program should integrate the expertise of individuals in pursuit of the program mission but long-term success depends on the participants remaining current in the disciplines by maintaining success-ful disciplinary research programs. The planning should be integrative and should draw on the scientific leaders among the faculty. Membership on the strategy team should be an honor and funding decisions should reflect the priorities established by the team.

4. Just to show that I am even-handed in this arrogance, I will also make:

A Recommendation. Corporations, commodity groups, and state and national agricultural research agencies should seek evidence of these kinds of approaches in providing funding. In particular, some of the funding for competitive grants should be directed toward the support of multidisciplinary centers.

5. The involvement of industry scientists in campus-based research can ensure technology transfer and enrich the teaching and research programs of the campus. It can be achieved without compromising the university commitment to openness and with the exclusion of proprietary work provided that the participating industries have the staff to pursue the development of applications in-house.

A Recommendation. Research-based corporation should adopt a "systems-view" of their products and processes. They should view uni-versity-based research as integral to their own mission and adopt man-agement strategies that reward their scientists for participation in uni-versity-based research and for bringing value to the corporation from that participation.

6. The preceding five recommendations imply that new organizations should be created in the universities that will foster interdisciplinary research and interactions between the universities and industries.

A Recommendation. University-based multidisciplinary research cen-ters should be created that integrate the research activities of scientists with complementary interests. The centers should provide some of the funds needed by participating scientists; additional funding for comple-mentary disciplinary research should be obtained from agencies other than the center. To ensure that centers are integral to the total mission of the university, faculty members participating in these centers should hold academic appointments in departments and colleges, not in a center. Centers should involve industry scientists and attract some industry funding. Other funding might be obtained from state and/or federal agencies, or by redirecting local funding. Center funds should provide short-term grants to initiate new multidisciplinary projects and support shared resources. Decisions on the directions to be taken by the center should be shared by the participating scientists and others such as representatives of participating corporations and agencies.

7. The problem of how best to do research and ensure technology transfer to fulfill the land grant mission of many universities is a difficult one. Most agricultural corporations are small and are not research-oriented. The value they have received from research has come from the Agricultural Experiment Stations and through the Cooperative Extension programs. Many think that the principal beneficiaries of this research and development have been the very-large-scale-agribusinesses. They may be right because there is probably a law of logic, if not of economics, that predicts that small increments of efficiency that depend on costly innovations can only be applied when the scale of operation is large enough to balance cost with gain in efficiency. The only practical way for the research community to deliver much of its services is through its traditional channel (the Extension Service), and through those corporations that provide services to the distributed agricultural production system. Another avenue may develop that involves providing assistance in the creation of new corporate ventures that serve the agricultural community. There is no doubt that the rapidly evolving technologies that impact agriculture will require the Extension services to respond very imaginatively if their mission is to be achieved.

A Recommendation. Land grant universities should continue to target research toward the needs of the farm community and to those businesses that serve it. They should work closely with state and federal agencies to ensure that innovations that can improve the efficiency of small producers are delivered, including those that require the development of new business to deliver services. The concept of university-based incubation facilities focused on services to the agricultural and food industries should be explored and developed.

8. Earlier, I referred to the fact that we should not look upon the world as the marketplace for our food production. While food production and processing will remain as the essential core of agriculture and a central focus for agricultural research, it is clear that agricultural production aimed at other end uses will increase. Agriculture for chemical feedstocks and structural materials will eventually be important.

A Recommendation. Agricultural research should, in a small way, address the use of natural products and their derivatives as structural materials. Linkages to the material sciences should be explored and funds should be committed to the application of advanced physical-chemical methods to structure elucidation. Similarly, work should be continued on plant materials for energy, for pharmaceutical and other chemical applications.

9. To demonstrate that my focus is not just on production agriculture, let me add the following.

A Recommendation. The research mission of agricultural institutions should increasingly encompass the food industry and other industries, present or potential, that support or are supported by agricultural production.

Conclusions

I was asked to deal with the changing world of research opportunities. I think the intent was for me to talk about how to get new funding for research; I have not done that. There are only four potential sources of funds: federal and state governments, industry, and foundations. All have established yet changing agenda. In agriculture, industry and foundations account for very little (less than 2%) while in the research universities these sources now account for 5 to 6% and, in some, to 10% or more. Agribusinesses (apart from agricultural chemicals) developed after the federal and state research and extension systems had been established. Food and fiber industries, while they benefited from the research done in universities and drew their trained people from them, are based on traditional methods and materials. Most do not see themselves as dependent on basic research. I think these perceptions will have to change but I do not expect the change to be rapid. Some far-sighted corporations will begin to build their research base and may be amenable to the suggestions I have made to work closely with the universities. I cannot see these developments, even if they are pursued with vigor, producing much by way of new revenues. What new funding is produced should be directed toward multidisciplinary centers so that they provide leverage to bring about structural changes that will enhance the research effort. I do not expect states or the federal government to do much incremental funding either. What is left is a do-it-yourself proposition.

I mentioned earlier that the molecular biology of plants had been neglected. Many agricultural scientists derive their research support from agencies such as the National Institutes of Health (NIH) and do not make their research choices in an agricultural context. Yet much of what can be accomplished in the improvement of crops, agricultural practices, and biotechnology depends on our building the knowledge base of the basic agricultural sciences. The kinds of collaborative interdisciplinary approaches to agricultural research that I have recommended can provide the incentive to redirect these energies and interests. They are also the most likely to attract the transitional funding that will allow the 1975 organizational structures and strategies to adjust to the needs of the 1990s.

We need new configurations and new players on the team, but I am fairly sure that at best we will only find the resources to start the ball rolling. It will be up to us to restructure what we have now to win the game.

REPORTS OF THE
NINE WORKING GROUPS

Genetic Improvement

Submitted on behalf of the group by:

KENNETH J. FREY   SHARON R. LONG

CAROLE P. MEREDITH

Crop productivity and composition are affected by the genetic makeup of the variety used, the production environment, and of paramount importance, the interaction between variety and environment. Genetic improvement of crop plants has occurred ever since agriculture began 12,000 years ago, and until 1900, plant breeding consisted of selecting among plant species or among genotypes within species. With the rediscovery of Mendel's laws in 1900, knowledge became available that permitted plant breeders to develop crop varieties tailor-made for new environments created by farmers—environments with adequate fertility, no moisture stress, and free from weeds, diseases, and pests. Genes from two or more parent lines were combined into a single cultivar via hybridization and selection.

Genetic potential for yield of cereals and soybeans has been increased by 40 to 100% (19, 24); host plant resistance has been used as an effective control for many diseases and pests (47); seed and plant composition have been genetically modified to meet specific nutritional and market demands (2); and plant architecture and development have been tailored to fit harvesting and marketing requirements. To accomplish these improvements, it was necessary to know the inheritance patterns of genes responsible for the traits. However, a number of crop traits have been resistant or intractible to improvement, *e.g.* drought and heat resistance, tolerance to salinity and toxic ions, and increased biomass productivity. Genetic variability for such traits has been demonstrated, but planned improvement in them will be limited unless their fundamental biological bases are elucidated. Some of these are especially important in light of the need to increase agricultural efficiency by reducing such inputs as irrigation, fertilizer, and pesticides.

The five traits exploited consciously as primary contributors to increased production are hybrid vigor, increased harvest index, semidwarfness, resistance to disease and insects, and date to maturity. Hybrid vigor, which results in increased growth rate and plant size, even though not understood physiologically, has been utilized in numerous field, horticultural, and forest crops. Harvest index, which measures the ratio of seed to biomass yield, is near its physiologic limit at 50 to 55%. Semidwarfness permits using heavy nitrogen fertilization without lodging. Resistance to diseases and pests protects plants from as much as 30 to 40% potential loss in production. Controlling time to maturity permits the farmer to better exploit a given climate.

Three factors that have developed somewhat independently and have had great impact on plant breeding are germ plasm collections, international agricultural research centers, and computers. Germ plasm collections contain the genes for crop improvement (7–9, 50); international centers have organized plant breeding for individual commodities on a global basis (49); and computers permit complex experiments to be conducted, instantaneous summarization of data, and instant communication among researchers.

Biochemical and molecular studies have begun to reveal the basis for plant traits, and to establish the principles of plant molecular genetics. For example, there have been some successes in identifying the genes that control photosynthesis and in elucidating their regulation. However, the fundamental basis of most plant traits remains unknown, and detailed analysis of major crop plants is especially needed. New biological techniques must be used (a) to analyze and elucidate molecular, biochemical, and genetic bases of plant traits, (b) to transfer genes asexually, and (c) to establish somatic cell selection schemes. In this section, we have given background information for and outlined the research that must be done to assure that genetic materials will be available and to provide the knowledge and the techniques for future crop improvement.

Germ Plasm

Germ plasm collections of crop species contain the genes needed for future crop improvement. The concept is that the genotypes in a germ plasm collection contain nearly all the genes that exist for a species (7). The rice germ plasm collection, which serves as a model system, contains 70,000 accessions resulting from systematic exploration and collection wherever cultivated or wild rices grow. These collections provide food, feed, and fiber security for humankind and materials to answer fundamental questions of biology.

The steps in assembling and utilizing a germ plasm collection are (a) collection, (b) documentation, (c) preservation, (d) evaluation, and (e) utilization. Even though some collections have thousands of accessions, most are deficient in weedy and wild species, and centralized collections of pests and parasites are nonexistent. Few collections have been evaluated systematically and current evaluation data are not available in a centralized file. Seed can be preserved easily but clonal species are difficult and expensive to maintain.

The germ plasm collections for cereals, grain legumes, cassava and potatoes, and most vegetable crops are quite adequate, but those for ornamentals and forest and fruit crops range from inadequate to nearly nonexistent. In general, evaluation records are not standardized.

Pressing limitations on assembling and utilizing germ plasm collections include the rapid erosion of germ plasm sources worldwide, a deficiency in funding, and a lack of appropriately trained personnel. To overcome these limitations would require a 4-fold increase in funding worldwide and the establishment of an education and training program in germ plasm science.

Sampling Strategies

The distribution of genetic variability in nature is influenced by environmental niches, the reproduction system of the species, and selection pressures. The ideal is to collect all genetic variants in nature without redundancy. Unfortunately, most accessions are collected without regard to appropriate sampling procedures and, as a result, much genetic variation is missed and the world collection contains considerable redundancy. Sampling procedures and frequency are dependent upon (a) the degree of genetic variation within a sampling area, (b) the reproduction system of the species, and (c) the extent and pattern of environmental variation in the sampling area. Research is needed to establish how many and what size samples should be collected for selfing, outcrossing, and clonal species and optimal collection patterns to obtain a representative and adequate sampling of natural habitats that vary in elevation, soils, and biotic communities.

Storage Methods

Seeds of most species remain viable for long periods if stored at low humidity and subfreezing temperatures. For example, most cereal seeds, if vacuum sealed into containers and stored at −20 to −30°C, will remain viable for a quarter century or more, and alfalfa seeds stored under these conditions will survive for a century. However, many root and tuber crops (*e.g.* cassava and potatoes), which are stored as vegetative tissue, must be propagated annually. Perennial fruit, forest, and ornamental species must be maintained in clonal repositories, *i.e.* grown in outdoor nurseries. It is difficult to keep accessions in germ plasm collections of the latter two categories free of viral and other systemic diseases, and they are continually subject to loss from epidemics or natural disasters. If *in vitro* cultures of these two categories of germ plasm collections can be stored, perhaps cryogenically, their maintenance will be more efficient, secure, and less expensive. *In vitro* cultures, if free of viral infection, are also a good means for international exchange of germ plasm (44).

Seed Physiology of Recalcitrant Species

Certain species of tropical crops, *e.g.* wild relatives of cassava, have evolved a seed physiology that requires special environmental conditions for survival and germination. Some must be stored at room instead of subfreezing temperatures to survive. And for germination, the seeds may need to be subjected to a sequence of changes in moisture and temperature to initiate germination. If these conditions are not known, the seeds may die during storage, or, if alive, may not germinate, and thus not be usable for crop improvement. Each recalcitrant species has a unique requirement for seed survival and germination that must be understood if germ plasm collections of these species are to be preserved.

Combining Genes by Sexual Methods

The tremendous genetic improvements in crop plants achieved to date are largely based on sexual hybridization and, as emerging cellular and molecular technologies develop further, sexual methods will continue to play a major role in crop improvement. In the cereals and grain legumes, especially, genetic improvement has accounted for approximately half of the remarkable increases in productivity achieved in the 20th century. Although plant geneticists have frequently been able to manipulate and recombine genomes into agriculturally effective combinations using sexual breeding methods, they are limited by a lack of understanding of interactions among genes. A better understanding of these interactions would enable greater control in assembling genes into optimal combinations.

Hybrids

Striking gains have been achieved in a number of crops with hybrid varieties produced by crossing select inbred parents. The hybrid typically exhibits higher and more stable productivity than either parent, a phenomenon referred to as heterosis, or hybrid vigor. This approach has had its greatest success in maize. The replacement of open-pollinated maize cultivars with double-cross hybrids in the 1930s resulted in an immediate 10 to 15% increase in productivity. Similar gains have been accomplished by the introduction of hybrid sorghum and, in China, hybrid rice.

Heterotic combinations have been demonstrated in many crops, suggesting that hybrid varieties of them would be valuable. The limitation in using hybrids, however, lies in the difficulty in mass-producing hybrid plants in crops where male sterility is not available for use in the large-scale production of hybrid seed. While several ways can be envisioned for producing hybrids, more research is needed on methods for either preventing self-pollination or for large-scale asexual propagation of hybrid individuals.

Several strategies can be used to prevent self-pollination. Cytoplasmic male sterility can be sought or developed for those crops where it does not occur. Concurrently, fertility restoration genes will be needed for seed crops. Cytogenetically mediated genetic male sterility gives virtually complete male sterility, and hybrids produced via this mechanism do not require restoration genes. Alternatively, male gametocides could be exploited to cause male sterility. These chemicals have advantages even if genetic male sterility is available because they permit the testing of many experimental hybrids without requiring that genes for male sterility be incorporated into the parental lines. Self-incompatibility alleles, which prevent selfing, can be introduced by sexual means but the possibility of introducing self-incompatibility genes from alien species by molecular transformation should also be investigated.

If a single hybrid plant could be multiplied asexually on a large scale, it would circumvent the laborious hand emasculation of the female parent, such as is done for hybrid seed production for cotton in India.

Obligate apomixis, if available, could be used to propagate hybrids. High fidelity, high frequency methods for producing somatic embryos from cell cultures derived from hybrids, and the technology for producing synthetic seeds from them should also be investigated for certain crops.

Heterosis

If the fundamental mechanisms underlying heterosis were known, it might be possible to assemble deliberately heterotic combinations of genes by other means than hybridizing inbred parents. Three genetic hypotheses are proposed to explain heterosis: (a) heterozygosis, (b) epistasis, or (c) partial dominance of linked alleles. Supposedly, any of these genetic mechanisms would be mediated via physiological reactions or biosynthetic pathways but none of these hypotheses has yet provided an adequate explanation of the phenomenon. Molecular genetic techniques may be effective in analyzing the contrasting interactions and gene regulation in hybrids and parents. Even though heterosis is likely the integrated effect of many interacting genes, analysis of single genes whose activity is altered in hybrids may provide incisive information.

Reproductive Biology

Genetic manipulation via sexual means exploits the natural reproductive systems of crop species. More fundamental knowledge of the nature and control of these mechanisms may facilitate their manipulation to increase the efficiency and power with which plant genes can be combined sexually.

The control of flower development at the fundamental level, including hormonal regulation of flowering and mechanisms controlling gametogenesis, needs to be elucidated. Investigation of the control of pollen development may lead to novel methods for (a) mediating male sterility for use in hybrid seed production and (b) for obtaining haploid plants via microspore embryogenesis or regeneration from microspore-derived cell and tissue cultures. Knowledge of the mechanisms underlying self-incompatibility, including the identification, isolation, and transfer of the genes involved might allow greater control of the reproductive process.

In many woody perennial species, genetic improvement by sexual methods is severely restricted by the long juvenile period that precedes reproductive maturation. Control of juvenility and phase change, if elucidated, might permit the reduction or elimination of the juvenile period in these species, and thus accelerate breeding programs.

Coadapted Gene Complexes

In certain instances, a trait may seem to be inherited oligogenetically, but refined analysis shows that the trait is multigenic with the genes being tightly linked into a coadapted complex. Such linkage complexes probably evolve because they assure that all genes needed for optimal trait expression, once assembled in a genotype, will be disrupted minimally by outcrossing and recombination. Such linkages may be more important and prevalent in outcrossing than in selfing species, and coadapted gene complexes may be important units of inheritance when germ plasm is introgressed from wild and weedy relatives into crop gene pools. Knowledge of the nature and frequency of coadapted gene complexes in outcrossing and selfing species and in wild and weedy relatives of crop plants is needed for formulating appropriate breeding strategies, especially for the introgression of exotic germ plasm.

Multigenic Traits

Many traits of interest in plant breeding are quantitatively inherited, but all genes probably do not contribute equally to trait expression. For example, genetic analysis of maturity date in wheat, a quantitatively inherited trait, showed that genes at four loci accounted for most of the variation (58), and a semidwarfness gene at any one of 20 loci will cause short plant stature in barley. This situation probably occurs for many or perhaps most multigenic plant traits, so it is essential to conduct genetic research to establish the relative contributions of individual genes to several such traits and to determine whether this situation is pervasive in plants. If only a few genes (of the many) are responsible for a large portion of the variation in a multigenic trait, this knowledge would be valuable in establishing a proper breeding strategy and might permit the molecular dissection of these traits.

Molecular Analysis of Plant Genomes

The basis for all genetic behavior lies in the arrangement and reactions of the nucleic acids of the genome. Molecular biology, the biochemical and genetic analysis of nucleic acids, thus gives us the most fundamental and detailed understanding of genetic behavior. The genetic material of plants resides in three organelles: nucleus, chloroplast and mitochondria (40). Basic information about the size, replication, organization into higher order structures, and the control of expression of these genomes is important for plant molecular biology. The stability and instability of DNA may underly important phenomena such as plant genomic variability. The arrangement of the genome can only be studied where individual genes or DNA segments can be detected and followed. In the past 5 years great advances have been made in DNA analysis; molecular studies have permitted analysis of existing gene arrangements and also the first directed genetic change in a plant species.

Gene Mapping

Molecular biology can and should be used to underpin and aid conventional plant breeding and cytogenetics. An example is the development of restriction fragment length polymorphism (RFLP) analysis of DNA, a technique that permits genetic markers to be tracked at the DNA level by means of cloned DNA fragments (42). This permits the construction of a genetic map for segments of the genome even where no phenotypic markers exist.

In addition, techniques are needed for molecular detection of the presence and position of genes on chromosomes, to permit refinement of genetic linkage maps. This has been accomplished in some plant species with cloned DNA segments representing repeated sequences (20) and must be extended to the analysis of specific genes. This would enhance the potential for following traits in hybrids and germ plasm introgressed from distantly or unrelated species. The accumulation of knowledge from these two techniques would permit a detailed analysis of new plant genotypes. These techniques will be especially useful for crop species that have not been mapped by traditional genetic analysis.

Chromosome Organization and Behavior

Analysis of gene position on chromosomes is the first of several levels of study that are required. Work in recent years, particularly on cereal crops, has demonstrated that chromosomes are not distributed randomly throughout the nuclear volume, but occupy rather specific physical locations. It appears that these locations influence a chromosome's tendency to be lost from the cell (4). This phenomenon may account for chromosome number instability in certain genotypes, and thus nuclear architecture and its relationship to chromosome stability and activity need to be understood. Furthermore, traditional and molecular genetics should be used to identify specific genes that control chromosome behavior, including pairing and meiotic activity.

In yeast centromeric and telomeric segments of chromosomes have been identified, isolated, and characterized. These advances have permitted the construction of artificial yeast chromosomes that are versatile transformation vehicles. Such research and techniques would be valuable for plant molecular transformation and should be actively pursued.

Genome Replication and Recombination

Central to the current power of molecular biology for manipulating microbial systems is the advanced understanding of the basic mechanisms of nucleic acid metabolism and of genome replication. Genetic recombination, mutagenesis, and repair are all intimately involved with, and to a great extent controlled by, the processes of DNA replication (*e.g.* see Walker [57]). These processes have not been well-studied in plants (37), but without further study our understanding of and ability to regulate plant mutation, transposable element activity, gene amplification, genetic exchange during recombination, and other fundamental genetic events will be very limited. In addition, an understanding of DNA synthesis mechanisms may be a substantial aid to the directed transformation of plant cells with exogenous DNA such as recombinant clones. In bacteria, the analysis of nucleic acid synthesis has been greatly advanced by studying how viruses utilize native replication systems, and this research direction is likely to be of great use in plant studies as well.

Organelle replication systems have been reported but have not been reliably characterized (37, 40). Chloroplast and mitochondrial division and genome replication are influenced by nuclear activity and by the state of differentiation of the cell. More understanding of the coordination of organelle and nuclear replication is required to permit analysis of the role of organelle inheritance and the control of genes introduced into organelles for genetic engineering purposes.

Genome Variability at the Molecular Level

The use of cloned DNA segments as probes has revealed that plant genomes may undergo relatively rapid fluctuations at the nucleic acid level, with or without accompanying changes in organismal phenotype (56). Flax displays changes in copy number of certain sequences, including ribosomal cistrons, during multigeneration treatment with varied temperature or nutrient regimes; however, some DNA sequences appear not to be subject to these variations. It is likely that these findings relate to the problem of cultivar stability; molecular genetics must be used to achieve an understanding both of the mechanism, and of the elements in a species or strain background that contribute to genomic fluidity and stability. It is particularly relevant to explore the relationship of genomic change in response to stress (12).

Somaclonal Variation

A specific example of instability is the phenomenon of somaclonal variation, in which *in vitro* cultures of clonally derived cells give rise to genetically variable plants at very high frequency. This variability occurs in the absence of selection pressure, and has resulted in phenotypic alterations in many important traits (17, 34, 54). However, the high apparent frequency of mutation in cultured plant cells is undesirable in cases where genetic constancy is required, such as in germ plasm maintenance. Recent research suggests that one possible cause of somaclonal variation is the activation of transposable elements in cultured plant cells. However, this same study also shows that many of the mutant types arising in culture are not due to a transposable element, but to some as yet unknown genetic event (R Phillips, private communication). It is essential that intensive study be carried out, including not only the analysis of transposon activation, but also of genome replication fidelity, DNA damage and repair processes, and other mechanisms that may lead to genetic variability in cultured plant cells.

Transposable Elements

The basic molecular biology of transposable elements is of fundamental importance in advancing our understanding of plants and in providing tools for genetic manipulation of plants. In bacteria, and more recently in *Drosophila*, transposons have been indispensable aids in the identification of genes by insertional inactivation and their subsequent cloning by use of transposon homology. Furthermore, transposons have provided the unique means of transformation in some systems such as *Drosophila*. Transposable elements were first identified in plants, and in the past few years our understanding of plant transposons has expanded greatly. Several transposons have been obtained as cloned DNA fragments, and sequence analysis has revealed some structural features that are similar in the various elements (15, 23). However, few plant systems and few transposable elements have benefited from this analysis. It is necessary to investigate transposable element properties, including definition of the minimum features of one- and two-element transposon systems, analysis of the mechanism and regulation of transposition and excision, characterization of the effects of transposon insertion and excision on the target sites in the genome, and identification of loci in a plant's genetic background that influence all of these transposable element functions (18).

A further objective is the development of transposable element systems for all seed and clonal crop plants. A preliminary report indicated heterologous transposable elements may be useful for this objective (3). Such tools will be invaluable for identifying the genes for defined phenotypes such as metabolic pathways, the production of toxins, and disease resistance. Because transposon-marked genes are straightforward targets for recombinant cloning, this technology will advance the genetic engineering prospects for all crop plants.

Transformation Technology

Current molecular biology techniques make it possible to manipulate the genetic composition of bacteria and, to some extent, of higher organisms such as animals and plants. For example, a structural (protein-encoding) gene from a given organism can be linked to any of various transcriptional control regions (promoters), so that the genes are expressed under specific conditions in a new species (45). Several major advances have been made in applying these techniques to model plant systems, but vigorous new research will be necessary to make transformation a reliable and useful technology. The advantages of these techniques for crop improvement will be many, including the prospect of introducing single traits into a variety without the complications of linkage, and of transferring to one species a desired trait from an unrelated species.

All genetic manipulations, traditional or molecular, have two major component processes: first, the identification of a trait or gene of interest; and second, the means to transfer that gene (trait) into a recipient organism. In molecular genetic techniques, both gene identification and transfer have seen considerable achievement, but require much further development. The major areas for research include molecular and genetic means of identifying specific DNA segments for structural genes and for regulatory function, new technologies for DNA transfer into plant cells, methods for regeneration of whole organisms from transformed plant cells, and techniques for the independent genetic manipulation of organelles and organelle genomes.

Gene Identification and Expression

In traditional plant genetics, genes are deduced from the inheritance of traits, and their positions and behavior are determined in crosses by their relationship to other genes. Molecular genetics has added several twists to this process. One new approach uses transposable elements (see "Transposable Elements" above): by mutating a gene of observable phenotype with a transposable element, the DNA of that gene is physically marked (tagged) with an inserted DNA segment. Recent research has permitted the cloning of transposable elements from maize and *Antirrhinum* (23). The isolation of these recombinant DNA segments will now permit the cloning of genes that have been tagged by transposable element mutagenesis. Genes for disease resistance, and for other traits whose biochemical basis is elusive, are among the targets to be cloned by transposable element tagging. It is clear that the availability of transposable elements for all major crop systems will be essential for advancing molecular genetics in those systems.

The other major route to identifying genes at the DNA level is the biochemical approach. If the enzymatic or structural protein responsible for a trait can be specified, current technology enables researchers to identify the RNA and DNA sequences responsible for encoding that protein. The techniques used often include protein and nucleic acid separation, immunological and enzymatic assay, and *in vitro* translation of RNA to produce protein. Although laborious, this is a reliable approach. It has been used to obtain cloned gene segments encoding various plant products including seed storage proteins and enzymes of intermediary and photosynthetic metabolism. The power of this approach clearly is dependent on accompanying studies of plant function at the cellular and biochemical level. Thus, it is essential that such research also be highlighted.

A variation on the biochemical approach, also dependent on background studies in physiology, biochemistry, and cellular biology, takes advantage of the fact that certain plant traits appear only at specific stages in development, or in response to certain environmental signals such as a change in incident light. In such cases, nucleic acid biochemical manipulations make it possible to identify directly those genes which are newly expressed. This approach has allowed the cloning of several genes induced by light (55), genes encoding seed-specific proteins, and genes whose products are involved in defense against pathogens (36).

Having in hand the DNA for a structural gene is only part of what is necessary for useful transformation. Such genes will not be expressed unless located in proximity to DNA segments that regulate transcription of DNA into RNA. Furthermore, the protein products of the gene will not be produced and directed to the appropriate subcellular location (such as membranes) without particular amino acid coding regions being present in the gene itself. Work to define such controlling or regulatory features of plant genes has begun. Upstream transcriptional control regions have been identified for several genes including some that are expressed uniquely in seeds, or in response to light (29, 55). These upstream sequences have been shown to function when linked to other genes and placed in new plant species. In addition, a transit peptide sequence that directs itself to the chloroplast has been identified and used to carry another protein product to that location (*e.g.* see Herrera-Estrella *et al.* [32]). These breakthrough achievements demonstrate the likelihood that genetic engineering of specific individual gene traits will work across, as well as within, plant species. The needs for new research are many. Regulation of all critical plant cellular functions must be characterized at the molecular level. Further biochemical and physiological research on the regulation of plant function will be essential underpinnings for the identification of regulatory DNA segments. Also, such levels of research must be pursued to permit identification of structural genes that control productivity traits. Molecular analysis must be combined with cell biology research to characterize the control of protein localization to all plant cell compartments.

Transformed Plants

Higher plant cells can now be transformed and functioning plants that express and transmit the introduced genes can be recovered. In most cases, the recipients have been solanaceous species (*e.g.* tobacco, petunia, tomato) that are both (a) hosts to *Agrobacterium*, the agent that introduces the Ti plasmid vector that carries the new gene, and (b) tractable in cell and tissue culture (33), although direct DNA transformation without the aid of *Agrobacterium* has also been successfully accomplished (30, 48). This latter approach has also been used to transform successfully cultured cells of monocot species that are not hosts to *Agrobacterium* (39, 51). Electroporation, in which DNA is taken up by a cell placed in an electric field, is an additional method shown to be successful in both monocots and dicots (26). These transformation methods, and others now emerging, must be extended to all major crop species if the power of transformation (both for genetic improvement and for the dissection of important plant processes) is to be applied to the improvement of crops.

Regeneration

Most crops can now be regenerated from primary tissue cultures (1, 21), but only a few can be regenerated from protoplasts (16). Since Ti plasmid-mediated transformation can be accomplished by cocultivating *Agrobacterium* with an explant tissue that will produce adventitious

shoots, such as leaf discs (33), the regeneration requirements for trans-
forming crops that are hosts for *Agrobacterium* are not stringent. For
other crops, however, transformation methods that require protoplasts
will be necessary, and thus regeneration from protoplasts will be an
essential component of the process. Other genetic manipulations involving protoplasts, for example somatic hybridization or transformation
with intact organelles, will also require regeneration from protoplasts.

Organelle Genomes

Chloroplasts and mitochondria in plants carry out essential physiological functions, prominently photosynthesis, biosythesis, and respiration,
and they carry endogenous DNA genomes that partially encode these
functions (40). Because chloroplasts and mitochondria are inherited
maternally, only the organelles of the maternal plant genetically determine the properties of progeny. Another consequence of organelle genetics arises from the dependence of pollen viability on mitochondrial
function, which is the basis for cytoplasmic male sterility (35). These
factors constrain the plant breeder's ability to introduce new genetic
variability and combinations for organelle-encoded traits. Thus it is
essential to develop the technical means to transform plants with intact
organelles having desired properties, and to introduce into organelles
specific new genetic determinants (14). Furthermore, we must understand
the molecular biology of organelle function to allow regulation of newly
introduced genes.

The genomes of plant organelles have been only partly characterized
(40). The chloroplast genome encodes ribosomal and tRNA genes, and
structural genes for stromal and membrane photosynthetic proteins.
Mitochondrial genomes in higher plants are puzzlingly large, orders of
magnitude larger than those of animal cells; the DNA molecules often
display distinctive physical organization, which varies with the plant's
genetic background. The mitochondrial genome has been shown to encode ribosomal and tRNA genes and genes for some proteins of respiratory electron transport. The significance of its large genome, such as
versatility of function, remains unknown. Recent evidence indicates the
likelihood that chloroplasts and mitochondria undergo genetic exchange
(56).

Molecular engineering of plants will require control of all three genomes. For organelles in particular, it is necessary to understand genome
replication and recombination, including native exchange mechanisms,
to permit control of genetic transformation. In addition, detailed understanding of gene regulation is required, including analysis of organelle-
nuclear coordination. Specific cases requiring analysis range from the
coupled production of large subunit (chloroplast-encoded) and small
subunit (nuclear-encoded) of ribulose bisphosphate carboxylase to the
effect of nuclear fertility restorer genes on cytoplasmic male-sterile traits
of mitochondria.

The consequences and advantages of organelle location for genes are insufficiently understood. Basic research is required to determine, for example, how genes encoded in animal nuclear genomes have come to be located in plant mitochondrial DNA; the regulatory features of such an arrangement are crucial to controlling introduced organelle genes or to engineering organelle genes into the nucleus for the purpose of improving traits. Finally, markers and techniques must be developed for detecting and stabilizing uptake of intact organelles into plant cells, which can then be regenerated into whole plants with new traits.

Genetic Manipulation of Crop Phenotype

The objectives of plant improvement programs usually include the genetic modification of specific agriculturally important phenotypic traits. Resistance to pests and pathogens is the most universal improvement imparted to cultivars, but is often ephemeral because these biotic stresses arise from genetically evolving entities (47). Breeding for tolerance to abiotic stresses has been less common even though significant genetic differences are known to exist in tolerance to temperature extremes, moisture stress, and soil toxicities and deficiencies (10). The capacity for productivity has been dramatically altered in some cereals through genetic alteration in plant form and in the partitioning of assimilate within the plant. However, in virtually all cases, the improvements have been accomplished either by empirically selecting for individuals expressing the trait or by introgressing phenotypic traits identified in other sources of germ plasm. In both cases, the process is often hampered by the inability to easily and rapidly identify individuals carrying the trait.

Very little is known about the biological mechanisms underlying many agriculturally important phenotypes. Most certainly they could be manipulated more deliberately and effectively if their fundamental bases were better known. Somatic cell selection of useful genotypes would be greatly facilitated by more fundamental biological knowledge that would permit the recognition of the cellular manifestation of important plant phenotypes (6, 41).

Resistance to Pests and Pathogens

Host plant resistance to pests and pathogens involves the biological interaction between two organisms and both must be investigated in elucidating the nature of resistance. The analysis of genes governing disease and pest resistance in plants and those for pathogenicity and virulence in pests and pathogens can reveal the mechanisms underlying these phenomena and facilitate the direct and deliberate manipulation of resistance (28). Plant and pathogen genes are now being studied at the molecular level for several plant diseases caused by fungal, bacterial, and viral pathogens and these efforts must be expanded. The same molecular tools must be applied to the study of microbial symbionts, namely nitrogen-fixing bacteria and mycorrhizal fungi.

Genetic research on pathogens and symbionts has already produced some noteworthy successes. In *Rhizobium*, the genes for plant invasion and nitrogen fixation have been identified and cloned, making it possible to alter the host range and regulation of bacterial nodulation ability (38). Genetic studies of *Rhizobium* have provided transposon, vector, and other molecular technology useful in the analysis and manipulation of bacterial plant pathogens such as *Pseudomonas* and *Agrobacterium*. In *Pseudomonas*, these new techniques have made possible the first cloning of any pathogen's host-specific avirulence gene (52). Basic genetic studies of *Agrobacterium* (43) have yielded an understanding of virulence and its regulation, and have provided the basis for rational biological control of crown gall using bacteriocins. Furthermore, *Agrobacterium* research has, by elucidating the hormonal basis of tumorigenicity, provided new impetus and insight to the study of hormone molecular biology in plants. Beyond these basic advances, of course, are remarkable achievements using *Agrobacterium* to engineer the transfer of new genes into plant cells. These research advances exemplify an important benefit of pathogen study, the critical new information often discovered about the host's own biology.

In genetically more difficult organisms such as fungi and nematodes, new techniques have been emerging for model systems. In yeast and *Aspergillus*, molecular cloning and transformation have been developed (59). Recent research indicates these approaches will apply to many plant pathogenic fungi, and should permit the identification of virulence and pathogenicity. For example, work on the biochemistry of fungal toxin synthesis has seen several advances, and paves the way for molecular cloning of toxin genes and the study of their regulation (46). For some fungal systems, though, many challenges remain. For example, the beneficial endomycorrhizae, as well as some pathogens, have so far eluded efforts to grow them in pure culture.

Nematodes that attack plant roots have also been refractory to genetic study, due to the difficulties of observing them *in vivo* and of culturing them *in vitro*. At the same time, however, remarkable genetic and developmental research has been carried out on a free-living soil nematode, *Caenorhabditis elegans* (53), and has demonstrated that this group of organisms should be amenable to genetic crosses, transformation, and developmental analysis.

It is imperative that research now proceed from the few systems where genetics has had an impact, to begin elucidating the fundamentals of plant-pathogen and plant-symbiont interactions in the major agriculturally important systems. Genes for avirulence and pathogenicity of bacteria and fungi need to be identified and their protein products and functions characterized. The regulation of such genes in disease needs to be determined, as does their role in race specificity on different crop genotypes. Central to these goals are new developments in vectors, transposable elements, and transformation procedures. For difficult systems, all techniques from basic to molecular must be pushed further. Knowledge about nematodes from the model system *C. elegans* should be applied to plant parasitic nematodes. Mycorrhizae need to be studied more intensively. Even for somewhat developed systems, it is important to develop more sophisticated, workable genetic tools.

The viruses and viroids present unique problems and opportunities (13). As the ultimate intracellular pathogens, viruses and viroids will provide us with a direct means to understand plant molecular biology, especially nucleic acid metabolism. In addition, they are elusive and cause devastating diseases, which deserve much more focused attention by all methods of experimental plant biology. It is important to understand viral replication and transcription, both to understand disease and to provide useful genetic tools for cloning. The disease aspect of viruses also demands study to address several critical problems, such as elucidating the functions of viral-encoded genes during plant cell infection, defining host cell factors needed for virus replication, and analyzing the mechanisms by which viruses cause symptoms in the host. The means by which cell-to-cell spread of virus occurs needs to be determined; finally, these analyses need to be brought together to research the question of what makes some plants immune to viral disease. Among the practical benefits of such research will be not just the understanding of disease and of basic plant functions, but also the means to diagnose plant disease by rapid nucleic acid or immunological methods.

Resistance to Abiotic Stresses

Crop genotypes with increased resistance to such adverse environmental factors as drought, salinity, high temperature, ion toxicities, and nutrient deficiencies are particularly important for reducing agricultural inputs and improving crop productivity on marginal land (5). While genetic variability in resistance has been described for all of these factors (10), it has not been exploited in plant improvement programs to any great extent because much of it is so poorly characterized, both genetically and physiologically (5, 22). If the inheritance of and the fundamental mechanisms underlying genetic adaptation to environmental stresses were elucidated, not only could this aid conventional breeding programs, particularly in facilitating the reliable identification of resistant individuals, but it might suggest somatic cell selection strategies and transformation schemes for obtaining useful resistant genotypes.

Additionally, genotypes that differ in response to an environmental stress can be invaluable tools in elucidating the biological mechanisms underlying the response. Such genotypes may be identified by screening existing germ plasm, as has been done in studies of drought tolerance in barley (31) or may be obtained by somatic cell selection, as has recently been demonstrated for aluminum resistance (11).

Simple Evaluation and Diagnostic Methods

Selection in plant breeding requires the evaluation of large numbers of plants and/or progenies, and thus rapid and simple evaluation methods are essential to making genetic progress. Many of the procedures used to evaluate plants for resistance to diseases, pests, and abiotic stresses (*e.g.* drought, heat, and salinity) and for chemical composition, however, are too cumbersome and unreliable to be used on large numbers of plants. Even when they give reliable results, their use is limited to evaluating a few genotypes as potential parents for crosses. Research to elucidate the fundamental bases of these traits may suggest simple and rapid tests for evaluating them.

Genetic Control of Assimilate Production and Partitioning

Genetic improvement of seed yields of many crops has been steady and large. For example, yields of cereals and soybeans have been increased by 40 to 100% (19, 24). These gains in grain yield have been due almost entirely to higher harvest index with little or no increase in total biological yield (27). In some cases (*e.g.* small grains) harvest index has been optimized at 45 to 55%, so further gains in grain yield will depend upon increasing total biomass productivity. Total biomass productivity of forage crops has not been increased very much. Manipulation of biomass productivity will require an understanding of the control of assimilate production and partitioning. Weedy and wild relatives should be explored as sources of genes for increasing biomass productivity (25).

LITERATURE CITED

1. AMMIRATO PV 1983 Embryogenesis. *In* DA Evans, WR Sharp, PV Ammirato, Y Yamada, eds, Handbook of Plant Cell Culture, Vol 1. Macmillan, New York, pp 82–123
2. AXTELL JD 1981 Breeding for improved nutritional quality. *In* KJ Frey, ed, Plant Breeding II. Iowa State University Press, Ames, IA, pp 365–432
3. BAKER BJ, L HERRERA-ESTRELLA, N FEDEROFF 1985 Ac: a generalized plant mutagen? J Cell Biochem 9C: 212
4. BENNETT MD 1984 Nuclear architecture and its manipulation. *In* JP Gustafson, ed, Gene Manipulation in Plant Improvement, Plenum, New York, pp 469–502
5. BOYER JS 1982 Plant productivity and environment. Science 218: 443–448
6. CHALEFF RS 1983 Isolation of agronomically useful mutants from plant cell cultures. Science 219: 676–682
7. CHANG TT 1985 Principles of genetic conservation. Iowa State J Res 59: 325
8. CHANG TT 1985 Evaluation and documentation of crop germplasm. Iowa State J Res 59: 379
9. CHANG TT 1985 Germplasm enhancement and utilization. Iowa State J Res 59: 399
10. CHRISTIANSEN MN, CF LEWIS, eds. 1982 Breeding Plants for Less Favorable Environments. John Wiley & Sons, New York
11. CONNER AJ, CP MEREDITH 1985 Large-scale selection of aluminum-resistant

mutants from plant cell culture: expression and inheritance in seedlings. Theor Appl Genet. 71: 159

12. CULLIS CA 1984 Environmentally induced DNA changes. *In* JW Pollard, ed, Evolutionary Theory: Paths into the Future. John Wiley & Sons, London, pp 203–216

13. DAVIES JW, ed 1985 Molecular Plant Virology. CRC Press, Boca Raton, FL

14. DEBLOCK M, J SCHELL, M VAN MONTAGU 1985 Chloroplast transformation by *Agrobacterium tumefaciens.* EMBO J 4: 1367–1372

15. DÖRING HP, P STARLINGER 1984 Barbara McClintock's controlling elements: now at the DNA level. Cell 39: 253–259

16. EVANS DA, JE BRAVO 1983 Protoplast isolation and culture. *In* DA Evans, WR Sharp, PV Ammirato, Y Yamada, eds. Handbook of Plant Cell Culture, Vol 1. Macmillan, New York, pp 124–176

17. EVANS DA, WR SHARP 1983 Single gene mutations in tomato plants regenerated from tissue culture. Science 221: 949–951

18. FEDEROFF N 1983 Controlling elements in maize. *In* JA Shapiro, ed, Mobile Genetic Elements. Academic Press, New York, pp 1–63

19. FEHR WR, ed 1984 Genetic Contributions to Yield Gains of Five Major Crop Plants, Special Publication No. 7. Crop Science Society of America, Madison, WI

20. FLAVELL R 1980 The molecular characterization and organization of plant chromosomal DNA sequences. Annu Rev Plant Physiol 31: 569–596

21. FLICK CE, DA EVANS, WR SHARP 1983 Organogenesis. *In* DA Evans, WR Sharp, PV Ammirato, Y. Yamada, eds. Handbook of Plant Cell Culture, Vol 1. Macmillan, New York, pp 13–81

22. FOY CD, RL CHANEY, MC WHITE 1978 The physiology of metal toxicity in plants. Annu Rev Plant Physiol 29: 511–566

23. FREELING, M 1984 Plant transposable elements and insertion sequences. Annu Rev Plant Physiol 35: 277–298

24. FREY KJ 1971 Improving crop plants through plant breeding. *In* JD Eastin, RD Munson, eds, Moving Off the Yield Plateau, Special Publication No. 20. American Society of Agronomy, Madison, WI, pp 15–58

25. FREY KJ, TS COX, DM RODGERS, P. BRAMMEL-COX 1984 Increasing cereal yields with genes from wild and weedy species. *In* VL Chopra, BC Joshi, RP Sharma, HC Bansel, eds, Genetics: New Frontiers, Proceedings of the 15th International Genetics Congress. Oxford and IBH Publishing Co., New Delhi, pp 51–68

26. FROMM, M, L TAYLOR, V WALBOT 1985 Expression of genes transferred into monocot and dicot plant cells by electroporation. Proc. Natl Acad Sci USA 82: 5824–5828

27. GIFFORD RM, JH THORNE, WD HITZ, RT GIAQUINTA 1984 Crop productivity and photoassimilate partitioning. Science 225: 801–807

28. GILCHRIST DG, OC YODER 1984 Genetics of host-parasite systems: a prospectus for molecular biology. *In* T Kosuge, E Nester, eds, Plant-Microbe Interactions. Macmillan, New York, pp 69–92

29. GOLDBERG R 1985 Regulation of higher plant gene expression. *In* M Freeling, ed, Plant Genetics. Alan R Liss, New York. In press

30. HAIN R, P STABEL, AP CZERNILOFSKY, HH STEINBISS, L HERRERA-ESTRELLA, J SCHELL 1985 Uptake, integration, expression and genetic transmission of a selectable chimaeric gene by plant protoplasts. Mol Gen Genet 199: 161–168

31. HANSON AD, CE NELSEN, AR PEDERSEN, EH EVERSON 1979 Capacity for proline accumulation during water stress in barley and its implication for breeding for drought resistance. Crop Sci 19: 489–494

32. HERRERA-ESTRELLA L, G VAN DE BROECK, R MAENHAUT, M VAN MONTAGU, J SCHELL, M TIMKO, A CASHMORE 1984 Light inducible and chloroplast-associated expression of a chimeric gene introduced into *Nicotiana tabacum* using a Ti plasmid vector. Nature 310: 115–120

33. HORSCH RB, JE FRY, NL HOFFMAN, D EICHHOLTZ, SG ROGERS, RT FRALEY 1985 A simple and general method for transferring genes into plants. Science 227: 1229–1231

34. LARKIN PJ, SA RYAN, RIS BRETTELL, WR SCOWCROFT 1984 Heritable somaclonal variation in wheat. Theor Appl Genet 67: 443–455

35. LAUGHNAN JR, S GABAY-LAUGHNAN 1983 Cytoplasmic male sterility in maize. Annu Rev Genet 17: 27–48

36. LAWTON MA, RA DIXON, K HAHLBROCK, C LAMB 1983 Elicitor induction of mRNA activity. Eur J Biochem 130: 131–139

37. LITVAK S, M CASTROVIEJO 1985 Plant DNA polymerases. Plant Mol Biol 4: 311–316

38. LONG SR 1984 Nodulation genetics. *In* T Kosuge, E Nester, eds. Plant-Microbe Interactions. Macmillan, New York, pp 265–306

39. LÖRZ H, B BAKER, J SCHELL 1985 Gene transfer to cereal cells mediated by protoplast transformation. Mol Gen Genet 199: 178–182

40. MARCUS A, ed 1981 The Biochemistry of Plants, Vol 6, Proteins and Nucleic Acids. Academic Press, New York

41. MEREDITH CP 1984 Selecting better crops from cultured cells. *In* JP Gustafson, ed, Gene Manipulation in Plant Improvement. Plenum, New York, pp 503–528

42. METZENBERG RL, TN STEVENS, EU SELKER, E MORZYCKA-WROBLEWSKA 1984 A method for finding the genetic map position of cloned DNA fragments. Neurospora Newsl 31: 35

43. NESTER EW, MP GORDON, RM AMASINO, MF YANOFSKY 1984 Crown gall: a molecular and physiological analysis. Annu Rev Plant Physiol 35: 387–413

44. NITZSCHE, W 1983 Germplasm preservation. *In* DA Evans, WR Sharp, PV Ammirato, Y Yamada, eds, Handbook of Plant Cell Culture, Vol 1. Macmillan, New York, pp 782–805

45. OLD RW, SB PRIMROSE 1981 Principles of Gene Manipulation. University of California Press, Berkeley, CA

46. PANOPOULOS N, JD WALTON, DK WILLIS 1984 Genetic and biochemical basis of virulence in plant pathogens. *In* DPS Verma, T Hohn, eds, Genes Involved in Microbe-Plant Interactions. Springer-Verlag, New York, pp 339–374

47. PARLEVLIET JE 1981 Disease resistance in plants and its consequences for plant breeding. *In* KJ Frey, ed, Plant Breeding II. Iowa State University Press, Ames, IA, pp 309–364

48. PASZKOWSKI J, RD SHILLITO, M SAUL, V MANDAK, T HOHN, B HOHN, I POTRYKUS 1984 Direct gene transfer in plants. EMBO J 3: 2717–2723

49. PLUCKNETT DL, NJH SMITH 1984 Networking in international agricultural research. Science 225: 989–993

50. PLUCKNETT DL, NJH SMITH, JT WILLIAMS, NW ANISHETTY 1983 Crop germplasm conservation and developing countries. Science 220: 163–169

51. POTRYKUS I, MW SAUL, J PETRUSKA, J PASZKOWSKI, RD SHILLITO 1985
    Direct gene transfer to cells of a graminaceous monocot. Mol Gen Genet
    199: 183–188
52. STASKAWICZ BJ, D DAHLBECK, NT KEEN 1984 Cloned avirulence gene of
    Pseudomonas syringae pv. *glycinea* determines race-specific incompatibility
    on *Glycine max* (L.) Merr. Proc Natl Acad Sci USA 81: 6024–6028
53. STERNBERG PW, HR HORVITZ 1984 The genetic control of cell lineage during
    nematode development. Annu Rev Genet 18: 489–524
54. SUN, Z-X, C-Z ZHAO, K-L KANG, X-F QI, Y-P FU 1983 Somaclonal genetics
    of rice, *Oryza sativa* L. Theor Appl Genet 67: 67–73
55. THOMPSON WF, LS KAUFMAN, JC WATSON 1985 Induction of plant gene
    expression by light. BioEssays 3: 153
56. WALBOT V, C CULLIS 1985 Rapid genomic change in higher plants. Annu
    Rev Plant Physiol 36: 367–440
57. WALKER GW 1985 Inducible DNA repair systems. Annu Rev Biochem 54:
    425–457
58. WEHRHAHN C, RW ALLARD 1965 The detection and measurement of the
    effects of individual genes involved in the inheritance of a quantitative
    character in wheat. Genetics 51: 109–119
59. YELTON MM, JE JAMER, WE TIMBERLAKE 1984 Transformation of *Asper-*
    gillus nidulans by using a trpC plasmid. Proc Natl Acad Sci USA 81: 1470–
    1474

Plant and Cell Physiology

Submitted on behalf of the group by:

D. DELMER   LAWRENCE E. SCHRADER

GARY H. HEICHEL

With recent emphasis on biotechnology research, major advances have been made in molecular genetics and molecular biology. Techniques for transformation, plasmid transfer, and gene cloning are now in use. Expression of some of the transferred genes has been observed. A major challenge to the application of the new biotechnologies is the identification of agriculturally important (productivity-enhancing) genes and gene products in major crops. For example, what biochemical, physiological, morphological, or other traits currently limit crop productivity, which genes control these traits, and at what stages of growth, differentiation, or maturation are these genes expressed? If these traits and their associated genes can be unambiguously identified, molecular techniques should be useful in increasing gene dosage or otherwise overcoming these limitations.

Because of the diagnostic and mechanistic approaches of plant and cell physiology, this discipline may serve as a uniquely important "bridge discipline" between molecular biology and genetics. We predict that the unique contributions of physiologists will be in the understanding of the mechanism(s) of agriculturally useful genes in the whole, intact organism throughout growth, differentiation, and maturation.

The role of the plant biochemist and physiologist clearly assumes new relevance as the need intensifies for the elucidation of productivity-enhancing genes and gene products. Understanding of the detailed mechanisms of regulation at the structural and biochemical level for mechanisms of hormone action, assimilate partitioning, plant development and reproduction, and the modification of these mechanisms by the environment, is crucial for the identification of the genes and gene products.

We recognize that a multidisciplinary approach is becoming more necessary for rapid and efficient problem solving. While continued exploration of the structural and biochemical bases of physiological processes must continue using traditional approaches, imaginative use must be made of naturally available and created genetic variation as tools to solve recalcitrant problems in plant and cell physiology. We advocate a mission wherein plant scientists from structural botany, physiology, biochemistry, genetics, and molecular biology cooperate in multidisciplinary programs to identify the physiological and biochemical determinants of metabolism, growth, and development essential to the genetic improvement of crop productivity and quality. This mission should be conducted with a view to producing food profitably, high in nutrient density, by methods sparing of natural resources, and with maintenance of a stable natural environment. Ten research imperatives are relevant to achieving this mission.

Strengthen Support for Fundamental Research on Metabolism, Enzymology, Protein Chemistry, and Plant Structure, Function and Development

The proceedings of the conference held a decade ago (6) included research imperatives for several aspects of plant and cell physiology. Substantial advances have been made in accomplishing several of the research imperatives identified in 1975. However, basic information on the biochemistry of several metabolic processes and regulatory steps is needed before molecular techniques can be used most effectively. A recent report from the National Research Council (48) reviewed the status of plant science research, and affirmed the need for continued basic research in plant sciences.

Substantial progress has been made since 1975 in accomplishing the first research imperative in "carbon input." Photorespiration and the adverse effects of O_2 on net photosynthesis are now understood. It is established that O_2 and CO_2 compete at the active site of the enzyme ribulose 1,5-bisphosphate carboxylase/oxygenase (RuBisCO) and that RuBisCO serves a dual function as either a carboxylase or oxygenase (43, 51). Inhibition of photorespiration by chemicals or by elimination of an enzyme of the photorespiratory pathway (63) is currently not a feasible approach. Either method leads to an accumulation of one or more intermediates of the photorespiratory pathway, and prevents the normal cycling of carbon to generate RuBP (substrate) for RuBisCO. Therefore, photosynthesis drops markedly within minutes after inhibition of photorespiration occurs. Based on the work with *Arabadopsis* mutants (63), it appears that the only way to reduce or eliminate photorespiration is through genetic modification of the active site of RuBisCO so that O_2 is unable to compete with CO_2. How soon will it be possible to use molecular techniques to modify the active site on the large subunit of RuBisCO? What role does the small subunit play in the holoenzyme?

Much has been learned about regulation of carbon metabolism and carbon flux. In the chloroplast and leaf cell, the regulation of fructose bisphosphatase and other enzymes in the chloroplast by thioredoxin is important (14, 15). Fructose-2,6-bisphosphate plays a key role as an effector in regulating carbon partitioning in the chloroplast between starch (for storage) and triose phosphates for export to the cytoplasm to make sucrose for transport (13, 66).

The enzymes for sucrose biosynthesis are localized in the cytoplasm, so earlier concerns about the inability of chloroplast envelopes to transport sucrose (p. 180 of Ref. 6) are alleviated. Sucrose phosphate synthase and cytoplasmic fructose-1,6-bisphosphatase may be regulatory enzymes of carbon flow in the cytoplasm (19, 20, 58, 67).

The transport of metabolites of the Calvin cycle between the chloroplast and cytosol is now understood. The phosphate translocator has been isolated (26) and provides a mechanism to export products of photosynthesis (*i.e.* principally triose phosphates) from the chloroplast to the cytosol with a concomitant import of inorganic phosphate or phosphoglycerate to keep the phosphate concentration constant inside and outside the chloroplast. Other mechanisms (*e.g.* the dicarboxylate translocator) also exist in the envelope, but appear to be less important for carbon transport. The transport of amino acids from the chloroplast is not well understood, even though the chloroplast is a major site of amino acid biosynthesis. Are there specific translocators for amino acids? What about transport across the membrane of peroxisomes?

Several aspects of the regulation of photosynthesis are not yet understood. For example, is the "source" or "sinks" more limiting? Is there a feedback-type of inhibition of photosynthesis when the sink lacks the capacity to use all the photosynthate translocated to it? What regulates starch mobilization? What regulates the partitioning of photosynthate to different products (*e.g.* sugars *versus* amino acids *versus* organic acids)? What controls the activation of RuBisCO and pyruvate, Pi dikinase? Are these two enzymes the rate-limiting ones in photosynthesis of C_3 and C_4 species, respectively, or are there other enzymes that may be more limiting? How does this regulation of photosynthesis change during different stages of development of crop plants?

Much remains to be learned about nitrogen metabolism in plants. Nitrogen is the element that commonly limits plant productivity. The cost of nitrogen fertilizer still represents a major variable input to crop production. Little progress has been made in N_2-fixing microorganisms for supplying nitrogen to grasses and cereals. The recovery of fertilizer-N by crop plants has improved only slightly with about 50% of the applied nitrogen being recovered on average. Further improvement in nitrogen-use efficiency by decreasing nitrification, denitrification, and leaching of nitrogen would reduce farmers' production costs.

Perhaps a more effective way to improve N-use efficiency is through improvement of crop plants. Corn inbreds and hybrids differ in their ability to absorb nitrate (8), but a rapid assay is needed to screen large numbers of lines or plants for increased uptake capability. Why are certain lines superior in nitrate uptake? Do they have more uptake sites, larger root systems, or more efficient uptake mechanisms? Why do corn plants accumulate so much nitrate in their roots and stems? Is this accumulation genetically controlled? How can this accumulated nitrate be moved to the leaf for assimilation?

In many crops, about one-third of the N remains in vegetative parts at maturity. What controls this partitioning of N among vegetative and reproductive parts, and is it possible to increase the nitrogen harvest index in reproductive parts, above two-thirds?

Recent studies (9, 10) indicate that certain corn genotypes with high yield potential have the ability to delay senescence (*i.e.* stay green and maintain photosynthesis) and also mobilize more N from vegetative tissues to the grain. Are these traits simply inherited so they can be incorporated into other corn lines and hybrids?

Although our understanding of photosynthesis and nitrogen metabolism has improved during the past decade, fundamental research on these and other metabolic processes must be continued to provide the framework for the remaining imperatives. Sustained research programs that advance our fundamental knowledge of these metabolic processes and their regulation are essential. These research efforts need to be expanded to examine structure-function relationships and plant development. These key processes and relationships must eventually be understood at the molecular level so that researchers can apply new techniques to manipulate genetic and chemical regulatory processes.

Reduce Energetically Wasteful Processes

There are several metabolic components of carbon and nitrogen metabolism that appear to be energetically wasteful and, by implication, detrimental to plant productivity and quality. For example, dark respiration may dissipate 40% or more of the daily carbon accretion by a plant. Whether this respiration is all coupled to the production of high energy intermediates of metabolism is open to question. Evidence that annual dry matter yields of perennial ryegrass were increased 6 to 13%, by selection for low rates of leaf dark respiration (75), supports the hypothesis that some dark respiration is not associated with synthetic processes.

Activity of a respiratory alternate oxidase pathway is evident during inorganic N assimilation by many plant species. For example, roots of *Lupinus albus* grown on NO_3^- had higher alternate oxidase activity than those from N_2-dependent plants (42). Alternate oxidase activity was higher in roots of *Triticum aestivum* grown on NH_4^+ than on NO_3^- (3). Physiological and genetic modification of the cytochrome oxidase and alternate oxidase respiratory pathways of crop species may result in improving productivity and input-use efficiency.

In addition to the putative inefficiencies embodied in mitochondrial respiratory pathways, molecular techniques may aid in the analysis and eventual modification of other enzymatic systems having energetic inefficiencies. For example, in the absence of significant natural genetic variation in the discrimination of RuBisCo for CO_2 and O_2, directed modification of the active site may provide the opportunity to investigate the mutability of oxygenase activity with a resultant increase in plant productivity. The modification of the active site of rhizobial nitrogenase to decrease hydrogen reduction may also be tractable by molecular methods.

A second strategy for avoidance of seemingly wasteful metabolic processes is to induce an enhanced activity of alternate, more efficient pathways, or to introduce altogether new pathways into the plant. For example, a CO_2 concentrating mechanism in the plasma membrane of certain algae has been identified (2). The elucidation of its mechanism may provide a model for the modification of the mesophyll cell plasma membrane of C_3 crop plants, and possibly improve plant productivity.

The energetic losses associated with nitrogenase activity are partly circumvented in those rhizobia having an uptake hydrogenase (22, 52). The introduction of the uptake hydrogenase gene into the many deficient strains would offer the opportunity to determine the physiological and practical consequences of hydrogen evolution during N_2 fixation. Enhancing the quantity and activity of legume nodule phosphoenolpyruvate carboxylase activity may reduce the carbon costs of N_2 fixation with a consequent increase in plant productivity and quality (71).

Regulation of DNA Replication, Cell Division, and Differentiation

The regeneration of plants from genetically transformed protoplasts in tissue culture is critical to the application of certain molecular techniques for crop improvement. However, current tissue culture systems are inadequate for routine large-scale and reproducible application. The genetic variability in cell cultures, although a potential source of novel plant genotypes, is a serious problem. Crops that must be reproduced vegetatively need to be genetically uniform. Traits introduced through gene transformation may be lost in the background of an unstable genome. This is quite serious for many crops because a high percentage of regenerants from cultures may be abnormal. The origin of the genetic instability of tissue cultures is not understood but is probably due to our inability to control properly DNA replication and cell division.

The inability to regenerate plants from single cells or protoplasts from some species is a serious limitation. Although the above-mentioned instability of the genome may be a factor, it is more likely due to our lack of understanding of how hormones and other factors act in controlling cell growth and differentiation. Plant hormones play a central role in regulating plant growth, but little is known about the mechanism of action of any plant hormone. Because hormones are undoubtedly involved in the processes discussed above, a renewed emphasis should be given to studies on mechanisms of hormone action. The application of new biotechnology techniques should lead to timely advances.

A more thorough knowledge of the fundamental biochemistry of the regulation of DNA replication, cell division, and cell differentiation promises to minimize genome instability associated with current tissue culture systems and to improve our ability to reproducibly regenerate plants from cells or cultures that have been genetically transformed. This knowledge may permit control of the synthesis of desirable and undesirable plant products in culture.

Control of Floral Induction and Development

Flowering is the necessary developmental event which must precede the development of seeds, and is thus a crucial step in the production of economic yield. While the environmental conditions, particularly photoperiod, which can control flowering are well known, very little is known about the actual developmental mechanisms that take place as a stem apex undergoes the transition to flower production. In animals, dedicated germ cells are always present. This is not the case in plants where the reproductive structures develop from undifferentiated apical cells that were previously giving rise to vegetative structures. Analysis of cell lines has shown that flowers develop from a specific cell or cells in the apex and that the number varies with the species. At either a certain point in the growth of the plant (if photoperiodically neutral), or on the arrival of a (presumably) chemical signal from the leaves (the hypothetical florigen), a pronounced shift occurs in the development of the cells produced by the stem apex. Instead of the cells differentiating into the cells of leaves and other vegetative structures, the cells develop into constituents of flower parts including the male and female reproductive structures (stamen and ovary, respectively). While under rare conditions a slow morphological shift can be seen, the change is, in general, quite abrupt. It is thus clear that pronounced changes in the enzyme complement must be occurring which in turn are controlled by changes in gene transcription. Investigations into changing enzyme and RNA patterns in the 1970s failed to pinpoint any of the changes. With the evolution of modern molecular techniques, such changes should be amenable to investigation and resolution. Such investigations are sorely needed so that we can better understand the processes taking place on floral evocation. This understanding will enable the manipulation of the flowering process so that the timing and extent of flowering can be controlled to optimize flowering with regard to both the climatic conditions and the capacity of the plant to support the developing seeds. For example, a plant should reach a certain size before flowering in order to support seed development, but flowering should occur before photosynthate is wasted on excessive vegetative development. The timing of flowering should be at the time most favorable to seed development from a temperature and light standpoint and the flowering should be continued through periods of transient environmental stress. A control of the number of flowers produced would also optimize seed size and prevent the wasteful abortion of young fruits early in development.

Molecular markers of the evocation of flowering could also provide an early precise assay for floral induction in the search for the endogenous chemical agents inducing flowering. Despite a 50-year search for "florigen" its nature remains unknown in part because of the lack of a good bioassay other than the flowering of the entire adult plant.

The development of male sterility has greatly assisted the production of hybrid seed in species displaying hybrid vigor. Such sterility is often associated with a specific gene (which may be cytoplasmic). Knowledge of molecular changes during flower development may make it possible to pinpoint those changes exclusive to pollen production and lead to the potential to block genetically those specific changes. This would result in the wider availability of male sterile plants for hybrid seed production.

Some species display the phenomenon of incompatibility so that closely related genotypes fail to produce seed. This may seriously hamper seed production in genetically homogeneous potentially high yielding varieties. Investigations into the molecular basis of incompatibility have identified the genes and proteins involved in regulating pollen stigma interactions, in both the male and female parents, in *Brassica* (47). Such research should be continued to enable the elimination of incompatibility where agronomically desirable. On the other side of the coin the introduction of incompatibility via gene insertion would facilitate hybrid seed production without the disruption of yield quality occasioned by the introduction of incompatibility genes by traditional plant breeding methods.

Metabolic and Genetic Control of Plant Senescence, and the Development and Function of Sinks

Crop productivity is directly related to the duration of functionality in physiological sources and sinks. In most crop plants the limits to such functionality are the establishment of the reproductive sink (the setting of fruit) and the termination or senescence of functionality in the source organs (usually the leaves).

The establishment of the reproductive sink involves not only the induction and development of flowers as addressed under "Control of Floral Induction and Development," but also the setting of the fruit from such flowers. Very little is known about this process of fruit set, except that it is apparently a complex process regulated in part by the availability of assimilates (7) and in part by the profiles of endogenous hormones (12) in the reproductive structures. A clearer understanding of the metabolic processes and gene products involved in this regulation holds the promise of being able to manipulate it in ways advantageous to productivity.

The termination of functionality (senescence) in source organs is often a very gradual process, which starts long before the economic yield of the crop plant has been fully formed. For example, leaf photosynthetic activities typically start to decline soon after full expansion of individual leaves (76), long before the grain is fully developed. In legumes, the N_2 fixation activity of nodules and the nitrogen assimilation processes in roots and shoots are other examples of a gradual senescence of assimilatory powers which starts before the grain filling period is complete (61). Any degree of amelioration of such processes of senescence has the potential to cause considerable yield increases.

The metabolic regulation of senescence is largely unknown. In many instances senescence appears to be related to the excessive demands put on the source organs by the developing sinks (61); however, it is not known by what mechanism such sink demand expresses itself to the sources.

Studies of senescence in the past have been primarily concerned with terminal symptoms of senescence (such as leaf yellowing) (44) and have seldom focused on the initial events in the process.

Enhance Partitioning of Desired Organic Assimilates and Plant Nutrients into Harvestable Components

Increased crop yields have resulted from genetic alteration in the proportion of biomass allocated to the yield component (28, 29), and from implementation of improved cultural practices. Assimilate partitioning is a complex whole-plant process that begins with biochemical partitioning of assimilates in organelles and cells of source tissues to provide the substrates for long-distance translocation to other plant parts (sinks). Partitioning also encompasses the distribution and allocation of these assimilates into the economically important plant part(s). Our current understanding of these processes is so deficient that any directed attempts to manipulate partitioning or source/sink relations are precluded.

Because of its complexity, assimilate partitioning must be studied at many levels of organization ranging from molecular to whole-plant levels. A multidisciplinary effort will be required to identify important regulatory points and relevant gene products, and to exploit genetic variability through gene manipulation or by other means.

1. *Determine the pathway and mechanism of assimilate transfer between cells to identify key regulatory sites.* Assimilates must pass from one cell to another either via plasmodesmatal connections or across cellular membranes. Both pathways of cell-to-cell transfer are probably operative in source and sink tissues. However, their relative contribution to overall assimilate flux is unknown (69). Structural and physiological studies are needed to resolve these questions. An understanding of these transfer mechanisms could provide the opportunity for their genetic manipulation as outlined below.

(a) Plasmodesmata: While it is clear that assimilates can move rapidly through plasmodesmata, the precise location (cytoplasmic annulus *versus* desmotubule) and mechanisms of transfer are unknown (30). The recent observation that cytoplasmic levels of calcium influence solute permeability of plasmodesmata (23) indicates potential for manipulation of assimilate fluxes in both sources and sink tissues. In order for this potential to be explored and possibly exploited, basic information is needed to isolate key transfer events that influence movement through plasmodesmata.

(b) Membrane: Transport across membranes is the only way plants concentrate solutes. This important function is the energy source for driving the movement of assimilates from sources to sinks. However, knowledge of the energy-requiring transport mechanisms for organic assimilates across plant cell membranes is rudimentary. Molecular biology techniques will permit isolating, producing antibodies against, and genetically modifying carrier proteins, so that localization, mechanisms, regulation, and eventual genetic modification will be possible.

Present knowledge indicates that transport across the plasma membrane is via a proton-cotransport system for sugars and amino acids. However, transport across the tonoplast is less well studied, but may involve an antiport system or group translocator for sucrose (56).

2. *Identify the gene products that determine quantity and composition of desired assimilates accumulated in the yield component.* Current evidence suggests that allocation of translocated assimilates into final storage products is controlled within sink tissues. The use of mutants such as shrunken-2 or opaque-2 in corn (49) will aid in dissecting the metabolic pathways and important control points regulating starch, protein, and lipid biosynthesis. Comparison of these mutants possessing decreased sink capacity (*e.g.* shrunken-2 endosperm accumulates only about 25% as much starch as its normal counterpart) with their isogenic counterparts also provides a genetic tool to compare the effects of decreased sink capacity on source leaf metabolism and translocation (40). Other potential control points that are vulnerable to molecular biological techniques include cell wall invertase thought to control phloem loading (24) and sucrose synthesis shown to have tissue-specific substrate preference (60). Information from these studies can be used to genetically modify and thus improve both the quality and amount of assimilates accumulated in sink tissues. For example, the nutritional quality of corn can be improved by introducing the opaque-2 gene, but economic incentives are needed to persuade farmers to produce it. If corn grain can be modified to contain more energy-rich compounds, ethanol production from grain may become more economically feasible as a renewable energy source, and replace nonrenewable sources of fossil energy.

The source determines the timing and quality of assimilates available for export in response to sink demand. The metabolic pathway of sucrose biosynthesis and its regulation are now sufficiently understood so that this metabolic pathway is ripe for exploitation using molecular techniques. In those species that transport principally sucrose from sources to sinks, why do some species hydrolyze sucrose to hexoses before entry into sink tissues whereas others import sucrose? Knowledge of these biochemical conversions during translocation is important in understanding limitations of translocation.

Considerable progress has been made in understanding the "loading" of sucrose for translocation (27), but much less is known about loading and translocation of amino acids (35, 54). Several other questions need to be answered. Are there specific carriers for each amino acid? What is the relative importance of symplastic *versus* apoplastic transport? How does translocation in C_4 species compare to that in C_3 species? What structure-function differences exist between the two types of species because of the modified morphology in C_4 species? What roles do the paraveinal mesophyll cells play in translocation in soybean leaves? Are they merely a storage site for surplus metabolites, or do metabolites from photosynthesis and other processes continue to pass through these cells before loading into the phloem? Much less is known about "unloading." Is a carrier involved, or is the process passive or diffusive? Is there regulation of unloading?

3. *Determine physical (e.g. turgor) and chemical (e.g. hormones) mechanisms of interorgan communication and competition for source assimilates.* Cell turgor is a potential signal for communication between sources and sinks, and may regulate the storage of soluble solutes in some sinks. This signal would be transmitted as a change in the hydrostatic pressure gradient in the phloem (62). Once the nature of turgor signal transduction is understood, membrane fluxes of assimilates may be susceptible to manipulation through genetic shifts in the turgor set point (11).

Hormones are thought to be involved in interorgan communication. However, it is not evident whether control is due to synthesis, catabolism, or sensitivity to the hormone. For example, Setter *et al.* (59) showed that abscisic acid (ABA) mediates source/sink interactions in soybeans. ABA was shown to move with photosynthate to the sink where ABA was metabolized, but when ABA was prevented from leaving the leaf, ABA accumulated and decreased photosynthesis, presumably by closing stomata. Is this phenomenon general for other plant species? Are other hormones involved in regulating source/sink relations? Is there a signal from sinks to sources?

Competition between organs for limited assimilates in poorly understood, but is the key to understanding assimilate allocation. Despite considerable research effort, our knowledge is limited to identification of the individual sink as the site regulating competitive ability. The biochemical basis of this phenomenon is unknown.

An interaction between source and sinks establishes source/sink balance between anticipated source supply and sink load early in the ontogeny of reproductive sinks. The mechanism of the phenomenon is not understood.

Improve Plant Performance in Unfavorable Environments

A major factor contributing to the difference between the attainable and the actual productivity of crops can be ascribed to (a) the inhibitory effects of unfavorable environments on metabolic processes, and (b) the adjustments in metabolism made by plants to adapt to the unfavorable environment. Two research scenarios are possible.

The first is to identify multigene traits controlling susceptibility or resistance to unfavorable environments. There is exceptionally broad inter- and intraspecies variation in plant response to specific environmental perturbations and extremes. In most cases there is only meager knowledge of the complex biochemical and physiological origins of tolerance and adaptation. There is a need to understand the physiological bases of adaptation to stress to allow identification of useful genes and genetic modification of valuable plants prone to environmental risk.

For example, certain plant species avoid or significantly delay the deleterious effects of water deficits by osmotic adjustment of the cytosol. Further investigation of the physiology of osmotic adjustment is likely to lead to identification of essential regulatory genes or gene products. This might permit an increased expression of drought tolerance or allow introduction of osmotic adjustment competence into deficient cultivars.

Preferential growth of roots relative to shoots under water deficits may be an important tolerance strategy. The role of cell wall extensibility in this differential response to stress may be the controlling factor in the contrasting growth of above and below ground meristems. Directed modification of the ratio of cell wall components and the degree of interconnections would provide an opportunity to assess the role of cell wall extensibility in drought tolerance.

The second approach is to identify traits involved in acclimation to unfavorable environments. There is a bewildering diversity in the response of plants to temperature extremes, which suggests both a tremendous genetic diversity within and among species and the involvement of many genes in determining tolerance. Elucidation of the underlying physiological and biochemical mechanisms will allow the eventual identification of critical genes and gene products. For example, there are direct inhibitory effects of exposure to cool temperature on the function of the chloroplast in soybeans. Once the biochemistry and physiology of chloroplast inhibition is understood, the controlling genes should become evident.

Certain species of plants adapt growth to the presence of normally toxic heavy metals. The response to heavy metals is associated with the production of significant amounts of several novel polypeptides. The role of these polypeptides in adaptation should be determined to allow genetic enhancement of adaptive competence.

Modify Enzymatic Activities and Intermediary Metabolism to Control the Synthesis of Desirable and Undesirable Plant Products, and to Maximize Detoxification of Xenobiotics

There is a wide range of phenotypic alterations that might improve the quality, nutritive value, and economic value of food and feed. A comprehensive understanding of the synthesis, composition, and structure of cell walls, and identification of the relevant genes would be extremely important steps in development of crops with improved nutritive value of forage, improved character of fibers, enhanced pest resistance, increased lodging resistance, and improved fiber quality of foods.

Modification of intermediary metabolism to enhance the nutrient density of plant components used as food would be desirable. By gaining an understanding of the relevant metabolic pathways and the hierarchy of regulation that establishes the partitioning of metabolic precursors into alternative pathways, modification of gene expression would allow diversion of precursors to enhance the production of desired products, *viz.* oils with modified composition, and food components with increased vitamin content.

The induction and activity of cytochrome P-450 genes, and other detoxification pathways, would enhance the capacity of plants to tolerate potentially deleterious agricultural chemicals and pollutants. For example, more rapid detoxification of pesticides by plants would facilitate the production of wholesome foodstuffs with reduced residues.

Other phenotypic alterations might lead to allocation of a greater proportion of metabolic precursors into secondary plant products of economic value or of protective value to the plant. There are a number of naturally produced plant compounds that confer pest resistance (allelopathic agents, insect antifeedants). Understanding the synthetic pathways and controlling genes may allow development of crops requiring few pesticides for control of insects, pathogens, or nematodes. A similar procedure might lead to new plant products with high economic value, for example flavors and fragrances, medicinal products, or substitutes for petrochemical feedstocks.

Exploit Plant-Microbial Interactions to Enhance Dinitrogen Fixation

For optimum N_2 fixation, plant-bacterial associations require metabolic energy in the form of ATP, an energized membrane, and a supply of low redox potential reductant. Carbon substrates from the host are oxidatively phosphorylated to provide ATP using a high flux/low concentration of O_2 supplied by leghemoglobin. The membrane potential with pH gradient probably regulates reductant supply. In addition a communication system involving hormones may be involved in regulating the N_2-fixation process.

The nitrogenase system contains an energetically wasteful process wherein protons are reduced to hydrogen. Some of this energy can be recovered via a rhizobial uptake hydrogenase which recycles the hydrogen and recovers some of the energy wasted in H_2 evolution (22, 52), and may also aid in scavenging excess O_2.

Limited progress has been made in developing strains of symbiotic root nodule bacteria that cause more efficient N_2 fixation in symbiosis with legume hosts. The incorporation of a gene for uptake hydrogenase into rhizobial strains lacking it may be desirable and has increased soybean yields in controlled environments (77). Use of molecular genetic techniques has enabled incorporation of hydrogenase into agriculturally important rhizobial strains (18). In the absence of competition from indigenous strains, field-grown soybeans nodulated with a *Bradyrhizobium japonicum* mutant with high nitrogenase activity showed significantly increased seed yields and seed N content (74). Should Hup$^+$ genes or other advantageous mutations be incorporated into all rhizobial inoculants? Will the large populations and aggressive competitiveness of indigenous rhizobial strains limit introduction of new strains into the rhizosphere? What biochemical and physiological properties of plants are important in enhancing the survival and competitiveness of introduced rhizobial strains? There is evidence of host genes controlling expression of the uptake hydrogenase in rhizobia (65). Identification and isolation of these genes may provide new opportunities for improving N_2 fixation.

During the development of a functional nodule, several host-specific plant proteins increase in parallel with nitrogenase activity. These proteins have been isolated and characterized (*e.g.* leghemoglobin [68], uricase II [5], glutamine synthetase II [16], and phosphoenolpyruvate carboxylase [70]). Can molecular genetic techniques be used to determine whether these gene products limit N_2 fixation?

Despite major advances in the molecular biology and genetics of nitrogen fixation in the past 10 years, the only clear improvements in legume (host) nitrogen fixation that have been observed in the field have resulted from the activities of multidisciplinary teams (including physiologists) who have emphasized selection for numerous, host-conditioned quantitative (multigene) traits (4, 34, 55). These results suggest that identification of and selection for biochemical and physiological traits that regulate N_2 assimilation (source activity) will lead to increased productivity only if complementary traits that regulate transport and utilization of assimilates (especially sink activity) can be identified and selected for. What biochemial and physiological traits associated with N_2 fixation are important to improvement of this process? To what extent, and at what developmental stages, does fixed or combined N regulate sink initiation and subsequent activity? Genes for the production of nitrogenase, uptake hydrogenase, and the induction of nodules are located on rhizobial plasmids (21). Can molecular genetic techniques be used to transfer desirable traits between rhizobial strains or genera, and facilitate increased nodulation and N_2 fixation?

Exploiting the genetic endowments of plant-microbial partnerships to convert nutritionally inert atmospheric N_2 to forms useful to plant and human nutrition hold great promise for increasing the sustainability of food production, substituting a regenerable N source for a manufactured fertilizer in food production, increasing farm productivity and profitability, and providing fundamental insights to allow the future genetic induction of this process into non-N_2 fixing crops (33).

Identify the Physiological and Biochemical Determinants of Metabolism, Growth, and Development Essential to the Genetic Improvement of Crop Productivity and Quality

1. *Exploit existing genetic variations as a tool to investigate the genetic bases of physiological traits.* In the past, plant physiologists have, more

often than not, relied upon easily grown or easily purchased plant
material with poorly defined genetic background for the study of complex
biochemical and physiological processes. While use of such plant material
may have been adequate for determining the general features of the
organization and mechanisms of specific processes, it clearly has its
limitations. One consequence may be the difficulty in obtaining independent verification of others' findings when the source of experimental
material used was not clearly defined. But more important, genetic
variation, when used in a controlled way, can often provide the key to
understanding confusing or conflicting results or provide important clues
to aid in understanding the mechanism and regulation of complex processes. The totally unexpected finding that some plants did not display
the traditional pattern of metabolite labeling when supplied with radio-
active CO_2, led to the enormously important discovery of C_4 plants by
Kortschak et al. (41) and Hatch and Slack (32).

C_4 photosynthesis was discovered by studying variation within "normal" plant species. Another exceedingly valuable approach to understanding complex processes is by use of the abnormal to explain the
normal. Beadle and Tatum's one-gene-one-enzyme hypothesis as well as
the elucidation of specific biosynthetic pathways resulted from the
imaginative use of mutants of Neurospora blocked in various steps in
amino acid biosynthesis. Plant physiologists have been slow to draw on
the large pool of existing mutations within germ plasm resources. One
example supports this. Dwarf mutants of corn blocked in various steps
of gibberellin biosynthesis have been available since the late 1940s, but
only recently have been used with remarkable success to clarify what was
considered to be an apparently hopelessly complicated biosynthetic pathway. Plants synthesize a large number of gibberellins through complex
branched and overlapping pathways. In any given plant, only one of
these products is biologically active. By the use of existing dwarf mutants,
the true pathway to synthesis of the important active compound was
elegantly elucidated by Phinney, MacMillan, and colleagues (64). Workers in the area of N_2 fixation are also beginning to recognize the value of
plants blocked in various stages of nodulation to dissect this complex
symbiotic process (37, 53).

The challenge is to identify existing mutations which are intimately
involved in specific physiological processes. The use of dwarf mutants
for the study of gibberellin biosynthesis was relatively obvious since it
has been known for years that such mutants revert to normal phenotype
upon addition of gibberellin. For many other pathways and processes,
finding the right mutant may not be so easy. The excellent summary The
Mutants of Maize (50) catalogs all of the known mutations of this
important crop plant; having more such summaries available for all the
other important crop plants would be extremely desirable. Unfortunately,
even for the maize catalog, most of the mutations describe morphological
variants and do not document which specific biochemical lesion is affected. Even so, developmental biologists should be able to exploit such

mutants more effectively than has been attempted to date. For example, analyses of viviparous mutants of corn (57) and of ABA deficient mutants of *Arabidopsis* (38) are beginning to shed light on the role of ABA regulating seed development and water relations. And mutants are known which accumulate excess starch or sucrose in the leaves or which are resistant to specific herbicides, and many more examples could surely be found. Through interaction and discussion with plant geneticists and breeders, physiologists can often uncover source material which can be used to surprising advantage to dissect physiological processes.

2. *Create genetic variation for the physiological and biochemical analysis of traits essential to crop productivity and quality.* The rapid advances in genetic engineering of the past decade create exciting possibilities for going beyond the use of existing genetic variation to the actual creation of directed mutations in specific genes of interest. Using site-directed mutagenesis (73) of cloned genes, it is now feasible to introduce specific changes in amino acid sequences in the active sites of enzymes to determine the relationship between structure and function and ultimately to design enzymes with modified characteristics. For example, can the active site of the RuBisCO large subunit be modified to alter affinities for CO_2 and O_2? Can we change the amino acid composition of storage proteins to enhance their nutritive value? Can we modify the specificities or enhance or reduce catalytic rates of key enzymes to alter metabolism in a beneficial way? We should also seek to collect and utilize a range of promoters which control high or low rates of constitutive expression or determine developmental timing of expression of genes. Replacement of normal promoter sequences with other promoters and reintroduction of such modified genes into plants allows scientists to alter the extent, timing, or pattern of expression of specific genes. Using such an approach, one can hope to assess the relative importance of a specific gene product, to determine if benefit could be obtained from amplification or depression of levels of a specific enzyme, and to assess better the role of specific gene products in the regulation of complex developmental processes. Construction and integration of genes which lead to expression of anti-sense mRNA (36, 46) for a specific gene can potentially create mutations allowing one to ask if that gene product is necessary at all under different circumstances. Many polypeptides of unknown function are known to be under developmental control or induced by external factors; creating an effective null mutation for such genes allows one to approach an understanding of the function of such polypeptides.

Genetic constructions employing sequences which code for unique signal or transit peptides can, in principle, be used to alter the localization of gene products. Such a technique should prove useful to biochemists interested in compartmentation of specific isozymes, in studying the interaction of nuclear and cytoplasmic-coded genes and their products, or in protection from degradation of gene products derived from inserted foreign genes by directing their compartmentation into specific organelles.

Another area in which molecular biology can contribute to our understanding of physiological processes is in the area of protoplast regeneration. Regeneration of plants from tissue cultures is difficult to monitor. Methods to monitor regeneration are needed. Such methods would include development of DNA probes, antibody markers to key enzymes and metabolites which increase during successful regeneration. Such probes, developed using easily regenerated plants such as tobacco, petunia, clover, or potato, might then be used to assess the course of regeneration of more difficult plants and plant cell fusion products.

The ultimate goal, of course, is to use knowledge gained from the combined efforts of physiologists and molecular biologists for the directed modification of agronomically important crop plants to enhance productivity.

3. *Determine the importance of genome fluidity in plant metabolism, growth, and development.* Most of the approaches described above are most easily applied to single gene mutations. Unfortunately, we know that many traits of agronomic importance are multigenic and hence quite complex to analyze. We also know that the genome is not always stable. Such genome fluidity can involve transposable elements which have been so well-documented in maize (25, 45), chromosome rearrangements, gene amplification or loss, or variation in DNA content, particularly for repetitive DNA sequences. The last phenomenon, *i.e.* a relatively rapid variation in DNA content, has recently been well-documented to occur rapidly in flax and the changes seem to reflect responses of the plants to stress (17, 72). Also exciting is the observation that a non-Mendelian pattern of inheritance for most repetitive sequences of DNA is observed in intraspecific crosses in maize (72). Although the copy numbers of all repetitive sequences were stable over several generations with an inbred line, F_1 hybrid progeny between inbred lines often showed deviation from the expectation that the copy number of repetitive sequence would be the mean of the parental values. Whether these observations may explain the phenomenon of hybrid vigor is not yet clear, but the results do suggest new approaches to the analysis of this important phenomenon. In any case, it seems clear that genome fluidity may regulate a vast array of complex processes in all eucaryotes. We already know that generation of antibody diversity (1) and of mating type in yeast (31) is controlled by programmed genomic change. Are developmental changes such as the establishment of a "sink" in plants related to changes in genomic organization as well? Does amplification or rearrangement of specific genes play a role in plant development? One recent study in maize does indicate that form of DNA amplification does occur during endosperm development (39). Recent examples such as the ones cited above indicate that the study of genome fluidity will be one of the most rewarding and challenging areas of research in plant growth and development in the next decade, and should be pursued by the combined efforts of geneticists and physiologists.

LITERATURE CITED

1. ALBERTS B, D BAY, J LEWIS, N RAFF, K ROBERTS, JD WATSON 1983 Molecular Biology of the Cell. Garland, New York
2. BADGER MR, A KAPLAN, JA BERRY 1980 Internal inorganic carbon pool of *Chlamydomonas reinhardtii*. Evidence for a carbon dioxide-concentrating mechanism. Plant Physiol 66: 407–413
3. BARNEIX AJ, H BRETELLER, SC VAN DE GEIJN 1984 Gas and ion exchange in wheat roots after nitrogen supply. Physiol Plant 61: 357–362
4. BARNES DK, DL JESSEN, GH HEICHEL, CP VANCE 1985 Selection of multiple traits increases alfalfa N_2-fixation and yield. *In* HJ Evans, PJ Bottomley, WE Newton, eds, Nitrogen Fixation Research Progress. Martinus Nijhoff Publishers, Boston, p 25
5. BERGMAN H, E PREDDIE, DPS VERMA 1983 Nodulin-35: a subunit of specific uricase (uricase II) induced and localized in the uninfected cells of soybean nodules. EMBO J 2: 2333–2339
6. BROWN AWA, TC BYERLY, M GIBBS, A SAN PIETRO 1975 Crop Productivity—Research Imperatives. Michigan Agricultural Experiment Station and C. F. Kettering Foundation
7. BRUN WA, KJ BETTS 1984 Source/sink relations of abscising and nonabscising soybean flowers. Plant Physiol 75: 187–191
8. CHEVALIER P, LE SCHRADER 1977 Genotypic differences in nitrate absorption and partitioning of N among plant parts in maize. Crop Sci 17: 897–901
9. CRAFTS-BRANDNER SJ, FE BELOW, JE HARPER, RH HAGEMAN 1984 Differential senescence of maize hybrids following ear removal; I. Whole Plant. Plant Physiol 74: 360–367
10. CRAFTS-BRANDNER SJ, FE BELOW, VA WITTENBACH, JE HARPER, RH HAGEMAN 1984 Differential senescence of maize hybrids following ear removal; II. Selected leaf. Plant Physiol 74: 368–373
11. CRAM JW 1983 Chloride accumulation as a homeostatic system: set points and perturbations. The physiological significance of influx isotherms, temperature effects and the influence of plant growth substances. J Exp Bot 34: 1484–1502
12. CROSBY KE, LH AUGN, GR BUSS 1981 Influence of 6-benzylaminopurine on fruit-set and seed development in two soybean, *Glycine max* (L) Merr. genotypes. Plant Physiol 68: 985–988
13. CSEKE C, BB BUCHANAN 1983 An enzyme synthesizing fructose 2,6-bisphosphate occurs in leaves and is regulated by metabolite effectors. FEBS Lett 155: 139–142
14. CSEKE C, M STITT, A BALOGH, BB BUCHANAN 1983 A product regulated fructose 2,6-bisphosphatase occurs in green leaves. FEBS Lett 162: 102–106
15. CSEKE C, NF WEEDEN, BB BUCHANAN, K UYEDA 1982 A special fructose bisphosphate functions as a cytoplasmic regulatory metabolite in green leaves. Proc Natl Acad Sci USA 79: 4322–4326
16. CULLIMORE JV, BJ MIFLIN 1984 Immunological studies on glutamine synthetase using antisera raised to the two plant forms of the enzyme from *Phaseolus* root nodules. J Exp Bot 35: 581–587
17. CULLIS CA 1983 Environmentally induced DNA changes in plants. CRC Crit Rev Plant Sci 1: 117–131

18. DE JONG TM, NJ BREWIN, AWB JOHNSTON, DA PHILLIPS 1982 Improvement of symbiotic properties in *Rhizobium leguminosarum* by plasmid transfer. J Gen Microbiol 128: 1829–1838

19. DOEHLERT DC, SC HUBER 1983 Spinach leaf sucrose phosphate synthase. Activation by glucose-6-phosphate and interaction with inorganic phosphate. FEBS Lett 153: 293–297

20. DOEHLERT DC, SC HUBER 1983 Regulation of spinach leaf sucrose phosphate synthase by glucose-6-phosphate, inorganic phosphate, and pH. Plant Physiol 73: 989–994

21. DOWNIE JA, CD KNIGHT, AWB JOHNSTON, L ROSSEN 1985 Identification of genes and gene products involved in the nodulation of peas by *Rhizobium leguminosarum*. Mol Gen Genet 198: 255–262

22. EISBRENNER G, HJ EVANS 1983 Aspects of hydrogen metabolism in nitrogen-fixing legumes and other plant-microbe associations. Annu Rev Plant Physiol 34: 105–136

23. ERWEE MG, OB GOODWIN 1983 Characterization of the *Egeria densa* Plauch. leaf symplast. Inhibition of the intercellular movement of fluorescent probes by group II ions. Planta 158: 320–328

24. ESCHRICH W 1980 Free space invertase, its possible role in phloem unloading. Ber Dtsch Bot Ges 93: 363–378

25. FEDOROFF NV 1983 Controlling elements in maize. *In* JA Shapiro, ed, Mobile Genetic Elements. Academic Press, New York, pp 1–63

26. FLUGGE UI 1985 Hydrodynamic properties of the Triton X-100-solubilized chloroplast phosphate translocator. Biochim Biophys Acta 815: 299–305

27. GIAQUINTA RT 1983 Phloem loading of sucrose. Annu Rev Plant Physiol 34: 347–387

28. GIFFORD RM, LT EVANS 1981 Photosynthesis, carbon partitioning and yield. Annu Rev Plant Physiol 32: 485–509

29. GIFFORD RM, JH THORNE, WD HITZ, RT GIAQUINTA 1985 Crop productivity and photoassimilate partitioning. Science 225: 801–808

30. GUNNING BES, R OVERALL 1983 Plasmodesmata and cell-to-cell transport in plants. Bioscience 33: 260–265

31. HABER KE 1983 Mating-type genes of *Saccharomyces cereviseae*. Annu Rev Genet 7: 559–619

32. HATCH MD, CR SLACK 1966 Photosynthesis by sugarcane leaves. Biochem J 101: 103–111

33. HEICHEL GH 1986 Legume nitrogen: symbiotic fixation and recovery by subsequent crops. *In* Z Helsel, ed, Fertilizers and Pesticides (World Agriculture Handbook Series). Elsevier, Amsterdam. In press

34. HEICHEL GH 1982 Breeding alfalfa for improved nitrogen fixation: A physiological perspective. Iowa State J Res 56: 255–280

35. HOUSLEY TL, DM PETERSON, LE SCHRADER 1977 Long distance translocation of sucrose, serine, leucine, lysine, and CO_2 assimilates; I. Soybeans. Plant Physiol 59: 217–220

36. IZANT JG, H WEINTRAUB 1984 Inhibition of thymidine kinase gene expression by anti-sense RNA: a molecular approach to genetic analysis. Cell 36: 1007–1015

37. JACOBSEN E 1984 Modification of symbiotic interaction of pea (*Pisum sativum* L.) and *Rhizobium leguminosarum* by induced mutants. Plant Soil 82: 427–438

38. KARSSEN CM, DLC BRANKHORST-VAN-DER-SWAN, AE BREEKLAND, M

KOORNNEEF 1983 Induction of dormancy during seed development of endogenous abscisic acid: studies of abscisic acid deficient genotypes of *Arabidopsis thaliana* (L.) Heynh. Planta 157: 158–165

39. KNOWLES RV, R PHILLIPS 1985 DNA amplification patterns in maize endosperm nuclei during kernel development. Proc Natl Acad Sci USA 82: 7010–7014

40. KOCH KE, C-L TSUI, LE SCHRADER, OE NELSON 1982 Source-sink relations in maize mutants with starch-deficient endosperms. Plant Physiol 70: 322–325

41. KORTSCHAK HP, CE HARTT, GO BURR 1965 Carbon dioxide fixation in sugarcane leaves. Plant Physiol 40: 209–213

42. LAMBERS H, DB LAYZELL, JS PATE 1980 Efficiency and regulation of root respiration in a legume: effects of the N source. Physiol Plant 50: 319–325

43. LORIMER GH 1981 The carboxylation and oxygenation of ribulose 1,5-bisphosphate: the primary events in photosynthesis and photorespiration. Annu Rev Plant Physiol 32: 349–383

44. MARTIN C, KV THIMANN 1972 The role of protein synthesis in the senescence of leaves. Plant Physiol 49: 64–71

45. McCLINTOCK B 1978 Mechanisms that rapidly reorganize the genome. Stadler Genet Symp 10: 25–48

46. MIZUNO T, M-Y CHOU, M INOUYE 1984 A unique mechanism regulating gene expression: translational inhibition by a complementary RNA transcript (micRNA). Proc Natl Acad Sci USA 81: 1966–1970

47. NASRALLAH JB, TH KAO, ML GOLDBERG, ME NASRALLAH 1985 A cDNA clone encoding an S-locus specific glycoprotein from *Brassica oleracea*. Nature 318: 263–267

48. NATIONAL RESEARCH COUNCIL 1985 New directions for biosciences research in agriculture. High reward opportunities. Committee on Biosciences Research in Agriculture. National Academy Press, Washington, DC

49. NELSON OE 1967 Biochemical genetics of higher plants. Annu Rev Genet 1: 245–268

50. NEUFFER MG, L JONES, MS ZUBER 1968 The Mutants of Maize. Crop Science Society of America, Madison, WI

51. OGREN WL 1984 Photorespiration: pathways, regulation, and modification. Annu Rev Plant Physiol 35: 415–442

52. PATE JS, CA ATKINS, RM RAINBIRD 1981 Theoretical and experimental costing of nitrogen fixation and related processes in nodules of legumes. *In* AH Gibson, WE Newton, eds, Current Perspectives in Nitrogen Fixation. Australian Academy of Science, Canberra, Australia, pp 105–116

53. PETERSON MA, DK BARNES 1981 Inheritance of ineffective nodulation and non-nodulation traits in alfalfa. Crop Sci 21: 611–616

54. PETERSON DM, TL HOUSLEY, LE SCHRADER 1977 Long distance translocation of sucrose, serine, leucine, lysine, and CO_2 assimilates; II. Oats. Plant Physiol 59: 221–224

55. PHILLIPS DA, LR TEUBER 1985 Genetic improvement of symbiotic nitrogen fixation in legumes. *In* HJ Evans, PJ Bottomley, WE Newton, eds, Nitrogen Fixation Research Progress. Martinus Nijhoff Publishers, Boston, p 11

56. REINHOLD L, A KAPLAN 1984 Membrane transport of sugars and amino acids. Annu Rev Plant Physiol 35: 45–83

57. ROBICHAUD CS, J WONG, IM SUSSEX 1980 Control of in vitro growth of

viviparous embryo mutants of maize by abscisic acid. Dev Genet 1: 325–330

58. RUFTY TR, JR, SC HUBER 1983 Changes in starch formation and activities of sucrose phosphate synthase and cytoplasmic fructose-1,6-bisphosphatase in response to source-sink alternatives. Plant Physiol 72: 474–480

59. SETTER TL, WA BRUN, ML BRENNER 1981 Abscisic acid translocation and metabolism in soybeans following depodding and petiole girdling treatments. Plant Physiol 67: 774–779

60. SILVIUS JE, FW SNYDER 1979 Comparative enzymic studies of sucrose metabolism in the taproots and fibrous roots of Beta vulgaris L. Plant Physiol 64: 1070–1073

61. SINCLAIR TR, CT DEWIT 1975 Photosynthate and nitrogen requirements for seed production for various crops. Science 189: 565–567

62. SMITH JAC, JA MILBURN 1980 Phloem turgor and the regulation of sucrose loading in Ricinus communis L. Planta 148: 42–48

63. SOMERVILLE CR, WL OGREN 1982 Genetic modification of photorespiration. Trends Biochem Sci 7: 171–174

64. SPRAY C, BO PHINNEY, P GASKIN, SJ GILMAN, J MACMILLAN 1984 Internode length in Zea mays L. The dwarf-1 mutation controls the 3-hydroxylation of gibberellin A20 to gibberellin A1. Planta 160: 464–468

65. SPRENT JI 1983 Adaptive variation in legume nodule physiology resulting from host-rhizobial interactions. In JA Lee, S McNeil, IH Rorison, eds, Nitrogen as an Ecological Factor. Blackwell Scientific Publications, Palo Alto, CA, pp 29–42

66. STITT M, R GERHARDT, B KURZER, HW HELDT 1983 A role for fructose-2,6-bisphosphate in the regulation of sucrose synthesis in spinach leaves. Plant Physiol 72: 1139–1141

67. STITT M, W WIRTZ, HW HELDT 1983 Regulation of sucrose synthesis by cytoplasmic fructose bisphosphatase and sucrose phosphate synthase during photosynthesis in varying light and carbon dioxide. Plant Physiol 72: 767–774

68. SUTTON WD 1983 Nodule development and senescence. In WJ Broughton, ed, Nitrogen Fixation, Vol 3. Legumes. Oxford University Press, Oxford, pp 144–212

69. THORNE JH 1985 Phloem unloading of C and N assimilates in developing seeds. Annu Rev Plant Physiol 36: 317–343

70. VANCE CP, S STADE 1984 Alfalfa root nodule carbon dioxide fixation; II. Partial purification and characterization of root nodule PEPC. Plant Physiol 75: 261–264

71. VANCE CP, S STADE, CA MAXWELL 1983 Alfalfa root nodule carbon dioxide fixation; I. Association with nitrogen fixation and incorporation into amino acids. Plant Physiol 72: 469–473

72. WALBOT V, CA CULLIS 1985 Rapid genomic change in higher plants. Annu Rev Plant Physiol 36: 367–396

73. WEISSMAN C, S NAGATA, T TANIGUCHI, H WEBER, F MEYER 1979 The use of site-directed mutagenesis in reversed genetics. In JK Setlow, A Hollaender, eds, Genetic Engineering, Principles and Methods, Vol 1. Plenum Press, New York, pp 133–150

74. WILLIAMS LE, DA PHILLIPS 1983 Increased soybean productivity with a Rhizobium japonicum mutant. Crop Sci 23: 246–250

75. WILSON D 1982 Response to selection for dark respiration rate of mature

leaves in *Lolium perenne* and its effects on growth of young plants and simulated swards. Ann Bot 49: 303–312

76. WOODWARD RG, HM RAWSON 1976 Photosynthesis and transpiration in dicotyledonous plants; II. Expanding and senescing leaves of soybean. Aust J Plant Physiol 3: 257–267

77. ZABLOTOWICZ RM, SA RUSSELL, HJ EVANS 1980 Effect of hydrogenase system in *Rhizobium japonicum* on the nitrogen fixation and growth of soybeans at different stages of development. Agron J 72: 555–559

Rhizosphere Dynamics

Submitted on behalf of the group by:

ELDOR A. PAUL   P. BERNARD TINKER

W. DIETZ BAUER

Scope and Definition

Interactions that involve the root surface-soil interface include areas of study such as associative and symbiotic N_2 fixation and mycorrhizal fungi. Microbial catalyses in nutrient cycling and toxic chemical degradation are at a maximum where plant roots and soil constituents interact. The border of the rhizosphere cannot be clearly delineated and the following discussion includes microbiologically mediated reactions in the soil generally. The study of these interactions in ecosystem processes and global nutrient cycling is providing new dimensions to rhizosphere dynamics. Scientists are now asking questions on a much broader range of plant microbial associations than those related to agricultural productivity.

New soil management techniques such as computerized calculation of the timing and rate of plant nutrient addition, minimum tillage, and alternate cropping require a knowledge of rhizosphere dynamics. At the same time, the impact of biotechnology is adding to the ferment. Available genetic engineering techniques are centered on bacteria. The genetic characteristics of soil bacteria such as *Rhizobium* and *Pseudomonas* are being determined with the goal of enhancing N_2 fixation, the microbial degradation of toxicants, the production of biological insecticides, and the control of pathogens.

The application of both advanced soil management techniques and of genetic engineering principles is being held back by a lack of knowledge of the basic physiology and ecology of the organisms involved (40). This lack of knowledge is highlighted by the present discussions concerning the possible introduction of novel organisms into the rhizosphere. The survival of genetically engineered organisms in nature, competition with other organisms and the possible transfer of genetic material to the great array of still unstudied organisms are major challenges in rhizosphere biology.

This chapter looks at the state of our science and develops research imperatives in the knowledge that there is great excitement about the possibilities of field management and of biotechnology. It is hoped that manipulation of the plant-soil environment and of the microorganisms therein will produce environmentally safe, economical, biotechnological applications at a time when applications in the plant sciences themselves are still being developed.

State of the Science

Nutrient Fluxes in the Rhizosphere

A plant's requirement for nutrients depends upon its growth rate and composition. This is expressed as a local demand at the root surface, the intensity of which depends upon the total requirement and the amount of actively absorbing root (11). The question of how this demand is distributed over the root surface, and its relation to the growth of the plant requires more research.

The principles governing the physical transport of nutrient ions to the root surface from the bulk soil are well-established. Root uptake follows movement of ions to the surface by mass flow or diffusion, the former being of little importance for strongly absorbed ions such as phosphate or micronutrients. Diffusion occurs only when a concentration gradient is established, so it requires a depletion zone around the root. Phosphorus has a very low diffusion coefficient in most soils, and the coefficient itself is concentration dependent. Consequently, it is difficult to deplete totally a soil of P (*i.e.* soils have a high buffer capacity for this and similarly absorbed elements). Fertilization with P on initially poor soils involves increasing P concentration, so that steeper gradients can form around roots, and also increase the diffusion coefficient. This often involves applying far more of the element than is needed by the crop. This excess can normally not be extracted so long as efficient cropping is to be continued. It is thus an investment which can only be recovered if a more efficient root-microbe absorbing system can be devised.

A number of factors affect the concentration which needs to be established in the soil to allow full crop growth. Different cultivars have different nutrient demands (22), and this is likely to be an important area of work in the future (51). However, where cultivar differences have been found (for P or other elements) there is little information about the mechanism whereby this occurs. Progress in this area seems unlikely unless more attention is paid to the mechanisms involved.

Uptake of Nutrients

The uptake processes of all major nutrients are highly efficient; micromolar concentrations of N, P, and K are adequate, if maintained at the root surface. The same seems likely to be true for S and Mg, though no data are available. By contrast, this relatively very high efficiency at very low concentrations is less well marked in trace elements, where uptake may continue to rise with external concentration over a wide range (58).

Potassium is unlikely to provide major research opportunities (27) unless means can be found for growing tree crops and forest trees with a much smaller total K content. If so, one could prevent the immobilization of large amounts of the element, that at present may lead to deficiency on poor soils. With the exception of the tropics, Mg is rarely deficient, but the same comment as for K applies.

Iron deficiency is common and damaging. It is the one element for which the mechanisms of efficiency and inefficiency have been investigated (50). Iron is reduced to Fe^{2+} at the point of uptake. Some species secrete siderophores which complex Fe, render it soluble, and thus allow a sufficient flux density into the root. Others excrete protons when they become Fe deficient. This is highly effective in controlling Fe deficiency, which is almost always found on alkaline soil. The possibility of transferring the genes that control these functions is very attractive, as it could simplify the growing of crops prone to Fe deficiency, such as lupins.

Copper deficiency is genetically controlled, and Cu deficiency in cereal crops has been linked to a single chromosome from rye. With the elucidations of the mechanisms involved, this opens up the possibility of more Cu-efficient cereals. Zinc deficiency is prevalent in many crops, especially rice. Some varieties are more susceptible than others (30), but the mechanism is not understood.

Membrane Transport and Rhizosphere pH

There has been considerable progress in the biochemistry of membrane transport. A reasonably clear understanding of the coupling between exergonic reactions and inorganic ion transport exists. It is no longer held that ATP serves as the immediate (primary) energy source for transport reactions, but rather that ATP is consumed by H^+ translocating ATPases of the plasma membrane and tonoplast. The end results of these activities is to generate a proton gradient (composed of both a pH and an electrical gradient) which represents the immediate source of energy for coupled solute transport. The flux of H^+ is viewed as the primary reaction of membrane transport. The proton gradient is consumed in coupled (secondary) reactions in which the free energy of the proton gradient drives the "uphill" transport of various solutes across the plasma membrane or the tonoplast. Strong evidence for such transport systems now exist for the absorption of K^+, NO_3^-, Pi, SO_4^{2-}, and organic solutes (sugars and amino acids). Recently workers have been successful in demonstrating the existence of proton translocating ATPases in the plasma membrane and the tonoplast.

Growing attention has been directed toward the regulation of solute absorpion, and the existence of complex feedback mechanisms, that appear to maintain the inorganic composition of plant tissues, have been inferred on the basis of kinetic studies (21). Considerably more work of a biochemical nature will need to be addressed to this area of root function. At the whole plant level, evidence is emerging for important regulatory signals that transmit information concerning the nutrient status of the shoot to the absorbing regions of the root. These may act at the xylem loading step but details of these processes are sparse.

The pH immediately adjacent to roots is strongly affected by the plant and may vary by 1 to 2 pH units from the non-rhizosphere values (54). This alters the sorption relationship of P, Zn, Cu, Fe, etc., and hence their availability. Recent work suggests that there are specific mechanisms which acidify the rhizosphere when certain plants become Fe or P deficient. These mechanisms could be useful if they could be transferred to species which do not possess them.

Root Morphology

Species vary in root density, rooting depth, and root hair production, as well as in internal anatomy. This is partly under genetic and partly under environmental control, but at present it can only be predicted in the crudest way; there is little or no hope of an accurate root-system model in the near future. This emphasizes the previous concentration of research on plant shoot architecture. The balance needs to be redressed.

Nutrient uptake effects may be due to simple factors such as growth rate, root-shoot ratio or specific root weight. These alter the volume of soil exploited, or the inflow of nutrients. Differing rates of root branching may be important. The function of root hairs is still not clear, but they are likely to play a large part in uptake of immobile elements and water. The factors controlling their density, length duration and efficiency are poorly understood.

Mycorrhiza

The primary role of *Vesicular arbuscular* (VA) mycorrhizal fungi in plant growth has been related to an increased efficiency of P uptake by roots (35). Uptake of Zn, Cu, and S also is increased. Mycorrhizae also interact with a variety of plant pathogens and rhizosphere organisms. There is a body of evidence that VA mycorrhiza do not play a major role in releasing bound soil phosphorus. The main mechanism of improved P uptake is spatial. Mycorrhizal hyphae grow beyond the depletion zone, absorb P and transport it to the root, thus bypassing the soil diffusion step in P uptake. The growth of hyphae can increase the absorbing area of a mycorrhizal root up to seven times that of an uninfected root.

Plant growth response to infection is affected by such phenomena as rate of fungal infection, inoculum potential, host endophyte-combinations, and edaphic and climatic factors. Physiological mechanisms on which symbiotic effectiveness may be based are beginning to be investigated. These include alkaline phosphatases specific to mycorrhizae and membrane bound enzymes (ATPases) which are likely to be important in nutrient transfer (20).

A large number of species of VA mycorrhizal fungi have been recently identified. We can observe, isolate, grow and purify VA fungi although we cannot yet grow them in host-free culture. Plant growth enhancement by mycorrhizal fungi is known for many economically important plants. The efficiency of the symbiosis depends on the proper selection of compatible host-fungus combinations. The development of structures involved in nutrient transfer in the root in arbuscules and nutrient uptake from the soil by hyphae varies from fungus to fungus and may determine the degree of utilization of soil phosphate by the plant (39).

Although superior mycorrhizal isolates, in terms of growth response, can be identified, they may not compete with well-adapted, indigenous populations. Pot-culture experiments have defined the processes of infection in many plant species, but our knowledge of this under field conditions is limited. Factors which affect root infection include inoculum density and viability, soil and environmental conditions, and the stage of plant growth. High P concentration reduce mycorrhizal infection, through effects mediated by the host plant (39).

The commercial application of mycorrhizal fungi is now being realized in areas where native mycorrhizal fungi are not present. These include fumigated soil, greenhouse, nurseries, desert, and strip-mine revegetation (36). There is considerable promise in tests of their use with clover in pasture.

The most critical questions in mycorrhizal research relate to the biology of the host-endophyte interaction: How is the growth of host and fungus kept in balance? What determines specificity? How are C and P fluxes mediated and controlled? What are the characters of a superior growth-enhancing fungus? These questions must be addressed urgently. Effects of mycorrhizas on drought resistance may arise from direct uptake of water by hyphae, effects on hormone relations or changes in the leaf hydration. Another intriguing question is the effect of the C demand by the fungi on the host. Values up to 50% have been ascribed to ectomycorrhizas from field studies (17), but the value is much less (6–20%) for endomycorrhizas (45). It is as yet unknown if this C demand causes yield reduction in the host, or is met by compensation mechanisms.

In practice, the establishment of VA mycorrhiza on the root is most critically limited at the present time by competition both from similar well-adapted native strains and by competition by general components of the soil biota. This problem must be addressed if mycorrhizal fungi are to be utilized.

The VA mycorrhizal fungi have not been grown in pure culture and their sexual mechanisms are unknown. This, together with the absence of genetic information, restricts the use of modern genetic approaches.

Soil Fauna

Soil fauna are among the most numerous biota in biomass weight but their direct contribution to total soil respiration has been shown to be low (46). Traditionally, investigation on soil fauna in root rhizosphere dynamics has concentrated on their damage to plants or alternatively as biocontrol agents. Their function and importance as part of the rhizosphere population in general needs more study (18).

Both meso- and macrofauna are intimately associated with their food sources and act in nutrient cycling by consumption of the large biomass of microorganisms. They are known to feed on mycorrhiza and may reduce the beneficial effects of the latter on host plants, but research on the effects of nematodes on VA-mycorrhizas are inconclusive (3).

Nitrogen Dynamics in the Rhizosphere

Hardy (26) in discussing the translation of basic research on N transformations to improved crop production, listed 85 major research advances in N input research since 1960 when nitrification inhibitors and nitrogenase were first identified. These include crystallization of the nitrogenase, cloning of the Nif genes and measurement of photosynthate limitation for legume N_2 fixation. He then went on to state "Biological N_2 fixation research has been outstandingly productive of sophisticated basic information during the past 20 years with, unfortunately, no significantly practical applications. The excessive energy requirement for biological N_2 fixation is a major, and possibly the major limitation. It is recommended that highly creative basic research on biological and abiological N_2 fixation as well as other N input processes, be continued and encouraged with about an equal emphasis on N_2 fixation and other N input processes."

Now, in 1985 we are beginning to see practical benefit emanating from the N research. Some applications of immediate significance are: (a) dissemination of improved *Rhizobium* inoculant technology and personnel training have facilitated increased acreages of legumes. Research on *Rhizobium* has shown that some infection characteristics are encoded on plasmids. Studies indicate that plasmid instability in *Rhizobium phaseoli* is a significant reason for inoculant failure; (b) the culturing of the N_2-fixing tree symbiont, *Frankia*, in 1978 and continued progress in its use has led to large scale inoculant production and commercial use in agroforestry; (c) research on the *Azolla-Anabaena* N_2-fixing symbiosis has led to an extension of this system as a green manure for rice in developing countries. Sporulation has been induced in several *Azolla* species leading to the possibility of using spores as a less labor-intensive means of inoculation of rice fields and to a means of breeding *Azolla*; and (d) methods of quantification of N_2 fixation in the field using ^{15}N techniques have given us: 1) an insight into the agronomic impact and potential of N_2 fixation in legumes and non-legumes; 2) the ability to evaluate the effect of superior N_2 fixing organisms, plant genotypes and agronomic practices.

Research areas that are near practical applications include: (a) recent information on the transfer of N from N_2 fixing plants to other associated species provides near-term promise of developing more efficient intercropping systems; (b) plant breeding has created improved nitrogen fixing alfalfa varieties. Mutagenesis and selection have resulted in the production of supernodulating (nitrate tolerant) soybean lines. Varieties obtained from these lines are now being field evaluated; (c) yield increases have been demonstrated at specific localities by inoculation with associative N_2 fixing bacteria. However, the role of these microorganisms in improving crop productivity may arise from hormonal and other growth effects; (d) the recent isolation and successful transfer to other *Rhizobia* of the genes of H_2 uptake provides the possibility of incorporating this trait into a wide range of inoculant strains if it proves beneficial; and (e) current research on microbial competition in the rhizosphere is becoming quantitative and analytical, but is highly constrained by methodology. Promising approaches involve: (a) fluorescent antibodies, (b) split root techniques, (c) cryogenic stage electron microscopy, (d) visual screens for competitive mutants, (e) the isolation of genes affecting colonization and competition, and (f) analysis of plant mutants with altered nodulation properties.

Further characterization of host and microbial regulation offers the promise of controlled, knowledgeable manipulations of the symbiotic systems for agricultural applications, whether by genetic engineering, traditional plant breeding, strain-cultivar matching or improved agronomic practices.

Nitrogen Mineralization-Immobilization and N Losses

The need to gain an understanding of C and N cycles on a global basis relative to the influence of atmosphere CO_2 on climate has led to a better understanding of nutrient dynamics. Zincke et al. (62), in a survey of 3600 profiles, concluded that on a global basis approximately 100,000 × 10^{12} g N are stored in the top meter of soil (Table I). Annual plant uptake of N, calculated as 1% of global primary plant productivity (2% of C photosynthesized) represents 1400 × 10^{12} g N or slightly greater than 1% of the soil N reserves. Plants are known to utilize only 30 to 60% of mineralized N (55). The actual soil mineralization capacity, therefore, can be calculated to range from 2400 to 4700 × 10^{12} g N or 2 to 5% of soil reserves. Symbiotic fixation estimated at 120 × 10^{12} g is low relative to soil N mineralization but represents 8.5% of the plant N uptake because of the direct transfer of biologically fixed N to the plant.

The dominance of mineralized soil N, except in agricultural fields receiving very high levels of fertilizer N, indicates a major opportunity

TABLE I. *Global Terrestrial N Fluxes on an Annual Basis*

Source	N
	$g \times 10^{12}$
Soil N content	105,000[a]
Plant uptake	1,400[b]
Soil N mineralized	3,500[c]
Symbiotic N_2 fixation	120[d]
Associative and free-living fixation	50[d]
Fertilizer N applied	65
Fertilizer N utilized	26[c]
Combustion atmospheric inputs	22[d]
Denitrification	135[d]
Run-off erosion	25[d]

[a] Ref. 62. [b] Two percent of 70 × 10^{15} g C photosynthesized. [c] Forty percent efficiency of uptake of mineralized N. [d] R. Knowles, private communication.

for biotechnology in its wider definition. Even small increases in the efficiency of uptake of mineralized soil or fertilizer N would have dramatic effects on the N available to plants. Microorganisms compete very effectively for mineral N and the N contained in the microbial biomass represents 3 to 10% of the soil N pool. Management of this biomass, so that release occurs during periods of plant growth and immobilization during fallow periods, is a meaningful approach. The timing of cultivation practices, the use of minimum tillage and alternative cropping techniques such that C is returned to the soil during periods when the soil is bare, have been shown to be applicable for both tropical and temperate agricultural regions.

A large number of chemicals have been evaluated for use as nitrification inhibitors, but only a few are commercially available. Benefit has been obtained under field conditions under situations where the production of nitrate would have resulted in N loss via leaching and/or dentrification. Current research is delineating cropping situations where use of nitrification inhibitors may be of economic benefit, for: (a) reducing N loss from the plant root system, (b) nutrient balance in the plant, and (c) reducing environmental pollution. The organisms responsible for nitrification are limited in their occurrence (53). Biotechnological approaches may lead to the production in soil of chemicals that inhibit nitrification. This is thought to occur in some climax ecosystems. Another approach would involve the attack on nitrifiers by specific predators. Problems associated with the use of urea-containing fertilizers, and manures can be alleviated through use of an inhibitor of soil urease activity. These problems include loss of NH_3 from surface-applications and possible damage to germinating seeds and seedlings.

Nitrification occurs in forest soils at pH values below those in agricultural soils. Large N losses occur in forest soils after clearcutting and during the initial stages of stand reestablishment. Forest management techniques that retain this N for future plant growth and keep it from contaminating groundwater supplies are necessary. The possibility of greater insect attack and frost sensitivity attributable to luxuriant growth in the presence of excess N from acid rain has been proposed. Enhanced denitrification under these conditions may have to be investigated as a means of forest protection as well as for the prevention of NO_3 contamination of groundwater. Dentrification is directly controlled by nitrate and organic substrate availability and indirectly by water through its effect on soil aeration. The control of dentrification by biotechnological or management techniques should be pursued.

Associative Bacteria

Bacteria associated with plants either on the root surface (rhizoplane) or intercellularly, as in the cortex (endorrhizal) have been recognized as N_2 fixers for 50 years. The association occurs throughout a wide host range. Largest N_2 fixation rates are found in plants having air passages (lucunae) within the roots (44). These occur in rice and the salt marsh grass, (*Spartina*) sugarcane and *Paspalum notatum*. Many of these have a C_4 photosynthetic metabolism.

Claims for associative N_2 fixation rates have generally been higher and more consistent in the tropics than in temperate climates (56). In North America, plant yield increases, acetylene reduction assays, and isotopic dilution experiments with fertilizer ^{15}N have indicated fixation rates up to 20% of the plant N uptake (42, 43). Exposure of the plants to atmospheric [15]N$_2$ usually has shown a fixation capacity of only 5% of the plant N and associative fixation accounts in general for less than 20 kg hectare^{-1} year^{-1}. There is consequently much doubt whether the responses that have resulted from bacterial circulation result from N_2 fixation. There is evidence that these bacteria also produce components with phytohormonal properties (33). Associative N_2 fixers have also shown interactions with mycorrhizal fungi and rhizobia. Inoculation with *Azotobacter* or phosphate solubilizing bacteria plus a VA fungus has resulted in increased host responses (5). The role of phytohormones, competition, and variable soil P contents should be examined relative to the erratic field results obtained after inoculation with associative organisms.

Different chromosome substitution lines of spring wheat have been shown capable of supporting different rhizosphere populations (48). These affect the levels of associative fixation. Differences have also been found in the transfer rate of fixed [15]N$_2$ to the above ground plant parts in associative systems. Some studies show only 5% of the N fixed by *Azospirillum* incorporated into plants within 3 weeks (33). Others show much larger transfer rates.

The ability of bacteria to infect intercellular spaces in the roots, the wide range of plants infected, the diversity in the microorganisms involved, the proven response to genetic manipulation of host plants, the interactions between symbionts, such as *Azospirillum* with *Rhizobium* or VA fungi, and the demonstrated involvement of phytohormones can help explain the diversity of results that have been obtained with this association. The diversity (16) and the potential for genetic engineering of the bacteria involved should prove fruitful areas for research and possible improvements in plant growth and increases in the present low levels of fixation. The problems encountered with the high demands for energy by the symbionts may, however, be difficult to overcome.

Nitrogen Inputs by *Azolla*

Azolla-Anabaena symbioses provide an alternative nitrogen source for lowland rice. The major constraint to the use of *Azolla* is that it is labor intensive. Currently it must be propagated, transported, and maintained in the vegetative state during adverse growth conditions. Other limitations include the fact that as a free-floating aquatic it is often limited by the availability of P since this element rapidly becomes bound in the paddy soil, that it is subject to attack by insects, and that users must be educated to consider it as a green manure crop plant which requires management, and not as a panacea.

The future of *Azolla* is largely contingent upon unraveling the precise factor(s) which trigger the induction of sporulation in these heterosporous ferns. Sporocarps afford a means of preserving germ plasm, open the way to breeding programs, and, if used as an inoculum in a nursery, may reduce the labor required for maintenance during adverse environmental conditions. There is continuity of the endophytic *Anabaena* through the sexual cycle. The endophyte is partitioned into the sporocarps, and the young sporophytes are reinoculated during their emergence from the megasporocarp apparatus. Some progress has been made in elucidating conditions which lead to the induction of sporulation in species other than *Azolla mexicana*, which continually sporulates under a broad range of growth conditions.

Limitations associated with P requirements and temperature tolerance during the rice growing season are currently pursued at several institutions via screening of various species and populations. Breeding programs to generate hybrids may afford a new approach in these areas as well as in resistance to insect pests. The P requirements may also be offset by preloading the *Azolla* inoculum in a confined area such as a nursery or by dropping the water level to a depth that enables *Azolla* roots to contact the soil.

Recognition and Infection in Rhizobium/Legume Systems

Efficient and compatible strains of rhizobia cannot be successfully introduced as inocula for legume crops in many field situations where competing indigenous strains are present. Without a solution to the competition problem the introduction of genetically improved symbionts will have little practical impact. The cellular, molecular, and genetic factors that govern competition are not known. Specific host and environmental factors such as soil pH and cultivar can strongly affect the outcome of interstrain competition (31).

The resistance/susceptibility of host plants to *Rhizobium* is analogous to that of pathogens. These often are controlled by corresponding single genes in the host and pathogen. A further extension of this concept relevant to *Rhizobium*-host range is the notion that pathogens in gene-for-gene systems are virulent only when they are able to escape from being recognized and inhibited by the host (2).

Current research on specificity is focused on the identification of the molecular mechanism underlying the microbial signal-host response phonemena and the *Rhizobium* genes affecting host range (25). The identification of molecular mechanisms of host specificity has major applications for the biological control of microbial pathogens and for solutions to the competition problem for inoculated symbionts (24).

Rhizobia enter their host plant either by penetrating between the cell walls of host epidermal and cortical cells or by stimulating the formation of infection threads on curled root hairs (6, 34). Despite recent ultrastructural analyses, the mechanism by which the rhizobia penetrate the host cell wall is still uncertain.

Nodule formation in many legumes appears to be regulated by a feedback control mechanism. This host regulation of nodule number operates at the level of infection development, blocking infections at stages just prior to nodule emergence (9). Supernodulating host plant mutants of pea and soybean have recently been described (23, 29), and it appears likely that these mutants are defective in the autoregulatory control of infection development.

When infections develop successfully into emergent nodules, the release and membrane packaging of rhizobia then become central to the control of specialized functioning in nodules and nutrient exchange. Current studies are focused on analysis of the peribacteroid membrane and its regulatory functions, on the release and differentiation of rhizobia into bacteroids, and on the characterization of metabolic pathways that support N_2 fixation, exchange of C and N, and bacterial nutrition.

Control of N_2 Fixation

Most symbiotic processes are under the direct control of the host plant. Yet in N_2 fixation research, little emphasis is placed on the plant compared to the microbial (*Rhizobium*) component. Genetic analysis of the plant host has used induced mutagens and selection. This has yielded plant mutants with altered symbiotic properties (23, 28). Soybean and pea mutants that are tolerant to the symbiotic inhibitor effects of exogenously supplied nitrate have been isolated (10, 32). The stem nodules of *Sesbania* also are not inhibited by nitrate (15). Nitrate-tolerant symbiotic mutants have an increased symbiont dependency on biological N_2 fixation.

The general biochemistry of N_2 fixation is relatively well defined (14), but important nodule-plant relationships are less well known. For instance, the rate of carbohydrate use in the legume symbiosis appears to be limited, in the short term, by the rate of O_2 diffusion into the nodule (38, 60). A greater understanding of these constraints is needed before the systems can be manipulated in the best possible way (12); similarly, the major limitation to the construction of superior rhizobia is not a lack of genetical techniques (7, 49). It is a lack of knowledge of desirable and quantifiable attributes which the geneticist might exploit. For instance, differences in efficiency of C use offer a real possibility for producing better symbiosis, but before this can be exploited more work is required to define the genetic loci and basic mechanisms involved. The amount of N_2 fixed by a legume depends upon both the duration and the rate of fixation. The former is dependent upon plant genotype and agricultural practice as well as *Rhizobium* strain (47).

The rate of fixation may be determined at several levels: (a) *structural*—air spaces, bacteroid/cytoplasm, vascular connections; (b) *physiological*—rate of carbohydrate supply and O_2 diffusion, translocation of fixed compounds, water stress; (c) *biochemical*—ratio of nitrogenase proteins I and II, ATP/ADP ratios, ATP/reductant ratios, assimilation of NH_3, and efficiency of C use; and (d) *genetical*—the presence of Nif-like protein activators.

During biological N_2 fixation, some energy is used in the reduction of protons to H_2 and is thus apparently wasted. Measurements of H_2 evolution and of the C costs of electron transfer through nitrogenase (61), show that they are dependent both on *Rhizobium* strain and plant genotypes. The amount of H_2 released into the rhizosphere of a legume crop lacking an H_2 uptake system is large. As much as 5% of the captured photosynthetic energy can be released into the rhizosphere as H_2. Little of this appears at the soil surface suggesting that it is utilized by soil micro-flora. Possibilities may exist for exploiting this energy source; the "Hup" system could, for example, be inserted into desirable rhizosphere microorganisms to increase their competitive ability.

Actinorhizal Associations

Actinorhizal plants are perennial, woody shrubs and trees which fix N_2 in association with *Frankia*. With the isolation of *Frankia* in pure culture (4, 8), a major obstacle to the studies of actinorhizal plants was overcome. At present, strains of *Frankia* are maintained *in vitro* for approximately half of the actinorhizal species. Methods developed for gel typing of protein patterns of *Frankia* show that a great diversity of isolates representing about eight protein patterns can be obtained from one species of *Alnus* over a small geographic area. One or two of these dominate indicating a possible competitive advantage. At the same time isolates from different areas of the world can be very similar as determined by DNA homology. Controlled studies of efficiency and contribution of actinorhizal plants are being undertaken (1).

There are at least two mechanisms whereby the microsymbiont *Frankia* enters the root system. The first method, root hair infection is very similar to the mode of entry of *Rhizobium*. A second mechanism for symbiotic development of actinorhizal root nodules has been described recently for members of the plant family, Elaeagnaceae (37). In this mechanism, the bacterium invades the intercellular spaces between epidermal cells by enzymatic digestion of the middle lamella.

The two known infection mechanisms suggest that host specificity may differ among plant families and genera. Even within host specificity groups, compatibility and efficiency in nodulation (41) and N_2 fixation (13) differs dramatically among symbiotic combinations. There is a need to define what determines host specificity among actinorhizal species beyond limitations due to infection mechanisms. It may be possible to extend the range of actinorhizal symbioses to genera other than the presently recognized 23 genera in 8 families.

Molecular genetic techniques for *Frankia* are in the early stages of development. The very slow growth rate of this organism has been a deterrent. Fragments of DNA have been found to hybridize to known nitrogenase structural genes in other organisms with this region being highly conserved in all *Frankia* strains. The structural genes for the molybdenum iron protein of nitrogenase have recently been isolated and characterized.

Nitrogen metabolism in the actinorhizal symbiont is also an area which has been approachable only quite recently. An inducible ammonium transport system synthesized in response to ammonia starvation has been demonstrated.

The utilization of actinorhizal plants is most extensive in the developing countries especially for fuel production. Genera such as *Elaeagnus*, *Shepherdia*, and *Hippophae* are used extensively for soil conservation and land reclamation. The usefulness of actinorhizal genera as nurse plants to important tree crops has recently been shown to result in increased soil fertility, temperature moderation, and/or beneficial competition leading to self-pruning of the tree crop (52). The greater use of actinorhizal plants in wild lands such as grasslands and forestry, will require an understanding of the trade-offs between increased N availability through the use of a cover crop relative to the needs of moisture retention and the problems of competition between the planted crop and the cover crop.

Carbon Utilization by Roots and Symbionts

The transport of photoassimilated C to plant root systems provides metabolic energy and communication with various plant parts. This appears to be controlled by biochemical mechanisms operating in source leaves and the competitive interaction among plant sinks brought about by the environment (57). A remarkably large fraction of total photosynthate is used by the plant below ground. Even where the fraction of plant mass in roots is only about 10%, the drain of C can be 20 to 40% of the total fixation throughout the plant's growth cycle (59). During the rapid growth stage, beneath ground allocation can account for 60% of the photosynthate in a young soybean plant supporting both *Rhizobium* and mycorrhizal symbionts. Tree mycorrhizas have been regarded as consuming up to 50%, VA endophytes 6 to 12%, and *Rhizobium* 10 to 20% of the C fixed. There is still uncertainty about whether this loss of C leads to slower growth by the plant, or whether some form of compensation occurs. Although exudation levels into the soil are generally low, some exudates have specific effects, such as the displacement of phosphate.

Toxic Substances and Engineered Microorganisms

Synthetic chemicals are pervasive throughout the industrialized world. If used, with careful controls, these substances can be extremely beneficial, but toxic effects may arise at various points in the manufacture, use, and the disposal of the chemical. By-products and impurities, and the persistence of the chemicals in the environment may increase the hazard associated with their use and add to technical problems in assessing risk. Many toxic chemicals are difficult to monitor. Data about environmental concentrations cannot be obtained with a high degree of confidence because of inadequate methods. There is a tendency to rely on large safety factors to ensure the protection of humans and the environment from poorly defined risks.

Research is needed not only to identify what the environmental responses should be, but also to determine the biological kinetics associated with effects on key species and ecosystem resiliency and recovery. Mathematical models of the fate of chemicals are needed to estimate the movement and concentration of toxic substances in the environment. Few of the physical models have been validated in the field; their precision and accuracy of prediction need to be defined for specific applications. Recombinant DNA technology should allow the construction of soil microorganisms with the potential to degrade many environmental pollutants such as polychlorinated biphenyl (PCB) and dioxin. The benefits and risks involved in releasing such organisms into the soil must be assessed.

Biological Control Agents

An increasing interest has developed in the use of biological control agents to control pests. Altering microbial populations and activities in the rhizosphere provide opportunities for: (a) modification of plant growth and development; (b) beneficial effects derived from pathogen, insect, nematode, and weed control; (c) enhanced nutrient availability; and (d) degradation of specific toxic substances. These microbial agents may be native or genetically altered organisms and include bacteria, fungi, protozoa, and viruses.

Excellent, but limited, work has been done in the use of *Pseudomonas* species in the control of diseases (take-all) and progress has been made in the development of similar organisms, through genetic engineering, for the control of frost damage and insect pests. Work in this area, however, is still in its infancy and many potential applications have yet to be explored. These include an extended use of organisms such as mycorrhizal fungi, *Rhizobium*, *Azospirillum*, *Frankia*, and the actinomycetes in achieving the above goals, either as control agents in themselves or as highly targeted and selective delivery systems for genes of interest. In order to realize fully the potential of these biological control processes and at the same time evaluate the potential risk associated with their introduction, greater information is needed on the factors which influence their population dynamics and function in the soil and rhizosphere.

Organisms derived via genetic engineering techniques and their products have potential to have direct effects upon untargeted organisms including humans and to modify environmental processes. To evaluate the environmental risk associated with the bioengineering technology, research is needed to evaluate: (a) new and existing methodology to measure potential effect of engineered organisms on other susceptible life; (b) the ability of the engineered organism to survive and grow under *in situ* environmental conditions; (c) the ability of the organism to transfer genetic information to native strains in the environment; and (d) the potential to interfere with natural environmental processes.

Research Imperatives

The microbe is so very small
You cannot make it out at all
But many sanguine people hope
To see him through the microscope.
His thousand tufted tails with lots
Of lovely pink and purple spots
His eyelids of a tender green
All these have never yet been seen
But scientist who ought to know
Assure us that it must be so.

(Apologies, Hilaire Belloc)

The suggested imperatives on rhizosphere biodynamics will require a major, coordinated effort that stresses the attainment of new knowledge and focuses the scientific attention on the methodologies that will give the required insights. Surveys of the potential application of biotechnology to various aspects of rhizodynamics (40) indicate that a knowledge about the techniques of genetic engineering are outstripping the knowledge of the basic biology of the plants and microorganisms involved.

Field research also shows great promise. The application of zero-tillage, the use of winter, leguminous cover crops to control weeds while adding fixed N to the soil, and the recent increased utilization of crop rotations and alternative cropping are examples of success. What is needed in future research is an integrated program that involves field and laboratory studies where the sharp eye and knowledge of the field researcher can be combined with the new technology of the laboratory investigator.

Improve Crop Productivity through Understanding Basic Processes of Root Growth

Plant root systems are the primary interface between the soil resources and the plant. Yet little is known about the processes controlling root growth, development, architecture, and function. These factors govern the efficiency with which a root system exploits the soil profile for water and nutrients. Efficient utilization of translocated photosynthate by root systems is essential for their development. A large fraction of the total host photosynthate is used by the root for growth and metabolism including the part lost to the rhizosphere. The architecture of root systems varies widely with plant genotype. It is strongly modified by biological factors in the surrounding soil such as associative, symbiotic or pathogenic organisms, and also by physical or chemical factors such as waterlogging or acidity. Root studies have been markedly neglected in comparison to studies on the shoot, and this should be redressed. Objectives are:

1. *Characterize plant factors which govern root growth and development and influence the rhizosphere.* The establishment of root systems depends on plant-determined factors such as plant genotype and stage of development which may be modified by the environment. Differences between species which affect the root architecture, rooting depth and capacity of the plant to use soil-derived nutrients, and water include rate of growth of root apices and rate and pattern of initiation of lateral roots. Information on these rates is available for very few species and quantitative data from field studies are almost entirely lacking. The physiological control of root development and the way this is modified by environmental factors such as availability of water and nutrients and the aerial environment requires intensive study. The pattern of colonization of the soil profile by roots determines the spatial distribution of inputs to the soil from the roots as well as use of soil resources by plants.

2. *Resolve uncertainties regarding root anatomy and function.* While the structure and anatomy of plant roots is documented for a large number of species, the quantitative relationships between structure and functions are less clear. In addition, the chemistry of the cell walls and products of cell metabolism which are secreted to the intercellular spaces or to the root surface have not been satisfactorily characterized. These must affect the relationships and communication between root and rhizosphere microorganisms including pathogens as well as providing nutrient substrates. One outstanding gap in our knowledge is in the distribution, turnover and quantitative significance of root hairs, particularly as they affect nutrient uptake.

3. *Define the mechanisms of organic and inorganic nutrient allocation in the plant and thereby enhance efficiency of nutrient utilization.* Inorganic and organic nutrients are distributed between shoots and roots in a way which is determined by plant genotype and by the availability of resources in the ecosystem, (*e.g.* nutrient availability, light) or environmental constraints (*e.g.* drought, pathogens). The genotypic differences in nutrient requirements and in partitioning must be understood and analyzed quantitatively. Very little is known of the way in which alterations in the total allocation to above or below ground components (root:shoot ratio) is translated to differences in the rates of root extension branching and anatomy.

4. *Characterize microbe-root interactions that result in the modification of root development and function.* Root growth and architecture can be modified by soil organism activity. Examples include: (a) increased growth in response to infection by nematodes; (b) changes in rate of root growth relative to shoots following relief of nutrient stress such as P deficiency either in mycorrhizal plants or after P addition; and (c) the transformation of roots by *Agrobacterium rhizogenes*. The way these changes affect nutrient acquisition by the plant C translocation in the plant and root C transfer to soil organism has only been quantitatively investigated in a few cases.

Increase the Efficiency of Utilization of Nutrients in the Soil and Plants

Improved strategies for increased nutrient use efficiency, reduced loss of nutrients to the environment and lower costs of agronomic inputs, can be derived from research on both plant and soil processes. Nutrient uptake by roots is complex; exudation of organic compounds and protons alter the availability of ions in the rhizosphere. There is a great genotypic diversity in the ability of plants to absorb sufficient nutrients from different soils, but the mechanism underlying this is not understood.

Nitrogen transformations in soils are vital in maintaining plant available N and the global N cycle. Fertilizer N accounts for approximately 5% of the global plant N needs. N_2 fixation and input by rain each provide an additional 10%. Losses from soil through leaching and denitrification probably approach 30%. Computer modeling of plant nutrient needs, the timing of cultivation practices and the management of the soil biomass, and the active fraction of soil organic matter to control immobilization-mineralization reactions on a temporal basis have the potential for reducing these losses by 50%. This will, however, require research knowledge and management tools.

Interacting biological and chemical mechanisms that control soil stability and erosion must be determined and applied. The effects of crop selection, soil tillage, methods of chemical management, irrigation and other agronomic processes on nutrient utilization and soil conservation are currently being evaluated by empirical, site-specific approaches. This must be supplemented with fundamental understanding of the processes and widely applicable predictive ability that involves mathematical modeling. Objectives are:

1. *Understand plant regulation of inorganic nutrient uptake as it affects tissue composition and crop nutritional quality.* The last 10 years have witnessed new insights into the processes of membrane transport of inorganic ions, but we are still very ignorant regarding the regulation of the transport processes. Ion transport into the plant is regulated to maintain tissue composition within relatively narrow limits. In turn, this composition is critical in determining cellular processes, and hence, plant growth and yield. Composition is also important that the regulatory constraints be clearly defined so that these plant characteristics may be manipulated.

2. *Exploit genetic diversity in ion acquisition to optimize utilization of soil resources.* There are considerable qualitative and quantitative differences in the absorption and utilization of inorganic nutrients by crop varieties. The underlying mechanism of these differences must be determined at the physiological and biochemical levels so that new varieties may be generated that are adapted to specific soil conditions. This basic biochemical and physiological information is needed for genetic engineering to deliver the required genotypes, but plant breeders should also

consider the incorporation of the above information into future breeding programs. By such approaches marginal and problem soils, such as those with extreme pH or high salinity can be utilized.

3. *Develop effective biological and chemical regulators to manage specific nutrient transformations.* The transformations of N, P, and other elements are vital links in the cycling of these nutrients and in their conversion into plant-available forms. They are mediated through microbes or enzymes. The control of these processes would allow more efficient use of fertilizer and soil nutrient and reduce pollution of groundwater. Better chemical, biological and soil management techniques should be developed for this purpose.

4. *Develop methods for control of mineralization of soil organic nutrients, to ensure their availability at peak plant growth periods.* Methods should be developed for enhancing mineralization during periods of high nutrient demand, and favoring immobilization when demand is low. Techniques for characterizing organic N and P that allow the prediction of their availability to plants should be developed. The mechanisms of regulation and the kinetics of N and P assimilation and release by microbes and fauna should be studied in greater detail. The capability to predict long-term effects of agronomic practices on organic matter and nutrient dynamics is urgently needed. This is particularly important in developing countries where new areas are being cultivated and where fertilizers are scarce.

5. *Use rhizosphere processes to improve soil structure and prevent erosion.* The role of soil microbes, microbial products, living and dead roots, and stable soil organic matter in formation and stabilization of soil aggregate structure should be more thoroughly investigated to allow methods to be developed for enhancing these effects. This would give easier cultivation and better crop growth, as well as lessening the danger of erosion.

Enhance Symbiotic Function and Control Root Diseases through a Better Understanding of Plant-Microbe Interactions

Symbiotic microorganisms supply N, P, and other nutrients to their host plants. To optimize their benefit it is essential to understand the underlying physiological and biochemical processes. Modern genetic techniques provide a powerful tool for the analysis and management of these interactions. This includes a better understanding of the microbe-plant communication system, which determines specificity and type of interaction. Objectives are:

1. *Take advantage of plant microbial genetic diversity to make more efficient use of soil resources.* The ability to form effective symbiosis, as well as the susceptibility to disease, varies widely with the genotype of both plant and microorganism. Further exploitation of this diversity by investigating new combinations of symbioses would allow the most effective systems to be identified. Such new combinations should also be

tested in stressful environments. It is essential to apply various genetic approaches, including mutagenesis, somaclonal variation and genetic engineering, to the complex problems of plant-microbe interactions in the rhizosphere. Genetic analyses of particular host plants and their associated microbes would be especially powerful in the dissection and eventual manipulation of key steps limiting crop productivity.

2. *Characterize the nature and effects of chemical signals exchanged between plant roots and microorganisms.* Microorganisms can interact with plants in both beneficial and detrimental ways. Diffusable chemicals exchanged between plant and microbe appear essential for establishment of the association. In addition, such communication is involved in the induction of plant defense responses to pathogens. Identification of communication molecules and elucidation of the regulatory circuits will allow manipulation of the communication system to either favor or discourage the establishment of plant-microbe interaction.

The outcome of direct cell to cell contact between plants and microorganisms depends on recognition between the interacting cells. Our understanding of such recognition processes at molecular, genetic and cellular levels is rudimentary, yet is of great practical importance for developing new technology for controlling diseases and symbioses. The genes, their products and regulation involved in controlling any interaction are not yet identified, but are amenable to identification using recombinant DNA technology. The walls of the cells are the first point of contact, and also present a barrier to movement of gene products. We need to understand the structure and function of cell walls and extracellular secretions. We presently have no understanding of how signals are transduced to cytoplasmic responses via the plasma membrane in plant cells.

3. *Study the physiology and biochemistry of plant-microbe interactions to improve symbiotic function.* The efficient functioning of symbiotic associations can have a major impact on the health and productivity of plants. However, the molecular, cellular, and genetic factors that determine symbiotic efficiency are almost wholly unknown. The following fundamental mechanisms involved in the control of the development of the symbiotic infection need to be explored and exploited: (a) efficiency of photosynthate utilization, (b) regulation of metabolite exchange between symbionts, (c) effects of host reproductive development, (d) induced senescence and incompatibility, and (e) microbial strain-plant cultivar matching.

Improve Plant Productivity by Altering the Soil and Rhizosphere Population through: (i) Introduction of Novel Organisms, and (ii) Crop and Soil Management

The organisms associated with the rhizosphere can benefit the plant; possible mechanisms are control of pests or pathogens, the productions of plant growth regulatory compounds or the degradation of toxic substances. It is essential to understand the factors controlling colonization, growth, and competitive success, if the rhizosphere populations are to be controlled. Current methods of *in situ* observation of organisms are at present barely adequate, and need to be improved urgently. This will allow technologies of inoculum preparation and delivery to be improved and assessed. The genetic exchange and stability of both introduced and soil microorganisms needs to be determined, especially if the former are genetically engineered. Objectives are:

1. *Define the genetic, biochemical and environmental factors contributing to the competitive success of desired organisms in the root environment.* The establishment of beneficial microorganisms on or near the root is limited by competition both from similar well adapted native strains and by components of the general soil biota. It is imperative to understand the genetic, biochemical, environmental, and ecological aspects of the competition process to assure that stable microbial communities with the desired biological properties are maintained. These communities include nitrogen-fixers, mycorrhizal fungi, pathogens, organisms which control pathogens, organisms which mineralize soil nutrients, and the soil fauna. Survival away from the host under generally unfavorable soil conditions is a particularly important consideration. Strategies to increase competitiveness will be as diverse as the organisms involved, but may take the form of: (a) survival away from the host, (b) enhancement of saprophytic ability, (c) specificity, (d) host defense factors, and (e) resistance to chemicals or tolerance of unfavorable soil conditions. Recently developed technology which can provide for significant gains in research upon microbial competition in the rhizosphere include genetic engineering, the application of population ecology mathematics, modelling, and computer technology.

2. *Define factors important to the growth, function, and decline of microorganisms in soil.* The successful development of an agronomically efficacious microbe requires that we understand those processes which influence the extent, uniformity, and stability of the microbes in the particular ecological niche where their activity is to be expressed. This requires a fundamental understanding of those factors which affect growth, colonization, and survival of the organisms in the soil and in, on, and around the plant root.

Recent studies have shown a large population of bacteria with similarly large nutrient reserves. These are largely stabilized by absorption on clays. Mathematical models of microbial growth and function are necessary to develop concepts and test hypotheses concerning regrowth and enzymatic processes in the soil. These are different from those in liquid laboratory environments. Data for solid substrates must be obtained relative to substrate effects, limiting concentrations of nutrients, and maintenance coefficients. Populations are affected by faunal predation, yet few field values that could be used in mathematical quantification exist, and more research on this is needed.

3. *Develop methods for in situ examination of processes and population interactions in the root environment.* A definition of the parameters which control microbial effects is not possible without the development of methodologies for *in situ* examination. Simple *in vitro* studies on an organism often lead to misleading results which do not translate effectively to field situations.

The inability to assess population and activity responses in the field remains a major obstacle to analysis and modification of rhizosphere populations. *In situ* techniques are particularly important for monitoring the ecological success of desired populations and in identifying the traits required for inoculation success. New methodologies have the potential to partly fill this need if adapted to rhizosphere studies. These include image processing coupled with microscopy, fiber optics, ELISA and monoclonal antibody technology, nucleic acid methodologies to monitor population structure and gene expression, and microelectrodes as sensors of the microenvironment.

4. *Improve techniques for the culture, introduction and establishment of desired populations in soil.* More effective means must be developed for the delivery of beneficial microorganisms to crop plants in the field. Both basic research and technical development are required to ensure that inoculation with improved microsymbionts, biocontrol agents, and genetically engineered microorganisms will be consistently effective, convenient, and economical. Critical areas for further study are the delivery of desired microbes with or within seeds, improvement of carriers for the transport and temporary storage of such microbes, mechanical means for introduction of inoculants or inoculated seed to the soil, and methods for ensuring a head start for desired microbes during seed germination and root development.

Delivery of the microbe to the farmer and subsequently to the field requires the development of formulation and inoculation technologies. Although some work has been done on *Rhizobium* inoculation technology, these technologies are in their infancy and are unlikely to translate to other organisms. It is necessary to determine the underlying principles so that techniques can be established for new organisms and new environmental conditions. We cannot afford to test empirically all the potentially important combinations of soil type, abiotic factors, shoot plant type, and microbial symbiont.

5. *Understand genetic exchange among engineered and native microbial populations, and their stability.* Genetic exchange of traits between organisms in the environment is a critical issue relating both to the stability (and thus efficacy) of an introduced trait and to the environmental issues pertaining to the spread and persistence of an introduced trait in the ecosystem. Research is needed to identify specific microbial populations in various sectors of the rhizosphere, their dynamics, and the basic mechanism of genetic exchange between these classes or organisms. The relative frequencies of genetic exchange depend on factors such as

whether the trait is plasmid or chromosomally encoded, plasmid compatibility with other populations and on the frequency of encounter between organisms capable of exchange. The soil is the home of diverse populations capable of transferring their genetic information to each other. The understanding of the mechanism involved and the possible controls that must be established is imperative to the successful release of any genetically engineered microorganism in nature.

LITERATURE CITED

1. AKKERMANS ADL, D BAKER, K HUSS-DANELL, J TJEPKEMA 1984 Frankia symbioses. Plant Soil (spec vol) 78: 1–258
2. ALBERSHEIM P, AJ ANDERSON-PROUTY 1975 Carbohydrates, proteins, cell surfaces, and the biochemistry of pathogenesis. Annu Rev Plant Physiol 26: 31–52
3. ANDERSON JM, ADM RAYNOR DWH WALTON 1984 Invertebrate-Microbial Interactions. Cambridge University Press, Cambridge.
4. BAKER D, JG TORREY 1979 The isolation and cultivation of actinomycetous root nodule endophytes. In JC Gordon, CT Wheeler, DA Perry, eds, Symbiotic Nitrogen Fixation in the Management of Temperate Forests. Oregon State University Forest Research Lab, Corvallis, OR, pp 38–56
5. BAREA JM, AF BONIS, J OLIVARES 1983 Interactions between Azospirillum and VA mycorrhiza and their effects on growth and nutrition of maize and rye grasses. Soil Biol Biochem 17: 525–531
6. BAUER WD 1981 Infection of legumes by rhizobia. Annu Rev Plant Physiol 32: 407–449
7. BERINGER JE, NJ BREWING, AWB JOHNSTON 1980 The genetic analysis of Rhizobium in relation to symbiotic nitrogen fixation. Heredity 45: 161–186
8. CALLAHAM D, P DEL TREDICI, JG TORREY 1978 Isolation and cultivation in vitro of the actinomycete causing root nodulation in Comptonia. Science 199: 899–902
9. CALVERT HE, MK PENCE, M PIERCE, NSA MALIK, WD BAUER 1984 Anatomical analysis of the development and distribution of Rhizobium infections in soybean roots. Can J Bot 62: 2375–2384
10. CARROLL BJ, DL MCNEIL, PM GRESSHOFF 1985 Isolation and properties of soybean (Glycine max) mutants that nodulate in the presence of high nitrate concentrations. Proc Natl Acad Sci USA 82: 4162–4166
11. CLARKSON DT 1985 Factors affecting mineral nutrient acquisition by plants. Annu Rev Plant Physiol 36: 77–115
12. COLLINS GB, JG PETOLINO, eds 1985 Applications of Genetic Engineering to Crop Improvement. Martinus Nijhoff/Junk, Doredrecht
13. DILLON JT, D BAKER 1982 Variation in nitrogen-fixing efficiency among pure-culture Frankia strains tested on actinorhizal plants as an indication of symbiotic compatibility. New Phytol 92: 215–219 ₁
14. DILWORTH M, A GLENN 1984 How does a legume nodule work? Trends Biol Sci 9: 519–523
15. DOMMERGUES, YR 1982 Scarcely explored means of increasing soil N pool through biological N fixation. In Whither Soil Research, Transactions of the 12th International Congress of Soil Science, New Delhi, India, pp 138–149
16. ELA SW, MA ANDERSON, WJ MURRIL 1982 Screening and selection of maize

to enhance associative bacterial nitrogen fixation. Plant Physiol 70: 1564–1567

17. FOGEL R, G HUNT 1979 Fungal and arboreal biomass in western Oregon Douglas-fir ecosystem: distribution patterns and turnover. Can J For Res 9: 245–255

18. FRECKMAN DW, EP CASWELL 1985 Ecology of nematodes in agroecosystems. Annu Rev Phytopathol 23: 275– 296

19. GAUTHIER DL, HG DIEM, YR DOMMERGUE 1984 Tropical and subtropical actinorhizal plants. Pesqui Agropecu Bras 19: 119–136

20. GIANINAZZI S, V GIANINAZZI-PEARSON, J DEXHEIMER 1979 Ezymatic studies on the metabolism of vesicular arbuscular mycorrhiza. III. Ultrastructural localization of acid and alkaline phosphatase in ion roots infected with *Glomus mosseae*. New Phytol 82: 127

21. GLASS ADM, MY SIDDIQI 1984 The control of nutrient uptake rates in relation to the inorganic composition of plants. *In* PB Tinker, A Läuchli, eds, Advances in Plant Nutrition, Vol 1. Praeger, New York, pp 103–148

22. GRAHAM RD 1984 Breeding for nutritional characteristics in cereals. *In* PB Tinker, A Läuchli, eds, Advances in Plant Nutrition, Vol I. Praeger, New York, pp 57–102

23. GRESSHOFF PM, DA DAY, AC DELVES, A MATTHEWS, J OLSSON, GD PRICE, K SCHULLER, BJ CARROLL 1986 Plant host genetics of symbiotic nitrogen fixation and nodulation in pea and soybean. *In* HJ Evans, W Newton, eds, Proceedings of the 6th International Symposium on Nitrogen Fixation, Corvallis, OR

24. GRESSHOFF PM, K SCHULLER, D HANOLD, AC DELVES, A MATTHEWS, D WHITMORE, D PRICE, D HERRIDGE, J BETTS, D DAY, D MCNIEL, BJ CARROLL 1985 Host plant genetics of symbiotic nitrogen fixation. *In* HJ Evans, W Newton, eds, Proceedings of the 6th International Symposium on Nitrogen Fixation, Corvallis, OR

25. HALVERSON LD, G STACEY 1985 Host recognition in *Rhizobium*-soybean symbiosis. Plant Physiol 77: 621–625

26. HARDY RWF 1980 Translating basic research on biological nitrogen fixation to improve crop production in less developed countries. A users viewpoint. *In* RC Staples, RJ Kuhr, eds, Linking Research to Crop Productivity. Plenum Press, New York, pp 137–151

27. International Potash Institute 1979 Potassium research—reviews and trends. International Potash Institute, Berne

28. JACOBSEN E, W FEENSTRA 1984 A new pea mutant with efficient nodulation in the presence of nitrate. Plant Sci Lett 33: 337–344

29. JACOBSEN E, JG POSTMA, H NIJDAM 1985 Genetical and graft in experiments with pea mutants in studies on symbiosis. *In* HJ Evans, W Newton, eds, Proceedings of the 6th International Symposium on Nitrogen Fixation, Corvallis, OR

30. KANWAR JS, LJ YOUNGDAHL 1985 Micronutrient needs of tropical food crops. Fertil Res 7: 43–68

31. KEYSER HH, PB CREGAN 1985 Diversity of Nodulation of Serogroup 123 Isolates in Cultivated and Exotic Soybeans, 10th North American Rhizobium Conference, Maui

32. KHEEN B, TA LARUE 1984 Nodulation resistant mutants of *Pisum sativum*. J Hered 75: 238–240

33. LIN W, Y OKON, RWF HARDY 1983 Enhanced mineral uptake by *Zea mays*

and *Sorghum bicolor*, roots inoculated with *Azospirillum brasilense*. Appl Env Microbiol 45: 1775–1779

34. LONG SR 1984 Genetics of *Rhizobium* nodulation. *In* E Nester, T Kosuge, eds, Plant Microbe Interactions. Macmillan, New York

35. MARX DH, NC SCHENCK 1983 Potential of mycorrhizal symbiosis in agricultural and forest productivity, pp 334–347. *In* T Kommedahl, PH Williams, eds, Challenging Problems of Plant Health. American Phytopathological Society, St. Paul, MN

36. MENGE JA 1983 Utilization of vesicular-arbuscular mycorrhizal fungi in agriculture. Can J Bot 61: 1015–1024

37. MILLER IM, D BAKER 1985 The initiation, development and structure of root nodules in *Elaeagnus angustifolia* L. (Elaeagnaceae). Protoplasm. In press

38. MINCHIN FR, JE SHEENHY, MI MINGUEZ 1985 Characterization of the resistance to oxygen diffusion in legume nodules. Ann Bot 55: 53–60

39. MOSSE B, DP STRIBELY, F LETACON 1981 Ecology and mycorrhizae and mycorrhizal fungi. Microbiol Ecol 5: 37

40. National Research Council 1984 Genetic Engineering of Plants; Agriculture Research Opportunities and Policy Concerns. National Academy Press, Washington, DC

41. NESME X, P NORMAND, FM TREMBLAY, M LALONDE 1985 Nodulation speed of *Frankia* sp. on *Alnus glutinos*, *Alnus crispa*, and *Myrica gale*. Can J Bot 63: 1292–1295

42. PACOVSKY RS, G FULLER, EA PAUL 1985 Influence of soil on the interactions between endomycorrhiza and *Azospirillum* in sorghum. Soil Biol Biochem 17: 524–531

43. PACOVSKY RS, EA PAUL, GJ BETHLANFALVAY 1985 Nutrition of sorghum plants fertilized with nitrogen or inoculated with *Azospirillum brasilense*. Plant Soil 85: 145–148

44. PATRIQUIN EG 1982 New developments in grass bacteria associations. *In* NS Subba Rao, ed, New Advances in Microbial Ecology. Butterworths, London, pp 139–190

45. PAUL EA, RP VORONEY 1985 Field interpretation of microbial biomass activity measurements. *In* MJ Klug, CA Reddy, eds, Current Perspectives in Microbial Ecology. American Society for Microbiology, Washington, DC, pp 509–514

46. PETERSEN H, N LUXTON 1982 A comparative analysis of soil fauna populations and their role in decomposition processes. Oikos 39: 287–388

47. PHILLIPS DA, LR TEUBER 1985 Genetic improvement of symbiotic nitrogen fixation. *In* HJ Evans, W Newton, eds, Proceedings of the 6th International Symposium on Nitrogen Fixation, Corvallis, OR

48. RENNIE RJ, RI LARSON 1979 Dinitrogen fixation associated with disomic chromosome substitution lines of spring wheat. Can J Bot 57: 2771–2775

49. ROLFE RG, J SHINE 1984 *In* DPS Verma, T Hon, eds, Genes involved in Microbe Plant Interactions. Springer-Verlag, Heidelberg, pp 95–128

50. ROMHELD V, H MARSCHNER 1986 Mobilization of iron in the rhizosphere of different plant species. *In* Advances in Plant Nutrition, Vol II. Praeger, New York. In press

51. SARIC MR, BC LOUGHAM, eds 1982 Genetic Aspects of Plant Nutrition. Nijhoff/Junk, The Hague

52. SCHLESINGER R, R WILLIAMS 1984 Growth response of black walnut to

interplanted trees. For Ecol Manage 9: 235–243

53. SCHMIDT EL 1982 Nutrification. *In* FJ Stevenson, ed, Soil Nitrogen in Agricultural Soils. American Society of Agronomy, Madison, WI, pp 253–288

54. SOON YK, MH MILER 1977 Changes in the rhizosphere due to NH_4 and NO_3 fertilization and phosphorus uptake by corn seedlings. Soil Sci Soc Am J 41: 77–80

55. STEVENSON FJ 1982 Nitrogen in agricultural soils. *In* Agronomy 22. American Society of Agronomy, Madison, WI

56. SUBBA RAO NS 1982 Biofertilizers. *In* Advances in Agricultural Microbiology. Buttersworth, London.

57. THOMAS RJ, K JONKINEN, LE SCHRADER 1983 Effect of *Rhizobium japonicum* mutants with enhanced N_2 fixation activity on N_2 transport and photosynthesis of soybean during vegetative growth. Crop Sci 23: 453–456

58. TINKER PB 1984 The role of microorganisms in mediating and facilitating the uptake of plant nutrients from soil. Plant Soil 76: 77–91

59. WHIPPS JM, JM LYNCH 1983 Substrate flow and utilization in the rhizosphere of cereals. New Phytol 95: 605–623

60. WITTY JF, FR MINCHIN, JE SHEEHY, MI MINGUEZ 1984 Acetylene induced changes in the oxygen diffusion resistance and nitrogenase activity of legume root nodules. Ann Bot 53: 13–20

61. WITTY JG, FR MINCHIN, JE SHEEHY 1983 Carbon costs of nitrogenase activity in legume root nodules determined using acetylene and oxygen. J Exp Bot 34: 951–963

62. ZINCKE PS, AG STANGENBERGER, WM POST, WR EMANUEL, JS OLSON 1984 Worldwide organic soil carbon and nitrogen data. ORNL Publication No. 2212

Biological Constraints

Submitted on behalf of the group by:

BRIAN A. CROFT   DAVID R. MACKENZIE
R. JAMES COOK

Cultivars of major crops grown in modern farming systems may yield only 60 to 75%, and often only 50% or less, of their poential or attainable yield as set by their genetic makeup, available water, fertilizer, climate, and weather. This difference between the actual and attainable yield results largely from biological constraints to the crop imposed by pests[1] such as plant pathogens, arthropods, vertebrate pests, nematodes, and weeds, hereafter referred to collectively as plant pests. Several authors have estimated that, worldwide, preharvest crop yields would be 30 to 40% more were it not for damage from pests (11, 32, 41, 46).

Figures such as 50 to 75% of potential crop production and yield gains of 100% from pest control may seem like exaggerations, but plants are affected by pests from the day of planting until the day of consumption, and perennial crops are affected every year. Moreover, pest problems continue to be a major constraint to crop productivity in the Third World. Research is just beginning to document the importance of chronic pest problems in the United States and elsewhere that were previously thought to be of minor significance. The effects of chronic pest problems may occur so uniformly that the pest-limited yield is accepted as the normal crop. The changes toward conservation tillage and less rotation in the United States have resulted in several previously minor or controlled pests becoming persistent constraints to crop productivity. Although about one billion pounds of pesticide are currently applied in the United States to contain these pests (31), the effects of certain pest groups on crop yields have not diminished appreciably since the 1940s. For example, due mostly to more intensive cropping, losses to insects and other arthropods have increased from about 7 to 13% over this time period, although there is considerable variation in annual effects of insects on crop yields (32). Environmental questions about the use of pesticides represent other reasons for developing new pest control technology.

It is important that we consider new horizons for research to find new, safer, and more sustainable ways to limit the effects of pests on crop productivity. Any improvement in plant health has the potential to

---

[1] Throughout this chapter we have used the term "pest" in its broadest definition to include biota of all kinds that damage, injure, or limit the productivity of crops. This definition, while arguable from several perspectives, is editorially convenient.

increase not only the capacity to produce, but also the efficiency of production through improvements in crop performance without requiring more water, fertilizer, or land. Five major research imperatives for improving and protecting plant health are set forth in this paper. In addition, 30 more specific research imperatives are given as subsets. The five major research imperatives for crop health are:

1. Improve crop health through better understanding and management of crop patterns, mixtures and rotations, plant residues, and soil (see "Cultural Control ").

2. Maximize the capacity of plants to resist pest attack through acquisition and application of knowledge of biochemical and physical processes and genetic determinants (see "Host Plant Resistance").

3. Develop new or more effective biological controls of pests using classical methods and new biotechnologies (see "Biological Control").

4. Develop new chemicals (pesticides) for pest control, along with improved and safer methods for their sustained use compatible with crop production strategies (see "Chemical Control").

5. Improve integrated pest management programs by enhancing data collections and assessment, decision supports, and system design (see "Integrated Pest Management").

Cultural Control

Cultural practices such as crop rotation, clean tillage, burning of crop and weed debris, choice of planting date, and method of planting were once the only tactics available to control most pests. Such practices are still among the most important methods of pest control (34). Yields decrease with crop monoculture because of the selective enhancement of populations of soil organisms and increases in above-ground pests that out-compete, parasitize, or otherwise live at the expense of the crop. Many of these pests live in the residue of the crop and are thereby vulnerable to tillage or other practices that accelerate residue decomposition. For example, pathogens, insects, weeds, and rodents that live in or gain protection from crop debris on the soil surface are vulnerable to plowing or to destruction by burning. Weeds are more manageable if some form of crop rotation and tillage is used. Row spacing, planting date, and fertilizer placement are other common tactics used to favor the crop relatively more than the pest, or help the crop escape pest damage.

A major trend in modern agriculture with great implications for pest control, especially with field crops, is more intensive cropping and the reduction or elimination of crop rotation and tillage practices. The advantages of conservation tillage and intensive cropping include greater efficiency with specialization of the farming operation and greater conservation of soil and energy. These new cropping systems, however, also improve conditions for root diseases, weeds, and soil- and residue-inhabiting pests. Moreover, crops in some management systems may be more stressed and are therefore predisposed to greater pest damage. It is challenge enough just to maintain the current level of crop productivity in the face of these changing agricultural practices (22).

Crops grown without adequate rotation can appear nutrient deficient because of poor root health (9). Such plants are also less competitive with weeds. This has resulted in greater use of fertilizers and herbicides. Plants stressed by soil salinity or those deficient in one or more nutrients may be more susceptible to damage by pests. The management of crops for a yield greater than possible with available water in some low rainfall areas can result in more damage by diseases favored by plant water stress (8). In many cases, the cause of poor crop performance is not properly diagnosed, perhaps being incorrectly attributed to a lack of soil fertility, toxicity of the surface residue, or simply unfavorable weather. An accurate diagnosis opens the way for selection of resistant cultivars, pesticides, or other tactics aimed specifically at the control of the responsible pest(s) in the agroecosystem.

These emerging relationships point to a strong need for research in the following areas of cultural control:

Investigate the effects of conservation tillage on soil properties and pest population dynamics. Conservation tillage will improve the sustainability and efficiency of agricultural systems. Reduced tillage alters the physical, chemical, and biological conditions of the soil compared with soils managed by conventional tillage. Pest populations are markedly altered by these changing production systems. If conservation tillage systems are to succeed, new production challenges will best be solved by interdisciplinary research aimed at improving and protecting plant health in these systems.

Determine the influence and mechanisms of crop patterns, mixtures, and rotations on the population dynamics and genetic diversity of pests and their natural enemies. Both spatial and temporal sequences of crops influence pest populations and the resultant crop damage. It is important to determine both short- and long-term impacts of such cropping patterns on pest abundance and crop health. Furthermore, the maintenance of a pest's natural enemies or the direct suppression of pest populations may be possible through the encouragement of certain plant associations or cropping sequences. An understanding of the basis for changes in population and genetic diversity of pests under variable cropping regimes will facilitate the manipulation of cropping system sequence as a component of effective pest management.

Determine the mechanisms by which environmental stresses predispose crops to pest damage and disease initiation. Plant health, and especially the ability of plants to resist pests and diseases, is greatly affected by environmental stresses resulting from adverse climate, weather, soils, and cultural practices. The mechanisms by which these stresses affect the crop and its vulnerability to pests needs investigation to facilitate more rational approaches to crop management for pest control.

Elucidate mechanism(s) of crop-weed competition and allelopathy. Allelopathy is the suppression of plant growth by the chemical substance(s) produced by another plant and released into the environment. Competition refers to the differential use, and, therefore, unavailability of resources by plants in the same environment. Both processes may result in lower yields of one or both associates in the interaction that may be used for improved weed control. Studies of the mechanism of allelopathy and competition are needed to define the relationship of total plant density, species proportions, spatial arrangements (proximity), and numerous plant developmental factors (*e.g.* emergence time, total size, leaf area, growth rate) on the observed suppression of plant growth. The elucidation of these factors, together with breeding for more effective allelopathic effects, will enable crop managers to manipulate both crop and weed populations to lessen the environmental impact of weed control and improve crop productivity.

Host Plant Resistance

Host plant resistance offers a time-tested, economical and safe method of pest control (5, 21, 43). The greatest use of this tactic has been for the control of specialized arthropod pests, plant parasitic nematodes, and plant pathogens. Historically, progress has been made in obtaining useful resistance within available germ plasm of a species of a crop. A major limitation to progress has been the lack of useful genes or combinations of genes that code for resistance. Recent developments in plant breeding, such as screening protoplasts or microspores for resistant cells and transformation of plant cells by genetic engineering, may greatly enhance the successful development of resistant crops.

Historically, each new source of resistance introduced into a crop cultivar tended to favor the evolution of new biotypes of the pest with ability to attack that cultivar. One consequence of the new races and biotypes has been lower crop productivity—sometimes catastrophic losses! This problem has been greatest where cultivars with a single gene for host plant resistance have been used to control a highly specialized race of a plant pathogen (*e.g.* rust, smut, or mildew fungi and certain viruses). The need in breeding plants for resistance is to move toward greater systematic use of the total genetic variability, even at the expense of high levels of resistance, to achieve continued, long-term disease control. On the other hand, some forms of high level monogenic resistance continue to be effective after many years of use (*e.g.* resistance in cabbage to *Fusarium* wilt) (44) and are obviously adequate. Pyramiding of several major genes for resistance has also been effective in limiting the evolution of new races of the pathogen (*e.g.* the wheat stem rust fungus). This approach requires a continual monitoring of the pathogen population for frequency of virulence genes and the deployment of appropriate resistance genes in the host (33).

The use of multilines (6) and cultivar mixtures (45) provides another approach to retard or prevent the evolution of new virulent biotypes of the pathogen. With this approach, several genes for resistance are deployed in genetic isolines or in different cultivars in a mixture. It is reasoned that the pathogens, in order to be successful, must have all the genes for virulence, to overcome all of the genes for resistance in the multiline mixtures, which is unlikely. The traditional concept of pure seed and homogeneity in our crops must be modified or abandoned if this approach is to be adopted. More research is needed on the effects of multilines and/or cultivar mixtures on virulence gene frequencies in the pathogen population and on the epidemiology of specific races (or virulence genes) in fields planted to known cultivar mixtures. A major concern with this approach is the evidence that the yield of resistant plants in a mixture is limited as a consequence of the energy expended in reacting to the avirulent inoculum produced on neighboring susceptible plants (37). Therefore, research is also needed on the cost of the resistance reaction as a biological constraint to crop productivity.

New research approaches offer the opportunity to complement the existing crop breeding strategies for pest resistance by determining the underlying factors that regulate pest/pathogen virulence or host resistance. Understanding the reasons for success and failure of host plant resistance should lead to fewer failures in the future. This would best be done by increasing basic knowledge on the biochemical nature of the plant-pest relationship.

A thorough understanding of the basis for plant-pest interactions is necessary if more resistant plants are to be developed by new biotechnologies such as genetic engineering. For example, the surface of roots, stems, or leaves acts as both a barrier and a cue to influence invasion and would be subject to genetic manipulation by both conventional and unconventional means if the molecular basis and genetic control for these recognition phenomena were understood. Plant metabolic pathways, under genetic and environmental control, determine the quantity and array of constituents that may either attract or repel insects and nematodes. In the case of viral, bacterial, and fungal plant pathogens, and probably also for insects, invasion can trigger metabolic responses by the plant that render the plant resistant to further infection or colonization. Research is needed to reveal general principles of plant biochemical and structural mechanisms for pest/pathogen resistance. Specific, detailed examples are needed of the resistance factors that play a role in important compatible plant-pest interactions. A parallel research effort is needed to analyze the genetic basis for virulence in pests corresponding to resistance in host crops. This knowledge will be useful in developing more durable crop resistance to pests and very likely contribute to the applications of biotechnology to develop host plant resistance where none currently exists.

The following areas of research in host plant resistance are of primary need:

Determine the genes and gene products of both plants and their pests that confer resistance. The identification of gene combinations and the gene products responsible for host plant resistance is important information for plant breeders. Recombinant DNA technology now provides an opportunity to determine the products of both genes in the host and in the parasite that elicit incompatibility or otherwise make resistance effective. The genes and their products can be used to develop strategies to get sustained resistance to pests. Knowledge of these defense processes will permit the development of new strategies in resistance.

Identify the molecular signals in host-pathogen interactions. In the early stages of pathogen attack, chemical triggers activate host resistance responses. Activation leads to counter-responses as molecular messages from the host. The products of this chemical interaction are fundamental to the host/pathogen relationships and knowledge about them should lead to more desirable use of host plant resistance for disease control.

Elucidate arthropod/plant communication systems and metabolic interactions involved in plant resistance. Elucidation of sensory physiological mechanisms related to location, recognition and acceptance of a plant by the insect pests, and the effect of plants' resistance factors in the plant on insect metabolism is essential for progress in generating plants with high levels of resistance to insects, either by conventional breeding methods or through genetic engineering. Plants often respond to insect attacks by compensatory growth (*e.g.* tillering), or through *de novo* synthesis of inhibitory factors (*e.g.* proteinase inhibitors in potatoes and tomatoes). Resistance induced by insect attack (post challenge) have potential applications in practical control of this pest group.

Investigate the biosynthesis and mobilization of secondary plant products and metabolic costs of plant defense mechanisms. Plants have evolved elaborate, multicomponent, chemical defense mechanisms to protect themselves against pests. Elucidation of metabolic pathways for synthesis and mobilization of these defense chemicals should be intensified. Attention must be paid to the overall physiological cost of the production of defensive compounds to the plants. This information is essential for manipulating the production of appropriate secondary metabolites to enhance resistance.

Design gene deployment schemes to manage genetic diversity for cultivated crops and to ameliorate pest problems. Research is needed to determine how genetic diversity can be used more effectively and safely to combat pests through strategies such as the use of genetic mixtures, multilines, cultivar mixtures, intercropping, and crop rotation. More information is needed on population dynamics, the amounts of variation, the control of plant variation on pests, and the evolution of new pest biotypes.

Identify the effects of plant defense mechanisms on biological control agents. Research is needed on the effect of chemical and physical traits of the crop on the biology, ecology, and population dynamics of biological control agents of plant pests. More particularly, information is needed to identify plant characteristics or compounds that play a role in attracting or stimulating the action of biological control agents. The nutritional quality and developmental biology of the pest may be affected by genetic traits introduced into the crop, which may then influence pest susceptibility to biological control agents. The resulting performance of the biological control agent also must be determined.

Biological Control

Biological control as a strategy for pest management is of intense research interest and is applicable to all pest groups (3, 8, 17). Of the many positive aspects to the use of biological control, one particularly favorable attribute is its low environmental impact.

Biological control of arthropods has focused on studies of the chemical signals by which natural enemies recognize their insect hosts. These chemicals can be used to enhance the effectiveness of natural enemies and to develop more selective pesticides. This will allow improved establishment of introduced natural enemies and reveal ways for the genetic improvement of native and introduced biological control agents (3). Methods of estimating the abundance and impact of arthropod predators and parasites have been improved, and systems-analysis techniques are emerging as tools to study the effectiveness of these agents once introduced or integrated with other pest-management tactics (17, 38).

Tactics currently used or attempted for biological control with plant pathogens are of three broad types (8):

1. Regulation of the pathogen population with natural enemies such as hyperparasites and predators,

2. Protection of plant surface with nonpathogenic epiphytes antagonistic to the pathogen, and

3. Enhanced resistance of the plant to pathogens by inoculation of the plant with nonpathogens.

Because of the close and often intimate association between pathogens and their hosts (*e.g.* some pathogens, such as viruses, complete their entire life cycle inside their host), it has been necessary to design biological controls for plant pathogens that operate on and within the host plant itself. Due to these close associations, distinction between host-plant resistance and biological control is, in some cases, not practical.

A major breakthrough for biological control of plant pathogens was the discovery by Kerr (20) of the nonpathogenic strain K-84 of *Agrobacterium radiobacter* as an effective root protectant against the crown gall pathogen, *A. radiobacter* var. *tumefaciens*. The nonpathogenic strain lacks the tumor-inducing (Ti) plasmid required to incite crown gall, but carries instead a plasmid that confers the ability to produce a bacteriocin (agrocin-84), to which the pathogen is sensitive. Strains of the crown gall pathogen insensitive to agrocin-84 have been reported (30), however, revealing that, as with other specific control tactics, selection pressure on the pest could favor evolution of resistant strains of the pest. The more specific the mechanism of biocontrol, the more likely the chance that a pest population will evolve with resistance to the control (8).

Another research breakthrough was the discovery of "plant growth promoting rhizobacteria" (PGPR) with the ability to colonize the rhizosphere, produce antibiotics and/or siderophores (naturally occurring, iron-chelating compounds), and thereby inhibit or suppress root pathogens (36). This approach, as a means to improve and protect root health, is now attracting research interest for virtually all major food crops (10). It may be possible in the future to transfer the gene(s) for inhibitor production from the antagonist to the host, in which case biological control could be achieved by the host directly.

Biological control of weeds has, in recent years, focused principally on the use of naturally occurring and genetically altered strains of weed pathogens and weed-feeding arthropods (40). Classically, an arthropod pest or pathogen from a native habitat is released into the habitat of the weed to inhibit growth of the weed. The use of "mycoherbicides" for biological control of weeds depends on mass culture of the pathogen and the inundative inoculation of the weed population in a manner similar to pesticide usage. Similarly, the introductions and management programs using arthropods as control agents for weeds have been developed and used successfully (2, 4). Success in the registration and use of plant pathogenic fungi as mycoherbicides to control weeds in crops such as rice (7) has been a major stimulus to the increased interest in using plant pathogens for weed control. Weed species are rarely, if ever, killed outright by biocontrol agents as they are with chemical herbicides. Weeds can, however, be weakened by a disease or arthropod pest so that they can no longer compete with desirable plants.

Work in the future will focus on the integrated use of pathogens or arthropod pests of weeds, as well as the use of selective synthetic chemical herbicides. Also, factors such as an allelopathic capability may be introduced genetically into a crop.

Biological control of nematodes, when compared with biological control of other pest groups, is not nearly as well developed, although recent progress in the identification of basic predator/prey or parasite/host relationships and the population dynamics of this group of plant pests is encouraging (42). Biological control of nematodes depends mainly on the use of natural enemies to help keep the nematode population low (23). In England, monoculture of wheat results initially in an increase in the population of the cereal cyst nematode, *Heterodera avenae*. If the monoculture is continued, however, fungi parasitic on eggs and cysts of *H. avenae* eventually lower the pest population below the threshold level associated with crop damage. Natural biological control of nematodes may occur more commonly than realized, but too little research has been carried out to document such effects. Nematode-trapping fungi have been a mycological curiosity for decades, but they have never been used to practical advantage except possibly where their populations have been elevated to unusually high numbers (19). Trapping individual nematodes in soil is inefficient when compared with agents that attack cysts and egg masses before the nematode larvae emerge (35). *Bacillus penetrans* is a highly destructive and efficient pathogen of several important plant parasitic nematode species (23) and could eventually be introduced commercially into soils for biological control. The major limitation to its practical use is the lack of a method for mass production and formulation. Results of Stirling and Wachtel (39) indicate that this limitation may soon be overcome.

The commercial application of biological control is often limited by lack of information on the biosystematics, basic biology, genetics, ecology, physiology, and behavior of the target pests and their biological control agents. This is especially acute in the case of biological control of nematodes and plant pathogens. Biosystematics research must be maintained and expanded to provide the necessary knowledge foundation for the identification of pests and biological control agents.

Biological control requires research to make it compatible with other crop protection and crop production strategies. The development of better monitoring techniques for pests and their biological control agents is also needed.

To overcome current restraints to biological control applications, further research is needed to:

Determine the chemical basis of physiological and behavioral interactions between plant pests and their natural enemies and use this information to improve biological control. To improve and manipulate the effectiveness of biological control agents, we must identify and quantify the molecular interaction between pests and their natural enemies and symbionts. This should include identification of the molecular basis of location, recognition and acceptance of pests by natural enemies, and the molecular interactions between pests and natural enemies in regard to defense and evasion, alteration of biochemical processes, and physiological interrelationships. Since hormones regulate the production of sex phermones, their implications span ecological as well as physiological/biochemical disciplines. Research that integrates the biochemistry and physiology of insects will have impact upon their mating success and population dynamics.

Improve biological control agents by selection and molecular genetic techniques to enhance their efficiency in cropping systems. Biological control agents can be improved in their responses to biotic and abiotic factors. Artificial selection makes use of intraspecific variability, and recombinant DNA techniques can provide new traits through interspecific transformations. Traits of immediate interest include pesticide resistance; more effective virulence/pathogenicity; broader host range; greater tolerance to abiotic factors such as relative humidity, temperature, ultraviolet radiation; adaption to crop phenology; and greater ability to compete and to produce inhibitory compounds. Genetic improvement requires identification of traits needing improvement and methods of maintaining and producing high quality biological control agents.

Identify key factors regulating the colonization of plant surfaces by microorganisms capable of biological control of plant pests. The successful introduction of biocontrol agents onto plant surfaces such as leaves and roots requires research on the principles involved in the population dynamics of these beneficial organisms on plant surfaces. It may be necessary to manipulate genetically both host and biocontrol agent to increase the effectiveness of this kind of biological control.

Develop methods for identification of biological control agents and their associated target pests. Basic systematics is the essential foundation for all programs of biological control. New technologies (*e.g.* monoclonal antibodies, enzyme-linked immunosorbent assay (ELISA) techniques, restriction fragment length polymorphism, and isosyme analysis) will be useful for more rapid and accurate identification of species, strains or variants that differ in anatomical, physiological, biochemical, and behavioral traits. Improved systematics will lead to rapid, definitive identification of pests and their biological control agents.

Develop an information base to predict the fate and effect of genetically engineered organisms in the environment. Biological control practices for pest control will increasingly use organisms that are genetically engineered to express a desired trait. Research is needed to establish the principles involved in the fate and environmental impact of organisms tested in containment facilities and under defined field conditions.

Develop technology for culturing, rearing, delivering and evaluating biocontrol agents under field conditions. The development of technology concerning the culturing, rearing, and delivering of biocontrol agents to targeted sites in the environment is basic to their safe and effective use in agriculture. Field evaluation of biocontrol agents is essential for obtaining required efficiency data and especially for determining the effect of the agent on the plant and other components of the environment. Such studies should provide data on dissemination of the biocontrol agents, possible alternate hosts, and a general investigation for possible undesirable characteristics of the introduced agent.

Develop methods to integrate biological control agents and pesticides in agricultural systems. Biological and chemical control agents can be used together for efficient and effective pest control. Assay methods are needed to determine the resistance of biological control agents to pesticides in crop ecosystems. Besides development of pesticide-resistant strains of biological control agents (see second imperative in section on chemical control), the relative timing, rates, and methods of applying biological and chemical control agents need to be investigated. Research could result in reduced pesticide use and increased biological control.

Chemical Control

The design and discovery of pesticides that have novel modes of action will continue to be a major objective to maintain and improve crop health in the foreseeable future for all pest groups and major crops (16, 24, 25). Pesticides are, in many situations, necessary to supplement other means of control, such as host resistance and biological and cultural controls.

There should, however, be a continuing effort made to move away from intensive pesticide usage, particularly those pesticides that have an adverse effect on nontarget organisms (12, 26).

In many crop production systems, particularly for crops in small acreages or grown with reduced tillage, available pesticides are inadequate, or too many pesticides are needed. In addition, many pesticides have lost their effectiveness due to the development of resistance in the target organisms. In spite of improvements in methods of pesticide application, only a small fraction of the pesticides applied reach their targets, and we lack information on interactions between pesticides, crops, and beneficial organisms. Beneficial organisms and other nontarget species can be affected significantly by pesticide applications.

Most pesticides have been discovered empirically by screening compounds from all sources followed by structure-activity optimization (25). Many authors have pointed out the trend of increasing costs for development of a pesticide and the decreasing probability of a product reaching the market place. For example, the cost of development now ranges from $15 million to $20 million and there is only a 1 in 15,000 to 20,000 chance of success for each potential compound.

For insecticides, new means of discovery using toxicant models fashioned after natural products must be vigorously pursued. Metabolic and mode-of-action studies of natural products can reveal sites that may lead to increased activity and improved qualities in related compounds. Synthetic pyrethroids are a recent product of this approach. In the future, research opportunities for improved insecticides and their use will come from development of better delivery systems, identification of new target sites in the pests, and development of natural-product compounds or mimics such as pheromones, allelochemicals, insect hormones, microbial agents, plant growth regulators or inducers of host plant resistance (16, 28).

Trends in herbicide synthesis and formulation will continue to include herbicide synergists, plant growth regulators, herbicide antidotes, controlled release from seeds, and improved foliar application techniques (16). However, there is a need to emphasize the mode of action of herbicides at the cellular and molecular levels, especially for understanding plant enzymes and membrane structure, function and turnover. Biochemical studies are needed to elucidate further the actions of herbicides (27).

New areas of herbicide research will include the development of substances that promote early weed seed germination (*e.g.* ethylene and ethephon) and incorporation of herbicide tolerance into crop cultivars through conventional breeding and by genetic engineering. The synergistic use of herbicides and plant growth regulators also shows promise for the future. Herbicides are beginning to be developed using natural-product models (*e.g.* from growth substances such as auxins, gibberelins, cytokinins, absicic acid, and secondary plant compounds such as lactones, terpenoids, steroids, and alkaloids). The possible benefits from allelopathic agents secreted from roots of plants to inhibit seed germination and growth were mentioned earlier in this paper.

Emphasis in the design and synthesis of fungicides is shifting toward biorational discovery. There is considerable work on structural modification of sulfonimides and ergosterol-inhibiting compounds, and the development of compounds that interfere with the pathogenic capabilities of fungi (e.g. Tricyclazol, Probenazol). Much more potential exists for discoveries in basic knowledge of immune responses in plants, which will provide opportunities to trigger natural defense mechanisms of the host plant against pest organisms. Pesticide-resistant strains of agriculturally important arthropods, fungal and bacterial pathogens, nematodes, weeds, and rodents are increasing in terms of number of species, the distribution of resistance, and species showing multiple forms of resistance (15, 29). Our inability to limit pesticide resistance is critical where alternate methods are not available to reinstate effective pest control. As a result of increases in economic and regulatory constraints on the development of new pesticides, appreciably fewer new pesticides appear on the market and some are being withdrawn (14, 29). New methods of resistance management are needed to prolong the effective life of currently available compounds.

Research attention must be given to the items listed below in order to address the problems of chemical control of pests:

Develop pesticides that control all or most components of the pest complex of a crop with minimal effects on beneficial species. Species-specific pesticides, although useful in some pest control programs, are too specific when an entire complex of pest and beneficial organisms must be managed. Activity that provides control over several pests but does not affect beneficial species is a preferred objective of future pesticide development. Research studies have shown, for example, that some beneficial species have very different detoxification mechanisms for pesticides compared to their hosts or prey. Although such ideal selectivity spectra will be difficult to achieve, their incorporation into integrated pest management systems could greatly reduce overall pesticide inputs while maintaining crop productivity.

Develop pesticide-resistant crop plants and beneficial species to minimize nontarget effects. Crops with resistance or tolerance to herbicides and some other pesticides can be developed through traditional breeding and recombinant DNA techniques. Strains of biological control agents and pollinators can also be selected for resistance to pesticides using traditional and new techniques. The use of recombinant DNA techniques, such as those developed for *Drosophila*, requires a deeper understanding of the molecular genetics of resistance in eukaryotes. Research is needed to develope vectors to carry foreign DNA into the recipient species, and to determine whether the inserted resistance genes are stable and appropriately expressed.

Identify mechanisms of chemical control in pests and develop novel chemicals from natural or synthetic sources to exploit these mechanisms.

In order to discover more selective and efficient pesticides, a better understanding is needed of metabolic pathways in target and nontarget species. Specific sites of pesticide action in the pest can be identified at the cellular and molecular level. This biorational approach may lead to the discovery of new modes of action and selectivity. Attention should also be given to developing chemicals that suppress pest populations by modifying behavior (*e.g.* reproduction, feeding, sporulation, infection, colonization, molting, seed or spore germination, repellants, and others).

Quantify the dynamics of pesticide interaction with crops, pests, natural enemies, and other nontarget species to achieve increased effectiveness and selectivity. Modeling techniques permit accurate and quantitative evaluations of the interactions between pesticides and the dynamic processes of crop growth, pest behavior, and the movement of pests and their natural antagonists. These evaluations result in more relevant determinations of pesticide effects, residue levels, necessity for treatment, and selectivity features of their use. The modeling effort will require collection of data in several areas, including crop growth rates and patterns, pesticide residue decay, and pest and natural enemy dispersal and reproductive behavior.

Develop diagnostic monitoring tools for resistant organisms and strategies to manage resistance to prolong pesticide effectiveness. The critical long-term effectiveness of pesticides may be limited by resistance in target pests. Diagnostic tools must be developed for rapid, quantitative detection of resistant strains. Strategies for pesticide use to avoid or delay resistance problems must be evaluated under a variety of field conditions.

Develop improved pesticide application techniques and delivery systems. New developments are needed in application technology to more accurately deliver the pesticide to the target pest, thereby reducing the amount of pesticide applied and minimizing off-target deposition through processes such as drift. Increased understanding of the relationship of the physical/chemical/biological properties of pesticides affecting their uptake and movement to the site of action is essential. New technology such as controlled-release delivery systems, additives to protect nontarget species, and synergists that enhance activity in target species should be the goals of this research.

Improve the quantification and management of the fate of pesticides in the environment, including processes for avoiding, reducing, or detoxifying them. This priority greatly affects the sustainability of crop production and continuing use of our valuable chemical resources. Evaluation systems describing the fate of pesticides in the environment must continue to be developed. Mathematical models of many aspects of environmental fate have been developed, but further validation in the field is needed to make them useful as predictive tools. In addition to accounting for pesticide fate under normal-use conditions, more research is needed to find or develop microorganisms to clean up toxic wastes, spills, and containers *in situ* and to minimize contamination of the environment.

Integrated Pest Management (IPM)

IPM is a holistic approach to crop health care for many annual and perennial crops. It involves integrated management of aspects of the crop (and even the larger agroecosystem) as a means to manage crop pests. An agroecosystem may be an individual field in a given rotation, tillage or planting date, or it may be an orchard, or an arrangement of fields and orchards within a defined geographic or climatic areas. Some of the features of IPM are summarized as follows:

1. IPM is a *design process*, based on a thorough analysis of the cropping system, the pests, and the available means to manage those pests.

2. IPM is a *decision-making* process that views control actions as a set of choices to be made, based on the current or expected status of the crop and pest populations.

3. IPM is an *information-based* approach that relies heavily on problem diagnosis and monitoring as essential tools to determine whether or not control is necessary and, if so, what tactics are most needed.

4. IPM is a *systems approach* to problem solving, identifying all relevant components of the agroecosystem that relate to pest/crop interactions, and considering the system-level effects of control strategies and tactics.

IPM is more than simply the use of multiple tactics to manage pests. Equally significant, the IPM philosophy has caused scientists and practitioners alike to consider pests and their control as aspects of an overall crop management strategy. As a result, creative interactions among disciplines at universities and research centers have developed, and farmers are benefiting from advice that relates to their total crop production needs.

IPM programs for major crops have achieved an improved level of economic benefit while minimizing environmental problems (1, 13, 18). IPM has developed models of crop and pest systems, and has led to sampling and interpreting biological and environmental information, improving information on thresholds of pest populations, managing multiple pest complexes, evaluating biological control agents, developing plants with multiple resistances to pests, improving economic evaluation; and increasing the success of implementing pest control tactics.

Efficient, and environmentally valid pest management programs must be developed. Research must focus on improving the theoretical, informational, and practical bases of the integrated approach. Greater knowledge is needed of the crop and environment, and techniques for supporting decisions in pest management must be made available to accommodate and analyze this complex information. Systems analysis and modeling are therefore essential to help establish priorities, goals, and objectives for effective research agendas.

Specific research imperatives are identified and described as follows:

Develop improved techniques to diagnose and quantify pest incidence and severity. Information on the accurate identification and geographical distribution of pests is crucial to both research and implementation of pest management programs. Rapid and accurate identification of plant viruses, viroids, and phytopathogenic bacteria can now be accomplished by monoclonal antibodies, DNA probes, and other biotechnological methods that must be refined even further to permit the precision necessary to identify individual virulent biotypes and races of a single species. Although arthropod species can often be more easily identified, identification of races and biotypes is often poor. Greater use must also be made of remote sensing and sampling techniques for more rapid and accurate assessment of pest occurrence and outbreaks over large areas. With most pests, complete and accurate quantitative data on pest abundance are rarely available.

Define dynamic pest control thresholds for individual species and multiple-pest complexes. IPM uses the threshold concept to indicate pest infestation levels where the benefits of control outweigh the costs of its implementation. Rarely has a threshold been used in practice that was based on a detailed economic analysis. In addition, current thresholds do not reflect that most crops are attacked by a complex of pests. A true threshold depends on several variables, including crop stage, expected price at harvest, weather, comparative costs of alternative control practices, choice of crop cultivar, and other considerations that change through time and space. Simulation models encompassing the crop, pest populations, and economics can be used to develop such dynamic approaches to decision making. Research, conducted by interdisciplinary teams, is needed to bring realistic, usable thresholds into pest management systems to provide greater efficiency and cost savings for farmers and a reduction in overall pesticide use.

Develop methodologies based on artificial intelligence to improve linkages between pest management strategies and other crop production practices for more efficient and effective pest control. IPM should be embedded into the crop production system and holistic plant health. This will benefit the way research is conducted on all aspects of crop production as they relate to plant health. Artificial intelligence, and specifically expert systems, is a highly researchable area that will provide new methods for integrating and transferring key agricultural production components, as well as marketing and financial planning techniques, to agriculture.

Conduct research to allow IPM programs to adapt to shifts in crop production factors, in order to avoid loss of effective pest control. Over time, major changes in pest status, pesticides, tillage practices, market conditions, and other factors can dramatically influence the effective operation of pest management programs. The current shift to conservation tillage systems in the United States, for example, substantially reduces weed control options and causes major shifts in the types and abundance of other pests. Research is needed to design features of IPM systems to respond to these changes. Such maintenance research must continue over time and will require considerable attention. Otherwise,

IPM systems will not be able to maintain their effectiveness or efficiency over the long term.

Determine the attainable yields of crops and quantify the factors that limit those yields. Better means of assessing constraints to crop productivity are needed. Current assessment methods are inadequate. Techniques are needed to determine the difference between the *actual* and the *attainable* yield and compartmentalization of the factors responsible for this difference, in order to inform policy makers, administrators, and researchers of the real problems in need of solutions.

Incorporate concepts of community ecology into IPM systems through modeling and experimentation. The design and effectiveness of IPM systems depends upon the dynamics of the entire community of organisms, ranging from microorganism, weed, arthropod, and vertebrate pests and their natural enemies. Experimental and modeling research provides the basis for linking ecological theory to the emerging concepts of integrated pest management. Such research will result in a better understanding of biological control, pathogen-vector dynamics, and pesticide resistance development. Furthermore, a greater understanding of crop and weed growth dynamics and threshold concepts for pest control in agroecosystems would thus be obtained.

Concluding Remarks

Comparison of the corresponding items listed in *Crop Productivity— Research Imperatives* of 1975 under the title "Plant Protection from Pests" shows a strong commonality with the imperatives listed above. This confirms that the frontiers of science move slowly on broad-based problems such as those of biological constraints in agriculture. However, an in-depth analysis of the progress of research in the last 10 years shows that progress has been made in solving 85% of the 33 imperatives listed in 1975 and significant progress has been made with 40% of them. Only 15% were rated as little as no progress. We judge this to be a remarkable success rate.

What of the next 10 years?

If the agricultural research community were to devote attention to these priorities and if they were given the needed resources, we predict the following applications and benefits would result: (a) significant contributions toward sustainable crop yields through soil and water resource conservation, (b) less dependence on and more rational use of pesticides, (c) increased safety through reduced pesticide exposure, (d) reduction of fossil fuel dependency, (e) new solutions for some crop pest problems currently without solutions, (f) a greater prospect for dependable food production systems, (g) attainment of yields now lost to biological constraints, and (h) increased farm profits through increased efficiency. We conclude that these potential impacts from plant health imperatives warrant the attention of the agricultural research community.

LITERATURE CITED

1. ADKISSON PL 1985 Impact of IPM on production of major crops. *In* National Symposium for IPM on Major Managed Agricultural Systems (Oct. 8–10, 1985). National Academy of Science, Washington DC
2. ANDRES LA 1981 Insects in the biological control of weeds. *In* D Pimentel, ed, CRS Handbook of Pest Management in Agriculture Vol II. CRC Press, Boca Raton, FL, pp 337–344
3. BATTENFIELD SL, MR MELSON, GE ALLEN 1983 Proceedings of the National Interdisciplinary Biological Control Conference (Feb 15–17, 1983). USDA/CSRS, Las Vegas, NV
4. BERNAYS EA 1985 Arthropods for weed control in IPM systems. *In* MA Hoy, DC Herzog, eds, Biological Control in Agricultural IPM Systems. Academic Press, Orlando, FL, pp 365–380
5. BOTRELL DR 1979 Integrated Pest Management; Council for Environmental Quality, Report. Washington DC
6. BROWNING JA, KJ FREY 1982 The multiline concept in theory and practice. *In* JF Jenkyn, RT Plumb, eds, Strategies for the Control of Cereal Disease. Blackwell, Oxford, pp 37–46
7. CHARUDATTAN R, HL WALKER 1982 Biological Control of Weeds with Plant Pathogens. John Wiley & Sons, New York
8. COOK RJ, KF BAKER 1983 The Nature and Practice of Biological Control of Plant Pathogens. American Phytopathology Society, St. Paul, MN
9. COOK RJ 1984 Root health: importance and relationship to farming practices. *In* DF Bezdicek, JF Power, DR Keeney, MJ Wright, eds, Organic Farming: Current Technology and Its Role in a Sustainable Agriculture. Special Publication No. 46. American Society of Agronomy, Madison, WI, pp 111–127
10. COOK RJ 1985 Biological control of plant pathogens: theory to application. Phytopathology 75: 25–29
11. CRAMER HH 1967 Plant protection and world production. Pflanzenschutz-nachr 20: 1–524
12. CROFT BA 1981 Use of crop protection chemicals for integrated pest management. Philos Trans R Soc Lond 295: 125–141
13. CROFT BA 1986 IPM: the agricultural environmental rationale. *In* National Symposium on IPM on Major Managed Agricultural Systems (Oct 8–10, 1985). National Academy of Sciences, Washington, DC
14. DOVER MJ, BA CROFT 1984 Getting Tough: Policy Issues in Management of Pesticide Resistance. World Research Institute Policy Paper Study 1
15. GEORGHIOU GP, T SAITO 1983 Pest Resistance to Pesticides. Plenum Press, New York
16. HENDIN PA 1983 New concepts and trends in pesticide chemistry. J Agric Food Chem 30: 201–215
17. HOY MA, DC HERZOG, eds 1985 Biological Control in Agricultural Systems. Academic Press, Orlando, FL
18. HUFFAKER CB 1980 New Technology of Pest Control. Wiley Interscience New York
19. JOHNSON LF 1962 Effect of the addition of organic amendments to soil on root knot of tomatoes; II. Relation of soil temperature, moisture, and pH. Phytopathology 52: 410–413

20. KERR A 1980 Biological control of crown gall through production of agrocin 84. Plant Dis 64: 25–30
21. KOGAN M Plant resistance in pest management. *In* RL Metcalf, WH Wickmann, eds, Introduction to Insect Pest Management. Wiley Interscience, New York, pp 93–134
22. KOMMENDAHL T 1981 Multiple grain rotations and minimum tillage in semiarid climate. *In* Proceedings of the IXth International Congress of Plant Protection, Vol I. Burgess, Minneapolis, MN, pp 67–88
23. MANKAU R 1980 Biological control of nematode pests by natural enemies. Annu Rev Phytopathol 18: 415–440
24. MENN JJ 1980 Contemporary frontiers in chemical pesticide research. J Agric Food Chem 28: 2–8
25. MENN JJ, CA HENRICK 1981 Rational and biorational design of pesticides. Philos Trans R Soc Lond 295: 57–71
26. METCALF RS 1980 Changing role of insecticides in crop protection. Annu Rev Entomol 25: 219–256
27. MORELAND DE 1980 Mechanisms of action of herbicides. Annu Rev Plant Physiol 31: 597–638
28. MULLIN CA, BA CROFT 1985 An update on development of selective pesticides favoring arthropod natural enemies. *In* MA Hoy, DC Herzog, eds, Biological Control of Agricultural IPM Systems. Academic Press, Orlando, FL, pp 123–150
29. NATIONAL ACADEMY OF SCIENCES 1985 Pesticide Resistance Management. Proceedings of Symposium and Workshop (Nov 27–29, 1984). Washington DC. In press
30. PANAGOPOULOUS CG, PS PSADILLIDAS, AS ALIVZATOS 1979 Evidence of a breakdown in the effectiveness of biological control of crown-gall. *In* B Schippers, W Gams, eds, Soil-Borne Plant Pathogens. Academic Press, London, pp 569–578
31. PIMENTEL D 1981 Energy use in plant protection. A global assessment. *In* Proceedings of the IX International Congress on Plant Protection. Burgess, Minneapolis, MN, pp 14–21
32. PIMENTEL D 1981 Introduction. *In* D Pimentel, ed, CRC Handbook of Pest Management in Agriculture, Vol I. CRC Press, Boca Raton, FL pp 3–11
33. ROELFS AP, DH CASPER, DL LONG 1984 Races of *Puccinia graminis* in the United States and Mexico during 1983. Plant Dis 68: 902–905
34. SAILER R 1981 Extent of biological and cultural control of insect pests of crops. *In* D Pimentel, ed, Handbook of Pest Management in Agriculture, Vol II. CRC Press, Boca Raton, FL, pp 57–67
35. SAYRE RM 1980 Promising organisms for biocontrol of nematodes. Plant Dis 64: 526–532
36. SCHROTH MN, JG HANCOCK 1982 Disease-suppressive soil and root-colonizing bacteria. Science 216: 1376–1381
37. SMEDEGAARD-PETERSEN V 1982 The effect of defense reactions on the energy balance and yield of resistant plants. *In* RKS Wood, ed, Active Defense Mechanisms in Plants. Plenum Press, New York, pp 229–315
38. STIMAC JL, RJ O'NEIL 1985 Integrating influences of natural enemies into models of crop/pest systems. *In* MA Hoy, DC Herzog, eds, Biological Control in Agricultural IPM Systems. Academic Press, Orlando, FL, pp 323–343
39. STIRLING GR, MF WACHTEL 1980 Mass production of *Bacillus penetrans* for the biological control of root-knot nematodes. Nematologica 26: 308–312

40. TEMPLETON GE 1982 Status of weed control with plant pathogens. *In* R Charudattan, HL Walker, eds, Biological Control of Weeds with Plant Pathogens. John Wiley & Sons, New York, pp 29–44
41. US DEPARTMENT OF AGRICULTURE 1965 Losses in Agriculture. USDA Handbook
42. VAN GUNDY SE 1985 Biological control of nematodes: status and prospects in agricultural IPM systems. *In* MA Hoy and DC Herzog, eds, Biological Control in Agricultural IPM Systems. Academic Press, Orlando, FL, pp 455–465
43. VANDERPLANK JE 1982 Host-Pathogen Interactions in Plant Diseases. Academic Press, New York
44. WALKER JC, R SMITH 1930 Effect of environmental factors upon resistance of cabbage to yellow. J Agric Res 41: 1–15
45. WOLFE MS, JA BARRETT 1980 Can we lead the pathogen astray? Plant Dis 64: 148–155
46. ZIMDAHL RL Extent of mechanical, culture and other nonchemical methods of weed control. *In* D. Pimentel, ed, Handbook of Pest Management in Agriculture, Vol II. CRC Press, Boca Raton, FL, pp 79–83

Environmental Constraints

Submitted on behalf of the group by:

JAMES M. DAVIDSON   ANDREW D. HANSON
             DONALD R. NIELSEN

Physical and chemical environmental stresses such as water deficits, temperature extremes, mineral nutrient deficiencies, salinity, and toxic constituents are primary constraints that prevent full expression of the genetic potential of crops with respect to both quantity and quality of yield (10). Moreover, there is growing evidence that climatic change is accentuating such stresses in some regions, for instance the increasing severity of winters in the Eastern United States (15, 21) and the increasing frequency of drought in the Sub-Saharan region of Africa (18, 42, 61, 62).

Ten years ago during the first conference on Crop Productivity, six working groups, composed primarily of biological scientists, focused their attention on basic inputs or resources required for maximizing crop yields. Attenion was given to improvement of the mineral nutrition of crops (N, P, water, and essential elements), to protection of crops from pests and environmental uncertainties, and to basic research aimed at a better understanding of plant development processes. The general philosophy implicitly adopted during the conference was that the level of crop productivity is highly correlated with the resources provided, and that if the research imperatives identified were addressed during the coming decade, there was a high probability of enhancing technologies for increasing crop productivity. A primary emphasis at the first conference was the improvement of knowledge of basic biological processes that contribute to or regulate crop productivity.

The emphasis on plant biology can be seen in the imperatives developed by the Environmental Stress group in 1975, which were:

1. Manipulate crops or their environments in ways which avoid or reduce stress injury and increase productivity.
   a. Develop crop management systems and cultural practices which reduce exposure of crops to stress;
   b. Reduce stress by modifying the microclimate in the vicinity of the crop;
   c. Develop treatments (*e.g.* chemicals) to increase stress resistance or to facilitate recovery from stress.
2. Exploit the genetic potential for developing new varieties of crops resistant to environmental stress.
   a. Collect and evaluate germ plasm of crop plant species for stress resistance;

    b. Develop criteria for screening large seedling populations for stress resistance;

    c. Increase the level of tolerance to yield-limiting stresses in food crop varieties.

3. Elucidate the basic principles of stress injury and resistance and evaluate the scope and nature of stress damage.

    a. Characterize the basic mechanisms whereby stress factors injure plants;

    b. Investigate the basic mechanisms of resistance to and avoidance of stress injury;

    c. Achieve an understanding of plant growth and productivity under stress.

The physicochemical constraints on crops can be alleviated by genetic modification of the plant and by environmental modification, including those modifications which change plant phenotype. Although there has been progress in understanding and applying genetic and environmental modification during the past 10 years, the research imperatives identified in 1975 remain in large measure valid and it is vital to maintain consistency in pursuit of these enduring imperatives. However, several factors dictate some revision of these imperatives. These factors are: (a) an increased environmental and societal requirement for improved efficiency in the use of all inputs to agriculture, (b) a sustained productivity within existing or shrinking agricultural lands, and (c) quality in the end products rather than an emphasis on all-out production (24, 59).

In 1972, the U.N. Conference on the Human Environment signaled growing concern regarding the sensitive and finite nature of the environment, especially when one considers the increasing world population and rising per capita demand for food and industrial goods. Degradation of our environmental resources (air, water, and soil) is accelerating because constraints of anthropogenic origin (SO_2, NO_x [oxides of nitrogen], ground water contamination, and acid rain) are being added to the natural constraints (temperature extremes, water excesses and deficiencies, and salinity) which have always beset agriculture, and which were the primary environmental factors considered during the first Crop Productivity conference. Thus, the imperatives identified a decade ago no longer describe all the environmental constraints that exist in agroecosystems in 1985 or those anticipated during the next decade. Environmental constraints require a wider view of the environment than that traditionally adopted by agricultural scientists.

Imperatives I and II (to be stated later) are concerned with traditional or natural constraints that are imposed on crops and their immediate environment. These two imperatives are focused on understanding physical and chemical environmental constraints and those genetic traits that might be identified and transferred to plants to provide avoidance or reduction of a natural constraint or stress.

A major factor that has limited research progress in the last 10 years is failure to appreciate fully and utilize the extent to which plants are able to adapt or cope with environmental stresses. This is true for a range of stresses. Advances in understanding plant adaptation stress will require using different time scales (seconds to months) as well as integration of research findings over a range of organizational levels (from subcellular to plant community). Advances that may further the progress in the next decade include the arrival of recombinant DNA technology as a means for genetic manipulation of plants, offering a new research tool and ultimately perhaps a novel set of breeding methods (34); and an increasing recognition that many environmental constraints (*e.g.* rainfall, temperature) are stochastic in nature (32). Also, crop productivity investigations must be designed with greater emphasis on the scale of observations stemming from autocorrelations or other regionalized variable or covariable analyses rather than, at the outset, assuming that all observations are spatially and temporally independent. Techniques to better monitor ecosystems also are needed.

Imperatives III through V are concerned with agroecosystems (field and regional level) that are constrained on a short- and/or long-term basis as a result of environmental chemical impacts resulting from man's activities and the need to reduce their presence and/or potential for degrading natural resources.

Human activities tend to have a degrading impact on the environment at local, regional, and global scales as resources are consumed and/or wastes generated. These factors affect the quality of soil, water, and air, and impact agricultural production. Having managed soil resources for countless human generations for the primary objective of food production, and having judged the success of this management on crop yield or "output," what opportunity exists for taking measurements at or below the soil surface to signal the long-term consequences of present-day agricultural technology to ascertain the relative "health" of land and water resources? With agriculture being viewed as irregular cyclic perturbations of a huge matrix of interdependent solar-driven ecological cycles, it is apparent that an opportunity exists to improve the management of our natural resources not only at regional and global spatial and temporal scales but at local scales as well.

The results and impacts of agricultural, technological and urban activities on a local scale are beginning to be contemplated or realized at regional and global scales. Modification of the stratospheric ozone layer, emission of NO_x from agricultural soils, decline of topsoil organic matter, accelerated erosion of topsoils, increased aerosol deposition, and rising atmospheric levels of CO_2 are several major concerns of this conference. These environmental concerns are becoming increasingly important and merit special attention.

Changes in environmental quality and the impact of such changes on crop production have scale characteristics, which differ in space and time. To understand and to predict how environmental constraints affect crop production, there is a need for measurements that can be integrated in terms of space and time. New technology for achieving these objectives will have to be developed. Accurate long-term monitoring for trends is a critical environmental need if reasonable policy and management decisions are to be established.

Because the nature and magnitude of environmental constraints to crop production vary from site to site and with time at the same site, no attempt is made in this report to rank the relative importance of different constraints. Also, each individual constraint has not been discussed as comprehensively as it was in 1975. Rather, specific examples are highlighted where progress is being made and where opportunities or needs exist.

Research Imperative I. Develop a Thorough Understanding of the Physiological Effects of, and Responses to, Environmental Stress on Plants in Order to Manipulate Genetically Crops for Greater Adaptation to Environmental Constraints

This imperative involves understanding the adaptation of crops to environmental stresses. Directing crop evolution at the target of stress adaptation depends on a number of components that are set forth in the objectives below. These objectives apply to a broad range of environmental constraints, and make no distinction between classical and molecular genetic technologies as a means to achieve them.

1. Understand the Mechanisms Underlying Stress Resistance, Stress Injury and the Efficiency with Which Environmental Resources Are Used in Growth

Stress Resistance and Injury. Research on stress resistance and injury is now passing from a descriptive to an analytical phase. Advances are being made in dissecting the causal physiological and biochemical mechanisms of resistance to, and damage by, environmental extremes. The following examples illustrate what is being achieved for a few cases.

As plants first experience stress, they generally respond in an active manner that tends to lessen the effects of the stress. It has become clear that for legumes, drought and high light stress can be reduced by certain leaf movements (37) and that drought or salinity stress in certain wild species can be tolerated by an induction of crassulacean acid metabolism (60). Similarly, accumulation of solutes (osmotic adjustment) can lead to turgor maintenance under drought and salt stress (41, 40). With air pollutant injury, stomatal closure avoids further injury (27) and in waterlogging stress, the induction of the enzymes of anaerobic glycolysis in roots leads to a tolerance of the stress (54). It is probable that these responses to counteract stresses involve a significant bioenergetic commitment or sacrifice by the plant (56). This is an area of uncertainty that needs clarifying.

The more severe and the longer the environmental stress, the greater the extent to which physiological processes of plants are driven into dysfunction. The development of these sequential injury events is only beginning to be understood. For instance, under an atmosphere of oxidant air pollutant, the permeability of the cell membrane is increased, leading to a drop in turgor pressure and an accumulation of water outside the cell. In this case, the dysfunction is permanent and leads to necrosis and an irreversible loss of photosynthetic capacity (28). For lesser injury, partial restoration of dysfunction to a normal state may require the expenditure of considerable resources, such that the plant may be unable to avoid successfully further stresses, such as O_3 injury and subsequent insect attack (22). However, quantitative understanding is completely lacking in this area.

Efficiency of Resource Use in Plant Growth. Efficiency has many facets. In general, efficiency is defined as the total output to total input ratio. In a more practical sense, efficiency is defined as the crop yield per unit of resource used, such as water use efficiency (kg dry matter/kg H_2O transpired) or nitrogen use efficiency (kg dry matter/unit nitrogen absorbed by the plant). In the economic sense, nitrogen use efficiency means to the farmer yield per unit of nitrogen applied. The specific efficiency of each crop can be optimized only under localized economic and environmental constraints. We need to understand the biological basis of output/input ratios for the major nutrients and water. Thus, understanding efficiency requires a knowledge of how resources are acquired and utilized for growth. We also need to know how stresses alter efficiency. In this way, it will be possible to determine, ultimately, the biological cost of stresses. There is a growing number of instances where significant intraspecific genetic variation for efficiency characteristics can be found. For instance, differences in plant water use efficiency have recently been demonstrated among wheat cultivars (23), and rice varieties (38a).

Potential Research Applications of Recombinant DNA. Recombinant DNA technology potentially provides novel opportunities to explore physiological mechanisms of stress injury and resistance. However, two major deficiencies limit the power of recombinant DNA techniques as research tools for understanding crop responses to stress. First, routine transformation and regeneration systems for most major crops are still lacking. Second, and probably more important, there are very few genes yet identified and isolated that are rational candidates for manipulation (9). It is therefore essential that basic studies of injury and resistance mechanisms be pursued wherever possible for the identification and isolation of the genes responsible.

2. Determine for Particular Environments the Physiological Characteristics that Help the Plant Avoid or Tolerate Stress

Past research has emphasized simple, constant stress situations and has often treated resistance traits as if they were a constant feature of the phenotype. However, environmental stresses are characteristically unpredictable with respect to time of onset, severity, and duration. Similarly, physiological traits conferring resistance to environmental stresses are complex, both in the genetic sense and in the way in which the expression is neither constant at all growth stages, nor independent of previous stress history (57). Also, a single environmental stress such as adverse temperature or salinity may have several facets. For example, temperature stress may affect leaf metabolism at entirely different thresholds than it does for pollen development or fruit set; likewise, salinity stress may be a result of specific ion toxicity, osmotic effects or interferences with nutrient uptake mechanisms. Stated another way, it may be predicted that because yield is quantitatively inherited and dependent on many components, stress may affect each component differently. Thus, the integrative relationships between specific growth stages and environmental stresses must be understood at both organismic and physiological-biochemical levels. The next step—using this under-standing of plant-environment interactions to define what kinds of resistance traits would help in what environment—needs to be taken to implant current and new knowledge into crop improvement and manage-ment strategies.

3. Demonstrate the Importance of Physiological Characteristics Considered to Be Adaptive before Recommending Them as Selection Criteria

Many morphological and physiological traits have been identified and recommended as selection criteria to reduce the impact of environmental constraints. However, rarely has the adaptive value been tested and demonstrated prior to the recommendation. One example is proline accumulation in response to drought stress. Tests made by Hanson *et al.* (26) failed to demonstrate that proline had any adaptive value in water-stressed plants. The absence of any demonstration of the value of suggested adaptive traits has generally led plant breeders to ignore these suggestions. In contrast, showing the importance of a morphological trait (17) resulted in its inclusion as one of several selection criteria to enhance winter survival of two subtropical forage legumes. Likewise, the recog-nition of osmotic adjustment as beneficial to grain yield in water-stressed wheat (40, 41) has led to it being used as a selection criterion in dryland wheat breeding in Australia.

Demonstration of the value of putatively adaptive traits is not simple. Although comparison between different cultivars or species that differ in a specific trait has often been used, it is usually difficult, if not impossible, to attribute results to the effect of any one trait. Development of near-isogenic lines or populations is the most desirable means of demonstrat-ing the adaptive value of traits, but few plant physiologists or plant breeders have resources to invest in this endeavor. The advent of recom-binant DNA technology and somaclonal variation may offer exciting opportunities for evaluating traits that are simply inherited. Another, but less satisfactory approach, is to establish internal consistency in the correlations between the presence of the trait, the intervening processes and yield (*e.g.* see Ref. 40).

4. Manipulate the Genetic Composition of Plants to Incorporate Desired Traits, Using Appropriate Technology

Genetic manipulations can in principle be accomplished at the molecular, cellular or whole plant level. In practice the method adopted will depend on various factors, including: basic understanding of the genome, number of genes involved, heritability, mode of reproduction, ability of cultured cells to express desired traits and to regenerate plants and availability of transformation systems. In some cases, manipulation by classical techniques at the whole-plant level will remain the best and perhaps the only route. However, although molecular and cellular technologies are not yet available for most crop species, this situation is likely to change in the next decade (12, 46). It is thus crucial to determine whether, and how, useful environmental stress-resistance traits could be handled by these developing techniques. Clearly the traits most amenable to molecular and cellular approaches are metabolic and physiological ones governed by very small numbers of genes. But the majority of valuable traits are likely to be polygenic, in which case molecular and cell approaches will be applicable only if individual components can be identified. A strong precedent for the effectiveness of dissecting a complex trait into manageable components is winter hardiness in cereals (45). In this case, several genetically distinct protective mechanisms contribute to total hardiness. They can be distinguished by screening tests for a biophysical and biochemical basis that can be linked with molecular genetics.

Research Imperative II. Develop a Thorough Understanding of How Environmental Modifications Can Minimize Constraints on Crop Productivity

To manipulate effectively the environment around the plant and improve cultural practices, it is necessary to understand the environment and how the plant "senses" it. To this end, three objectives are addressed.

1. Determination of the Way Plants React to Environmental Constraints and How These Affect Crop Growth in the Field

Although plants respond to the environment and environmental changes in a recognizable and consistent manner, the mechanisms whereby they "sense" their environment and transduce this into a response have received only limited study in the past decade. Study of these mechanisms is therefore a priority.

Leaves of several plants follow the movement of the sun such that they are normal to the incident beam (solar tracking), thereby maximizing the interception of radiant energy. Studies have shown that the leaves "sense" the change in sun angle and that changes in turgor of the pulvinus provide the mechanism for changes in leaf angle (55). Likewise, many plants respond to change in air humidity (atmospheric drought) by changing their stomatal aperture. Mechanisms whereby leaves react to the change in atmospheric humidity and transduce this into a change in turgor of the guard cell appear to reside in the epidermis, but full details of the mechanism are unclear. Until recently, soil water deficits were considered to reduce leaf growth and leaf photosynthesis through changes in meristematic and guard cell turgor arising from the lowering of the water potential in the leaf. Recent evidence clearly shows that leaf growth and stomatal conductance are reduced despite a lack of any change in leaf turgor (39); rather, regulation of leaf growth and photosynthesis appears to reside in the root and the signal for changes in the root environment arising from a change in the balance of plant growth regulators (19).

Little is known of how plants respond to and transduce other environmental stresses. However, the above illustrations suggest that progress has been made and point to potential opportunities for research. Such studies will require experimentation under carefully controlled environmental conditions, but in order for their importance for crop growth in the field to be elucidated, they will ultimately require studies under field conditions.

2. Evaluate the Effect of Modifying the Root and Aerial Evironment to Mitigate the Impact of Stresses

Root Environment. The root environment is now recognized as just as important as the aerial environment for controlling plant growth (8a). Removing adverse factors of the root environment can be an important means of improving crop productivity.

Manipulating the root environment by removing excess water through drainage has long been recognized as a means of increasing yields in soils where episodic waterlogging occurs. High mechanical impedance also restricts root growth. Recent evidence suggests that deep tillage of light textured soils that compact under mechanization can improve yields by 30% on an average (31). In water-limited environments this results from a deeper root penetration, greater water extraction, and delay in the development of plant water deficits.

Thus, the importance of environmental constraints on root growth and development is highlighted. Yet, because of the difficulties of observation and measurement, studies on the root environment and root development are often avoided. There is a clear need for studies of root function as well as shoot function under environmental stresses and a need for the development of methods for the measurement of the root environment and root function, particularly in the field. Methods such as three-

dimensional observations of root systems using nuclear magnetic resonance (NMR) imaging offer new opportunities (9a, 52).

Aerial Environment. Aerial environment constraints to crop productivity result from deficiencies or excesses of factors such as solar radiation,
CO_2 concentration, temperature, humidity, and wind. Modifying the
aerial environment can augment the benefits gained by genetic modifications of plants. Moreover, in many cropping systems it may be the
most practical way of alleviating environmental constraints.

Traditionally, the aerial environment of crops has been modified
through passive devices such as windbreaks and shade screens, and active
devices such as heaters and wind machines. For example, rice grain yield
has been increased by 10 to 15% in Northern Japan by windbreaks that
raise the temperature of paddy water and plants by up to 2 to 3°C (38).
However, new environmental problems are arising that require new
emphasis on quantifying the effectiveness of traditional and novel modifications under a range of adverse weather conditions. For instance,
winter temperatures have been steadily decreasing in the Eastern United
States over the last 30 years (15, 21). Thus, cold protection is of even
greater concern now that the probability of killing freezes is increasing.
Irrigation techniques have been used to reduce frost damage in fruit trees
and vegetable crops, but it is often ineffective or even damaging unless
it is managed according to weather conditions. Consequently, quantitative studies are required for plant protection from extreme cold temperatures; specifically, analytical studies on energy balance, turbulence, and
heat transport mechanisms are needed to quantify and predict the effects
of modifying the aerial environment for crop yield protection.

3. Develop Cultural Practices and Crop Management Systems that Mitigate Responses to Stress

To utilize established knowledge and new progress in understanding
mechanisms of stress injury and resistance, research is required that will
develop cultural practices and crop management systems which reduce
or avoid adverse responses to environmental stresses. The research
approaches should include development of predictive capabilities; *i.e.*
general crop models that simulate the effects of various stresses. Ideally,
the models should predict phenotypic responses to all relevant environmental factors and several types of environmental constraints such as
soil water deficits, salinity, high temperature, low temperature, high
vapor pressure deficits, and atmospheric gases (both essential and nox-
ious).

Research Imperatives III. Determine Impacts of Agricultural Practices on the Environment

Soil, water, and atmospheric resources are consumed in food and fiber
production. In addition, agricultural practices may themselves contribute

natural and anthropogenic chemicals to these resources that in some cases can seriously degrade the environment. The extent to which the environment is affected needs to be continually assessed on a local, regional, and global scale.

1. Quantify the Rates of Erosion and Depletion of Soil Organic Matter as a Function of Agricultural Management Practice, Soil, and Landscape

Rates of soil loss and depletion of soil organic matter and soil nutrients are comparatively small on an annual basis, but their cumulative effects over decades may result in significant degradation in the quality of soil resources. In contrast, the impacts of soil erosion and subsquent runoff of sediments, nutrients, and organic matter are more quickly perceived by the public in accelerating eutrophication of streams and lakes. Although soil and water conservation practices are fostered, soil loss is a serious problem in many regions of the United States where intensive cultivation of what was once native grasslands and forested lands is practiced.

There is a need to assess quantitatively the losses of soil, organic matter, and plant nutrients as well as to study their movement into the environment by taking into account the soil and landscape, cropping systems, tillage practices, crop residue management, mineralization of organic matter and plant uptake, irrigation and drainage, and climate and the stochastic nature of the weather. Such a quantitative assessment can best be achieved using a systems-based computer simulation model, *e.g.* the U.S. Department of Agriculture's Erosion Productivity Impact Calculation (EPIC). This and other modeling approaches need to be field validated at benchmark locations using site-specific practices and conditions.

2. Determine the Extent of Depletion and Contamination of Surface and Ground Waters by Nutrients, Salinity, Pesticides, and Trace Elements

Agriculture withdraws about 85% of our annual water supply for irrigation in the Western United States (44). Unlike other uses of water, irrigated agriculture contributes significantly to the depletion of our water resources because of its comparative high use. Of particular concern are the regional water shortages manifested by ground water depletion in the Great Plains and Western United States.

Moreover, agricultural practices may contribute to the degradation in quality of surface and ground water through runoff and percolation (35). These agricultural return flows contain both natural and anthropogenic chemicals. Surface runoffs may contain significant loadings of sediments, nitrogen, phosphorus, and pesticide residues. In contrast, percolation and drainage waters may contain significant amounts of nitrate, dissolved mineral salts, and trace elements. Depending on the dilution volume of receiving water bodies and unit mass emission rates, these chemicals may degrade surface and ground water supplies to an extent that the receiving water is less usable for agriculture and/or other uses.

The salt load in irrigation return flows is highly dependent on the quality of the irrigation water, leaching fraction and evapotranspiration losses, and effective rainfall as well as other sources and salt sinks. It is clearly evident that salt emission from gypsiferous salt-affected land contributes substantial salt loadings to the environment.

It is also common to find hazardous chemicals such as pesticide residues in agricultural return flows even though the pesticides were applied according to recommended methods and rates of application. The detection of ethylene dibromide (EDB) and 1,2-dibromo-3-chloropropane (DBCP) and other confirmed animal carcinogens in ground waters are of prime concern (48). In addition to pesticides, other natural and anthropogenic sources of trace elements such as selenium, boron, cadmium, arsenic, and molybdenum are being detected in surface and ground water supplies (20). The presence of these metals and metalloids in subsurface drainage waters and perched water tables are of concern because of their bioavailability and bioaccumulation in aquatic and terrestrial food chains (11).

In recent years, it has also become increasingly clear that some of the nitrogen added with chemical fertilizers, animal manures, and municipal and industrial wastewaters is being leached to the ground water (14). Surface waters can also be degraded by nitrogen and phosphorus discharges resulting in eutrophication.

Contamination of water supplies must be continually assessed and when degradation occurs, agricultural management practices must be developed that are environmentally sound. Because of the complexity of chemical reactivity and mobility in agroecosystems, additional research is needed to predict the effects of alternative agricultural practices taking into account reaction rates, solute transport and travel times, spatial and temporal variabilities, and the numerous sources and sinks to name but a few variables.

3. Quantify Gaseous Emissions from Agroecosystems and Their Possible Adverse Effect on the Atmosphere and Climate

Agricultural practices contribute a number of gases that can affect the atmosphere. They include oxides of nitrogen, ammonia, and methane.

The emission of nitrogen compounds may affect climate and stratospheric ozone contents on a global scale and lakes and forests on a local and regional scale. Nitrous oxide is produced in agroecosystems as a result of microbial denitrification of nitrate under relatively anaerobic conditions. Increased fertilizer use has led to greater nitrous oxide losses to the atmosphere. In addition, acidification of soils as a consequence of ammoniacal fertilizer usage, increased use of legume crops and atmospheric deposition is apparently increasing denitrification.

Ammonia volatilization losses are especially large from fresh manures as well as significant losses where aqueous ammonia fertilizer is applied on neutral to alkaline soils. In addition, clearing of forested lands and burning of vegetation results in large losses of nitrogen, especially in tropical forests where much of the nutrients are found in the above-ground biomass.

The production of paddy rice contributes methane to the atmosphere. Methane is one of the end products of anoxic decomposition processes prevailing in paddy rice fields. Increases in emission of nitrous oxide and methane may lead to a global warming as high as that predicted from increased CO_2 concentrations in the atmosphere. Previous concerns that increased nitrous oxide production would lead to decreased concentrations of stratosphere ozone concentrations seem to be less serious.

The rise in global atmospheric CO_2 concentrations has been attributed by most studies to burning of fossil fuel (16). Other sources include the biosphere. The rapid deforestation of tropical forests and burning as a part of the clearing practice has also contributed to a rise in global CO_2. Although the direct effect of rising CO_2 will be to increase photosynthesis and crop productivity (1), there is some uncertainty among scientists about the other environmental consequences of continued increases in atmospheric CO_2. However, there is general agreement that this trend of rising CO_2 will lead to an increase in air and sea-surface temperatures and a change in rainfall patterns (13).

Clearly, the emission of gaseous compounds from agricultural practices is of concern from a local to global scale. There is a need to monitor continually for this quality of the atmosphere and to develop quantitative estimates of gaseous emissions.

Research Imperative IV. Understand the Impacts of Anthropogenic Chemicals on Agroecosystems

Chemicals released by man's activities may adversely affect agricultural production as well as the quality of the harvested product. These chemicals are transported from sources primarily through atmospheric processes and are deposited on agricultural ecosystems. Chemicals can be released into surface or ground waters and arrive in agroecosystems through irrigation waters. These chemicals may enter the plant system directly from the atmosphere (through the leaves) or through the soil (roots). Four primary concerns are identified as deserving intensive study.

1. Determine Direct and Indirect Effects of Increasing Atmospheric CO_2 on Agroecosystems

Increasing CO_2 concentration affects plant growth and development (1, 36) and may also induce climatic changes (13), thereby affecting plant

growth (33, 53). Thus, increasing CO_2 concentrations are perceived to
have both direct and indirect effects on agroecosystems.

Carbon dioxide concentration could double over the next 100 years
based on current projected fossil fuel uses (16). Reviews and recent
experiments show that a doubling of CO_2 could increase plant biomass
and seed yield of some C_3 crops by more than 30% (3, 33). Positive CO_2
effects include: (a) larger plants and plant parts, (b) increased leaf turgor,
(c) decreased stomatal conductance, (d) decreased transpirational flux
density (51), and (e) increased storage of carbohydrates in leaf. Increased
growth and yield occurred even when nutrient supply was below normal.
Effects of elevated CO_2 on crop growth are global because increasing CO_2
concentration induces partial stomatal closure and may alleviate the
negative impact of other environmental constraints i.e. O_3 (27) or high
vapor pressure deficits (4).

Rising atmospheric CO_2 also may cause climate modifications, including an average increase in global surface temperatures (13). Lower
stomatal conductances may help alleviate effects of climatological
drought, but several additional questions include: (a) can plant breeding
increase the harvest indexes beyond those presently expected using
increased CO_2; (b) will preferential stimulation of C_3 plants encourage
better competition, production and survival of legumes in grass-legume
mixtures (pastures and range lands); (c) will forage quality be affected;
(d) will insect and/or disease infestation be enhanced or reduced; and (e)
will soil organic matter and litter be increased and thus improve soil
properties? Additionally, possible interactions of increasing CO_2 with
other components of the agricultural production system and other environmental constraints need to be studied (67). Finally, the long-term
consequences of an increasing CO_2 concentration on agroecosystems on
a global basis needs to be assessed.

2. Assess the Effects of Photochemically Produced Ozone on Agroecosystems

Ozone is both an essential component of the stratosphere (protecting
life from UV radiation) and a natural component of the troposphere (66).
Additionally, through photochemical reactions involving NO_x and hydro-
carbons, O_3 is produced as a direct result of man's activities (64, 65). Due
to long distance transport and periods of air stagnation, O_3 concentrations during the growing season are sufficiently high to cause crop losses
throughout the United States (7). Estimates of yield reductions have
been reported as negligible to as high as 25% depending upon the crop,
the location and the season (2, 29).

Ozone is considered to be one of the most damaging anthropogenic
chemicals to agroecosystems in the United States and Canada (30, 64,
65). It is an important problem in all industrialized countries and will
probably become a global problem as less developed countries become
more industrialized (30). Currently we know that O_3 affects crops and

crop systems in a number of ways: (a) stomatal functions may be directly affected; (b) membranes are affected as are a number of cellular processes; (c) photosynthesis is reduced and partitioning favors vegetative growth of the top over the root or reproductive growth; (d) plant response to O_3 is affected by both abiotic and biotic stresses; (e) stomatal closure, whatever the cause, acts as a protective mechanism; (f) pesticides can protect plants from O_3 damage; and (g) species and cultivar sensitivity are known to be different (30, 63–65).

Available data pertaining to O_3 effects on agroecosystems justify an intensive effort to study systematically and to model the effects of O_3 on crop production systems (30, 63–65). Likewise, research should be undertaken to identify ways to manipulate the crop or environment to study the impact of O_3 and to increase production efficiency (49). A systematic study should include: (a) measurement of O_3 flux to the plant and uptake by the plant; (b) determine mechanism(s) of plant response to O_3 and identify resistance mechanisms; (c) understand effects at the cellular, whole plant and crop systems scale; (d) determine how abiotic and biotic factors affect crop response to O_3; and (e) develop different levels of models to assess local, national and global impacts on crops (30, 63–65).

3. Determine the Effects of Acidic Deposition (Acid Rain), Heavy Metals, and Other Atmospheric Deposits on Agroecosystems

The principal components of acidic deposition are SO_2 and nitrogen oxides (NO_x—found principally as nitrogen dioxide [NO_2] and nitrogen oxide [NO]) (5, 7, 8). These are the precursors for the principal components of acid precipitation (SO_4^{2-} and NO_3^-) and are the primary chemicals of concern to crop production, when they reach the plant as a gas in acid rain or as "dry deposition" (5, 29). In parts of Europe, these gases are the principal atmospheric chemicals affecting crop production (63). These gases are emitted in large quantities from power stations, smelter operations, and other industrial sources (5). The automobile also is a primary source of NO_x. Heavy metals and other atmospheric chemicals are principally local problems associated with specific sources. Heavy metals and soluble components of particulate matter when dissolved in water or on leaf surfaces, may enter the plant through the leaf or be taken up through the root (5, 29).

Research has identified SO_2 and NO_2 as the important phytotoxic constituents of acidic deposition (8). Sulfur dioxide affects the plant at several levels and has been shown to affect agricultural production in the vicinity of large sources of SO_2 emissions (29, 63). Long-term exposures of plants to NO_2 has affected plant growth and productivity (63). Recent research has shown that plants may be more sensitive to mixtures of these acid gases than to the individual gas (50). Both gases trend to increase the sensitivity of some plants to O_3. Although SO_2 dose-plant response information is available, very little research has been done in the field. There are no clear estimates of crop losses associated with either SO_2 or NO_2 (30).

Although considerable fundamental research has been done with SO_2, there is no clear picture of the plant response mechanism (63). However, there is considerable information on the effect of SO_2 on plant growth and productivity. Numerous studies have attempted to define SO_2 flux to the leaf surface under a variety of environmental conditions (63). Reduction in plant growth and yield has been identified under some atmospheric conditions, but no attempts have been made to assess effects on a regional scale (30).

Although some growth and yield reductions are reported for NO_2, little definitive research exists. The primary areas of interest are associated with NO_2 when it occurs in mixture with SO_2 and/or O_3. Under these conditions, a number of studies have identified reduced biomass, flowering and yield for several crop species (50).

Research should focus on the interactions of SO_2, NO_2, simulated acidic precipitation, and heavy metals on the response of plants to O_3; biochemical and physiological studies should be undertaken at the cellular and whole plant level. Additional research should be directed at understanding growth dynamics and the effects on crop yields. Where possible, biotic and abiotic stress interactions should be investigated (5, 7, 8, 29).

4. Determine Effects of Chemicals in Surface and Ground Waters Used as Irrigation Water for Agroecosystems

Chemical dumps, septic tanks, and leakage from other contaminated areas may lower the quality of ground water. Likewise, sewage (especially untreated) releases from chemical industries, and surface runoff may adversely affect the quality of surface waters. Irrigation water from such contaminated sources may adversely affect crop production. Studies should include effects at the rhizosphere-soil-interface so that effects on soils, soil microorganisms, and root functions can be determined. If uptake occurs, direct effects on the plant should be studied at all levels.

Research Imperative V. Develop Alternative Cropping Resource Management Strategies to Minimize Environmental Constraints

Modern agricultural practices have, in some cases, impacted the environment in a negative manner. These consequences have been discussed in the introduction. To assess alternative cropping and resource management strategies to counter these issues, we must have a quantitative understanding of the interactions between the environment and plant (Imperatives I and II). Further, we must optimize crop productivity with due consideration to the environment (soil, water, and air). For example, there may be a reduction in yield because a certain pesticide must be withheld at a particular time on a particular site in order to avoid pollution of surface or ground water. Prediction of the problem would permit alternatives such as a selection of another crop or cultivar not affected by the pest or planting at a different time in order to minimize yield reduction by the pest. In order to predict properly the fate of a particular pesticide, the environment (*e.g.* soil temperature and moisture) must be characterized as well as biochemical reactions and and their rates. This characterization requires an interdisciplinary effort.

There are several alternative cropping and resource management strategies. These include: (a) tillage (from no till to full cultivation); (b) land forming; (c) fertilization (amount, timing, placement and formulation); (d) herbicides; (e) pesticide application; (f) irrigation (timing, distribution and amount); (g) crop and cultivar selection; (h) plant population; (i) planting date and depth; (j) residue management; (k) cropping sequence; and (l) intercropping or mixed cropping (25, 58).

Any one or any combination of these strategies could be used to optimize crop productivity (or profit) and to minimize specific adverse effects on environmental resources. A matrix of field experiments does not provide an efficient methodology to address these issues. Further, the complexity is considerably increased by the stochastic nature of the weather, spatial variability of solid and weather, and consideration that the environment extends beyond the boundaries of the individual farm. For example, fertilizers and pesticides from an individual field may become the contaminant in a water reservoir serving another farm or urban community. A systematic approach that considers the full range of interaction between the environment and the crop given a specific management strategy must be applied (43). An integrative approach needs to be developed which permits optimization and results in quantitative projections (47). This would result in quantitative analyses of various management strategies with different sets of scenarios and permit an analysis of risk due to the stochastic nature of the weather.

The world's native forests are being cleared at an accelerating pace. Much of the land is infertile and being settled by subsistence farmers. Large international lending agencies support land clearing schemes but do not provide guidelines for making impoverished soils productive. Without machinery or fertilizer, the farmer on impoverished soil has little chance of extricating himself from the grip of poverty. The land is unproductive and therefore neglected; neglect leads to erosion and exposure of acid and even more impoverished subsoil. Failure in development schemes cannot be eliminated but repeated errors that are predictable must be minimized. The knowledge and technology to prevent failures are largely known. Lending agencies and governments do not apply what is known because the knowledge has not been organized in a manner that is understandable or useful.

Answers to the above questions demand interdisciplinary efforts and collaboration with agencies who need precise answers to complex questions. In many parts of the world, subsistence agriculture is practiced by

212   WORKING GROUP PAPERS

a large number of the population. These areas are typified by low resource
inputs, and poor soil and water resources. In these situations, the adverse
effects to the environment by farm management is secondary to short-
term crop productivity. However, irreversible damage to the soil or water
base must be avoided. The flexibility in applying management strategies
is reduced in these situations. Social and cultural constraints play a major
role in the kinds of management strategies to be considered. Crop risk is
a major consideration for the subsistance farmer in a cropping strategy
(18). Management strategies which impact the environment the least can
be applied to farming systems; however, social and cultural constraints
also must be considered.

LITERATURE CITED

1. ACOCK B, L H ALLEN JR 1985 Crop responses to elevated carbon dioxide
   concentrations. *In* BR Strain, JD Cure, eds, Direct Effect of Increasing
   Carbon Dioxide on Vegetation, Chapter 4. US Department of Energy
   Report. In press
2. ADAMS RM, SA HAMILTON, BA MCCALL 1984 The Economic Effects of
   Ozone on Agriculture, EPA-600/3-84-090, US EPA. Environmental Research Laboratory, Corvallis, OR
3. ALLEN LH JR, KJ BOOTE, JW JONES, PH JONES, RR VALLE, B ACOCK,
   HH ROGERS, RC DAHLMAN 1986 Response of vegetation to rising CO_2:
   photosynthesis, yield, and potential for sequestering carbon, TRO.
   DOE7ER/60001-1, US Department Energy, Carbon Dioxide Research
   Division. Avail: National Technical Information Service, Springfield, VA.
   In press
4. ALLEN LH JR, PH JONES, JW JONES 1985 Rising atmospheric CO_2 and
   evapotranspiration. *In* National Conference on Advances in Evapotranspiration. American Society of Agrictural Engineers, Chicago, IL (December 16–17), pp 13–27
5. ALTSHULLER AP, RA LINTHURST, eds 1984 The Acidic Deposition Phenomenon and Its Effects: Critical Assessment Review Papers. Vol I—Atmospheric Sciences, EPA-600/8-83-016AF, Vol II—Effects Sciences, EPA-
   600/8-83-016F. US EPA, Office of Research and Development, Washington, DC
6. Anonymous 1983 Changing Climate. Report of The Carbon Dioxide Assessment Committee. National Research Council, NAS; National Academy
   Press, Washington DC
7. Anonymous 1984 Acid Rain and Transported Air Pollutants: Implications
   for Public Policy. OTA-0-204, Office of Technology Assessment. US Congress, Washington, DC (June)
8. Anonymous 1984 National Acid Precipitation Assessment Program: Operating Research Plan, Vol 1, Research Framework. Interagency Task Force
   on Acid Precipitation, Washington DC
8a. ARKIN GF, HM TAYLOR, eds 1981 Modifying the Root Environment to
   Reduce Crop Stress. American Society of Agricultural Engineers Monograph No. 4, St. Joseph, MI
9. BARTON KA, WJ BRILL 1983 Prospects in plant genetic engineering. Science
   219: 671–676

9a. BOTTOMLEY PA, HH ROGERS, TH FOSTER 1986 Nuclear resonance imaging shows water distribution and transport in plant root systems *in situ*. Proc Natl Acad Sci USA 32: In press

10. BOYER JS 1982 Plant productivity and environment. Science 218: 443–448

11. BURAU RG 1985 Environmental chemistry of selenium. Calif Agric 32: 16–18

12. CAPLAN A, L HERRERA-ESTRELLA, D INZE, E VAN HAUTE, M VAN MONTAGU, J SCHELL, P ZAMBRYSKI 1983 Introduction of genetic material into plant cells. Science 222: 815–821

13. Carbon Dioxide Assessment Committee 1983 Changing Climate. National Research Council. National Academy Press, Washington, DC

14. CAST 1985 Agriculture: Ground Water Quality. Council for Agricultural Science and Technology, Report No. 103

15. CHEN E, JF GERGER 1985 Minimum temperature cycles in Florida. Fla State Hort Soc Proc 98. in press

16. CLARK WC, ed 1982 Carbon Dioxide Review: 1982. Contract DE-AC05-760R00033 between US Department of Energy and Oak Ridge Associated Universities. Oxford University Press, New York

17. CLEMENTS RJ, MM LUDLOW 1977 Front avoidance and front resistance in *Centrosena virginianum*. J Appl Ecol 14: 551–566

18. DANCETTE C, AE HALL 1979 Agroclimatology applied to water management in Sudanian and Sahelian zones of Africa. *In* AE Hall, GH Cannell, HW Lawton, eds, Agriculture in Semiarid Environments (Ecological Studies 34). Springer-Verlag, Berlin, pp 98–118

19. DAVIES WJ, J METCALFE, TA LODGE, AR DA COSTA 1986 Plant growth substances and the regulation of growth under drought. Aust J Plant Physiol 13. In press

20. DEVERAL SJ, RJ GILLIOMN, R FUJII, JA IZBICKI, JC FILDS 1984 Aerial Distribution of Selenium and Other Inorganic Constituents in Shallow Ground Water of the San Luis Drain Service Area. San Joaquin Valley, CA. US Geological Survey. Water Resources Investigation Rpt 84-4319.

21. DIAZ HF 1984 The role of January in the character of recent winters in the United States. J Clim Appl Meterol 23: 177–186

22. ENDRESS AG, SL POST 1985 Altered feeding preference of Mexican bean beetle *Epilachna varivestia* for ozonated soybean foliage. Environ Pollut 39: 9–16

23. FARQUHAR GD, RA RICHARDS 1984 Isotopic composition of plant carbon correlates with water-use efficiency of wheat genotypes. Aust J Plant Physiol 11: 539–552

24. FOY CD 1983 Plant adaptation to mineral stress in problem soils. Iowa State J Res 57: 339–354

25. GEBHARDT MT, C DANIEL, EE SCHWEIZER, RR ALLOMARAS 1985 Conservation tillage. Science 230: 625–630

26. HANSON AD, CE NELSEN, AR PEDERSEN, EH EVERSON 1979 Capacity for proline accumulation during water stress in Barley and its implications for breeding for drought resistance. Crop Sci 19: 489–493

27. HARRIS MJ, RL HEATH 1981 Ozone sensitivity in sweet corn (*Zea mays* L.) plants: a possible relationship to water balance. Plant Physiol 68: 885–890

28. HEATH RL 1980 Initial events in injury to plants by air pollutants. Annu Rev Plant Physiol 31: 395–431

29. HECK WW, WW CURE, JO RAWLINGS, LJ ZARAGOZA, AS HEAGLE, HE HEGGESTAD, RJ KOHUT, LW KRESS, PJ TEMPLE 1984 Assessing impacts

of ozone on agricultural crops. II. Crop yield functions and alternative exposure statistics. J Air Pollut Contr Assoc 34: 810–817

30. HECK WW, AS HEAGLE, DS SHRINER 1986 Effects on vegetation: native, crops, forests. In AC Stern, ed, Air Pollution, Chapter 5, Vol VI, Ed 3. Academic Press, New York

31. JARVIS RJ, GP REITHMULLER, C HENDERSON, J HAMBLIN, BJ HILLMAN 1985 Deep Ripping. West Australian Department of Agriculture Farmnote No. 50/85

32. JONES HG 1980 Interaction and Integration of Adaptive Responses to Water Stress: The Implications of an Unpredictable Environment. In NC Turner, PJ Kramer, eds, Adaptation of Plants to Water and High Temperature Stress. John Wiley & Sons, New York, pp 353–365

33. KIMBALL BA, SB IDSO 1983 Increasing atmospheric CO_2: effects on crop yield, water use, and climate. Agric Water Manage 7: 55–72

34. KOSUGE T, CP MEREDITH, A HOLLAENDER, eds 1983 Genetic Engineering of Plants—An Agricultural Perspective. Plenum Press, New York

35. KRUSE EG, CR BURDICK, YA YOUSEF, eds 1982 Environmentally Sound Water and Soil Management. In Proceedings of the Specialty Conference, American Society of Civil Engineers, New York

36. LEMON ER, ed 1983 CO_2 and Plants: The Response of Plants to Rising Levels of Atmospheric Carbon Dioxide. In AAAS Selected Symposium 84. Westview Press, Boulder, CO

37. LUDLOW MM, O BJÖRKMAN 1984 Paraheliotropic leaf movement as a protective mechanism against drought-induced damage to primary photosynthetic reactions: damage by excessive light and heat. Planta 161: 505–518

38. MAKI T 1980 Studies on the windbreak nets. 2. Micrometeorological modification of a cool weather damage paddy rice displayed by two kinds of windbreak nets. J Agric Meteorol Jpn 36: 161–172

38a. Maruyama S, N Kabaki, K Tajima 1985 Water consumptions in Japonica and indica rice varieties. P Jpn J Crop Sci 54: 22–28

39. MICHELENA VA, JS BOYER 1982 Complete turgor maintenance at low water potentials in the elongating region of maize plants. Plant Physiol 69: 1145–1149

40. MORGAN JM 1983 Osmoregulation as a selection criteria for drought tolerance in wheat. J Agric Res 34: 607–614

41. MORGAN JM 1984 Osmoregulation and water stress in higher plants. Annu Rev Plant Physiol 35: 299–319

42. NICKLESON SE 1979 Revised rainfall series in the West Africa subtropics. Mon Weather Rev 107:620–623

43. NORMAN JM, G CAMPBELL 1983 Application of a plant-environment model to problems in irrigation. In D Hillel, ed, Advances in Irrigation Vol 2. Academic Press, New York, pp 155–188

44. Office of Technology Assessment 1983 Water-related Technologies for Substantial Agriculture in US Arid/Semiarid Land. Washington, DC

45. OLIEN CR, MN SMITH, eds 1981 Protective systems that have evolved in plants. In Analysis and Improvement of Plant Cold Hardiness. CRC Press, Boca Raton, FL, pp 61–87

46. PASZKOWSKI J, RD SHILLITO, M SAUL, V MANDAK, T HOHN, B HOHN, I POTRYKUS 1984 Direct gene transfer to plants. EMBO J 3: 2717–2722

47. RAJU KS, ES LEE, AW BIERE, ET KANEMASU 1983 Irrigation scheduling

based on a dynamic crop response model. *In* D Hillel, ed, Advances in Irrigation, Vol 2. Academic Press, New York, pp 257–271

48. RAO PSC, AG HORNSBY, RE JESSUP 1985 Indices for ranking the potential for pesticide contamination of groundwater. Soil Crop Sci Soc Fla 44: 1–8

49. REINERT RA, HE HEGGESTAD, WW HECK 1982 Plant response and genetic modification of plants for tolerance to air pollutants. *In* MN Christiansen, CL Lewis, eds, Breeding Plants for Less Favorable Environments, Chapter 9. John Wiley & Sons, New York

50. REINERT RA 1984 Plant response to air pollutant mixtures. Annu Rev Phytopathol 22: 421–442

51. ROGERS HH, JF THOMAS, GE BINGHAM 1983 Response of agronomic and forest species to elevated carbon dioxide. Science 220: 428–429

52. ROGERS HH, PA BOTTOMLEY, TH FOSTER, FA JOHNSON 1985 In situ root imaging with nuclear magnetic resonance. Agron Abstr 77: 87

53. ROSENBERG NJ 1982 The increasing CO_2 concentration in the atmosphere and its implication on agricultural productivity. II. Effects through CO_2 induced climatic change. Clim Change 4: 239–254

54. SACHS MM, M FREELING, R OKIMOTO 1980 The anaerobic proteins of maize. Cell 20: 761–767

55. SATTER RL, AW GALSTON 1973 Leaf movements: Rosetta stone of plant behavior. BioScience 23: 407–416

56. SCHWARTZ M, J GALE 1981 Maintenance respiration and carbon balance of plants at low levels of sodium chloride salinity. J Exp Bot 32: 933–941

57. SHANNON MC 1986 Principles and strategies in breeding for higher salt tolerance. Plant Soil. In press

58. STEWART BA, JT MUSICK 1982 Consumptive use of rainfall and irrigation on semiarid regions. *In* D Hellel, ed, Advances in Irrigation. Academic Press, New York, pp 1–24

59. TAYLOR HM, WR JORDAN, TR SINCLAIR, eds 1983 Limitations to Efficient Water Use in Crop Production. American Society of Agronomy, Madison, WI

60. TING IP 1985 Crassulacean acid metabolism. Annu Rev Plant Physiol 36: 595–622

61. TODOROV AV 1985 Sahel: the changing rainfall regime and the "normals" used for its assignment. J Clim Appl Meteorol 24: 97–107

62. TUCKER CJ, JRG TOWNSEND, TE GOFF 1985 African land-cover classification using satellite data. Science 277: 369–375

63. UNSWORTH MH, DP ORMROD, eds 1982 Effects of Gaseous Air Pollution in Agriculture and Horticulture. Butterworth Scientific, London

64. U.S. Environmental Protection Agency 1978 Air Quality Criteria for Ozone and Other Photochemical Oxidants, EPA-60018-78-004. Office of Research and Development, Washington, DC

65. US Environmental Protection Agency 1984 Air Quality Criteria for Ozone and Other Photochemical Oxidants, EPA-600/8-84-020A. External Review Draft, Office of Research and Development, Research Triangle Park, NC

66. VIEZES W, HB SINGH 1982 Contribution of Stratospheric Ozone to Ground-Level Ozone Concentrations, A Scientific Review of Existing Evidence. Technical Report Task 3, SAI Project 3643. Environmental Protection Agency, Research Triangle Park, NC

67. WITTWER SH 1985 Carbon dioxide levels in the biosphere: effects on plant productivity. CRC Crit Rev Plant Sci 4: 171–197

Production Systems

Submitted on behalf of the group by:

R. R. HARWOOD   R. J. BATTENFIELD
B. D. KNEZEK   J. L. DAVIDSON

> ... a single leaf turns not yellow but
> with the silent knowledge of the whole tree...,
> —KAHLIL GIBRAN, *The Prophet* (30)

Production systems is the study of a complex set of related components within the context of a relevant system. The underlying theme is that the complex interrelationships among components precludes studies of components in isolation. Thus, systems research is the study of systems; typically, it involves an analysis of components and the relationships within a system and, secondly, a synthesis phase.

In a problem-solving context, systems research involves both (a) development of new agricultural systems based on new components such as new varieties of cultivars, harvesting technologies, abilities to monitor the status of the system and markets; and (b) improved management of existing systems. Therefore: *The greatest need in agricultural research is to know the relationships between all the biological parts that comprise production systems.*

Most applied research is site specific and requires an understanding of the role of particular components in a system setting. Fundamental understanding of underlying processes and their interrelationships is necessary to make the best use of limited research resources, particularly given the large number of soils, microclimates, and social systems that agriculture is embedded in. These factors also make it difficult to develop general research imperatives since applications are site specific, but general themes emerge. That is the focus of this report.

Cropping Patterns

Integrative cropping systems are highly economical when production resources are scarce or expensive, as is true for much of U.S. agriculture and for all resource-limited[1] regions. In the United States, farmers are again making greater use of crop rotations and simple crop sequences.

---

[1] Resource-limited regions (or low resource farms) are those with low quality production potential either because of limited land area or poor land quality. They often have limited crop water resources for at least part of the year. A lack of access to rural infrastructure such as roads, markets, and credit is common. Limited access to or the cost of inputs follows.

Others are overseeding standing grain crops with grasses and legumes to establish ground cover before harvest, to protect the soil, to promote the uptake of residual soluble nutrients, and to increase biological N_2 fixation during the off-season (54).

Tropical and low resource regions use complex intercrop systems of annual crop trees and tree/annual crop mixtures (33). These systems have maintained good levels of production for very long periods of time. In the U.S. Midwest, there is evidence that input costs can be reduced significantly with integrated crop/livestock farms with carefully designed rotations (49) (see also Ref. 31). Such systems will tend to be more biologically stable, sometimes requiring fewer pesticide inputs. They have a greater potential for nutrient recycling, thus reducing loss to the environment.

Research alternative rotations to use the growing season more completely. This is particularly important for production research in tropical countries where production environments and their crop pattern potential are highly variable. Soil type, water management, rainfall, and field elevation change significantly over even short distances. As crop intensity is increased, the "fit" to these agroclimatic determinants becomes increasingly specific (see Ref. 78). The crop pattern potential (and the rotations) thus vary greatly over space. The identification of areas of relatively uniform production potential and the definition of alternative patterns that fully exploit that potential must continue to be a key element of the farming systems research approach. The continued development of a "design capability" will significantly reduce the expensive and resource-requiring empirical crop production research now being undertaken.

There is increasing research interest in the effects of modern crop rotations on the suppression of weeds, pathogens, and crop insect pests. For example, weeds tolerant to both the crop and its management practices build up under any continuous production scheme. No weed species is equally competitive in both warm and cool seasons. For the most part, weeds that increase under continuous corn reduce the incidence of cool season or perennial weeds which compete with fall or spring-sown small grains. These crop shifts then are done to counter weed buildup. They make effective use of weed shifts as a part of a management strategy. Additional effects are seen from crop allelochemical exudates that suppress weed growth (68).

Develop nontraditional methods, such as overseeding, for increasing cropping intensity. There is a significant opportunity in most crop systems for incorporating additional crops or cover crops for soil protection. Much more work is needed in this area, however. Currently most work on the benefit of overseeding to increase soil nitrogen levels has focused on nitrogen inputs (54).

Study the efficiencies of tropical intercrop production systems. Tropical crop systems are often intercropped. These systems have higher production, lower pest incidence, and more constant labor demand than do monocultures (38, 46). They seem to be highly desirable for small, labor-intensive farms, but for reasons that are not well understood. Thus it is difficult to import them or to prescribe their use in other locations.

Identify and genetically improve plant species that are rarely cultivated, but which can be usefully incorporated into cropping systems. New or underexploited plant species are ever needed in cropping systems. Many plant species provide food, feed, chemicals, fiber, wood, and other commodities (18). Nontraditional crops often have high levels of protein, minerals, or vitamins. These crops could become critical supplements to human or animal diets. Examples of such crops are the many tropical species that have been identified, such as grain amaranth. Other crops have potential for producing pharmaceuticals or various industrial products of high value.

Some "new" plant species could expand the agricultural land base due to their greater tolerances for unfavorable climates (high or low temperatures, drought) and soils (salinity, low mineral content). Jojoba, a desert plant from which high quality wax can be extracted, is an example of a new crop species (60). The benefits from such "new" crops to worldwide agricultural production systems can be significant. More crop options will contribute to greater diversification in the production system, resulting in long-term economic stability and increased productivity.

Base genetic improvement programs on criteria that "fit" crops into intended production systems. While the genetics of a crop species limits the crop's potential contribution, cultivars vary greatly in efficiency and adaptability to cropping systems. Traditionally, plant breeders have tended to select for high yielding-high quality cultivar types with little regard to other components of the production system. Consequently, the cultural environment often had to be modified for the crop to achieve its genetic yield potential. As the availability of critical resources such as land, water, minerals, and energy for crop production diminishes, crop genotypes will need to be made more compatible with existing environments and farmer needs. Although short-term crop yields might be compromised by such production strategies, long-term economic production and the resource use efficiencies within the cropping systems potentially can be enhanced.

Environmental stresses are a predominant force limiting crop yields and the variety of crop species that can be grown. Stress tolerance or avoidance traits bred into all economically important crop species would lead to better crop "fit." Considerable gains have been made in identifying genotypes with adaptive potential to drought (75), radiation (48), mineral nutrient toxicities or deficiencies (12, 26, 43, 85), and air pollution (50, 57). However, the incorporation of many of these traits into commercially acceptable cultivars of crop species is still lacking.

Mineral element uptake and use are genetically controlled (16) in plants. Because these traits are manipulable, they could be valuable for improving plants to adapt better to mineral stress conditions. For example, wheat has been adapted to produce in Brazil's soils. Maize hybrids tolerant to aluminum also have been developed. At the International

Rice Research Institute (IRRI), rice genotypes have been screened for relative responses to deficiencies of zinc, iron, and phosphorus, and tolerances to excessive salt, alkali, iron, aluminum, and manganese, and tolerances to organic and acid sulfate soils. Some successes have been made.

Fit also includes technological and societal constraints. Labor, cultural practices, mechanization, harvesting strategies, postharvest handling procedures, and consumer use all should be considered as characteristics of cultivars selected for particular systems. Plant genotypes that are compatible with available resources and technologies will make cropping systems more efficient and profitable.

Some plants also may contribute to the growth and health of other crop species in cropping sequences. Research to identify and promote these beneficial interactions would do much to improve the efficiency and sustainability of agricultural production.

Livestock Needs

Animals/livestock are a vital and often necessary part of crop production systems, especially for range and small-scale systems. Worldwide, 40 to 80% of the livestock are associated with mixed crop/livestock farming systems. In the warm climate regions, animals provide 150 million horsepower per year—mostly for cropping. Needs for animal power will increase up to 100% by the year 2000 (69). Crop residues are highly important as feed. In the semiarid and subhumid zones of West Africa, cattle spend 40% of their time grazing on crop residues, where they obtain almost half of their annual feed (66). Crop residues provide almost half the feed for sheep in North Africa and West Asia (40) and more than 70% of the feed for cattle and buffalo in India (51).

Despite the need for animals as power and food, little attention has been given to the quality and supply of their feed. Small holders are rejecting new varieties of barley in North Africa and West Asia because the feed value of their residues for sheep feed is lower than traditional varieties (39). In Mexico, there is a 50% price differential in favor of stover from conventional varieties due to their higher feed value (2). In warm climates, cereal grain crop residues from traditional varieties have a digestibility index (DIG) in the range of 42 to 56% (80). Most of the "improved" varieties are 10 or more points lower: 35 to 45% DIG. Ruminants require a DIG level of at least 45% to obtain sufficient energy for body maintenance.

Digestibility and intake are positively related in animal diets high in straw or stover; the bulk in these foods limits the amount an animal can ingest. Straws high in lignin limit the ability of animals to consume more feed; digestibility of plant cellulose is inversely related to lignification.

With the strong relationships of crop residues and animal performance, animal scientists are highly concerned when plant breeders change the distribution of plant nutrients in a crop to achieve increased grain yield at the cost of poorer quality residues for animal feed. Quantity and quality of crop residues are important factors in farmer decisions to grow a particular crop (32).

Identify the nutrient needs of livestock and provide a mechanism for ensuring that these are included in plant breeding programs. In pursuit of higher yields, pest resistance, and other crop productivity requirements, plant breeders often sacrifice nutrient quality, digestibility, and other characteristics of byproducts and residues needed for livestock feed. For example, scientists at the International Center for Agricultural Research in the Dry Areas (ICARDA) examined barley selections and found that (a) grain yields tended to be lower and straw yield higher in varieties with good straw, (b) leaf production declined as height increased, (c) variation in leaf proportion is a major factor in straw quality, (d) increased plant height decreased DIG, (e) greater leaf proportion increased DIG, (f) increased days to heading and days to maturity added to leaf production and DIG, (g) tall varieties contained more lignin in the leaf sheath than shorter varieties, and (h) high grain yield and good quality straw are compatible breeding objectives (40).

In 1984, scientists at the International Crops Research Institute for the Semi-Arid Tropics (ICRISAT) found that small land holders were not using new sorghum varieties, because they produced less stover and were less palatable to livestock than traditional varieties. When cowpeas are selected for yield, crop residue decreases, the lignin content in stalks increases, and leaf drop before harvest increases. Therefore, these varieties are rarely used in erratic rainfall areas, such as Botswana and northern Mali where cowpeas are traditionally used as an insurance crop for human food when pasture is plentiful and for livestock feed when pasture is poor. Centro Agronomico Tropical de Investigacion y Enseianza (CATIE) currently recommends "new maize" varieties only when farmers are aware of likely changes in stover quality or if other feed resources can be developed to offset lower quality stover (4, 52).

Improve techniques for handling and storing crop residues. Feeds are generally needed throughout the year. Technologies for handling and storing crop residues, however, limit full utilization. Although crop residues are readily available during harvest, feed supplies are limited during many months of the year. In some countries where farmers have no access to handling or storage facilities, crop residues are burned in the fields or left to rot. Research is needed to develop handling techniques and storage of crop residues. Storage systems that are simple and inexpensive would benefit the greatest number of farmers.

Identify and develop varieties, and commensurate production systems, of leguminous and dual-purpose crops that can produce high quality food and fodder. Forage crops have generally not received a great deal of attention in cropping systems research. Attention has focused on large-scale livestock production. Small land holders, however, have pertinent and unique needs. They rarely grow forage crops because it reduces the area needed for producing food crops. Residues from their food crops (rice straw, peanut hay, wheat straw, barley straw, and sweet potato leaves) are their main livestock feed.

Production systems and crops need to be developed that will best meet the dual-purpose needs for small holders. In time, this research will mean greater flexibility for all production systems—large and small, with and without livestock. Crop breeding programs should include characteristics such as low tannin content, consistent yield, and high protein content—without sacrificing grain yield. Several leguminous crops give high grain yield and high biomass production for livestock feed (cowpea, mungbean, peanut, and pigeon pea). Production systems should be developed that use these types of crops to best advantage in dual cropping systems. One type of system would use intercropping and relay cropping of leguminous forage crops.

Rotations of forage legume crops with food crops that can enhance the yield of the subsequent crop and sustain soil fertility should be investigated. Brumby (13) found that grain crops grown after 1 year of legumes yielded in excess of one additional ton. Similar results are occurring with the use of stylosanthes in the sub-humid zone of Nigeria and with browse legumes in the humid zone (alley farming) (14). Intercropping and sequential cropping of dual-purpose crops also need to be studied. The advantages of this research include keeping land in continuous crop production, increasing output of food grains without risk of rainfall-fertilizer interactions and through livestock feeding, and permitting more efficient use of crop residues from grain production.

Multipurpose Trees

Identify agroforestry systems with nitrogen-fixing perennial species that optimize the provision of nitrogen and other nutrients to permit a sustainable high level of crop production. Nitrogen-fixing trees have long been used as a soil-restoring land cover in shifting agriculture, and as "shade" or nurse trees for food and industrial crops. Such trees are grown increasingly as alleys providing rich green manure for tropical farm crop systems, or as hedges along food crops, or as interim crops between plantings of forest tree species (44). Almost 700 species of trees and shrubs are known to fix N_2, many relying on actinomycetes rather than rhizobia (1, 61). Their nitrogen-rich leaves are viewed as "green gold" in some countries, with reported annual harvests of 500 kilograms/hectare of nitrogen or of litterfall returns of 100 kilograms/hectare of nitrogen annually. "Grow your own nitrogen" has become a realistic goal of small low-input farmers. Little research has focused specifically on the nitrogen fixation of such species or of the quality and quantity of other nutrients returned as litter to the soil surface by these species.

Research needs to focus on the following areas: (a) quantify nitrogen-fixation and cycling to crops by nitrogen-fixing trees in tree/crop association; (b) identify land-use ratios of alley-trees and crops for optimized economic returns, quantifying the biological and economic effects of competition for light, water, and minerals; (c) search for food-bearing nitrogen-fixing trees suitable for alley cropping, and for trees producing high quality fodder suitable for nonruminant as well as ruminant animals; (d) develop agroforestry systems that will stabilize and reclaim degraded, desertine, and other marginal lands; and (e) develop "nurse-crops" systems that optimize the use of nitrogen-fixing trees when plantation crops are being established.

Identify trees suitable for alley cropping agroforestry combinations, and optimize their production in such systems. Many types of crop production systems involve trees as sources of food, feed, shade, industrial, and other products. However, few trees have been identified or bred specifically for such use. "Giant" cultivars of leucaena provide an illustration of the wide deployment and use by rural poor of improved varieties of fast-growing fuelwood trees (58). Fast-growing trees of the secondary forest, normally hardwoods, are vigorous, have a wide site adaptability, regrow rapidly from coppice, and are easily managed to any height or form. They have been little studied botanically or agronomically.

Research in this area needs to: (a) identify species and cultivars of trees especially suitable to alley cropping and other agroforestry systems, with descriptions of natural distributions and available genetic resources; (b) provide basic biological data on the taxonomy, morphology, nitrogen-fixing and mycorrhizal associations, coppice ability, pest and stress tolerance, and wood and forage properties; (c) establish site adaptabilities and limitations of such trees, especially for problem soils; and (d) determine yields and qualities of wood and fodder under management systems that optimize yields of associated crop species.

Establish agroforestry systems that maximize production of high quality animal feeds. Tree foliage has significance as a highly digestible, high protein supplement in low input animal feed systems. It is especially important as dry-season fodder. The highest animal gains on tropical pastures have been achieved on grass supplemented with nitrogen-fixing tree foliage (11). Most flowering trees can serve as browse fodder, but few provide highly digestible foliage and can be integrated into pastures with rapid regrowth suitable to grazing demands (47). Research needs in this area are: (a) develop standard methods for forage quality, analyzing tropical fodder trees, and evaluating the roles of tannins and toxins in such foliage; (b) identify superior, multipurpose fodder tree cultivars and species for cut-and-carry feed on small farms; and (c) develop grass/fodder tree intercrop systems that maximize animal gains.

Identify productive cultivars of food trees and production systems that optimize their contribution in small-farm cropping systems. Food-producing trees are an integral part of most small-farm cropping systems. They serve multiple purposes, often providing shade and shelter, wood and fuel, fodder and nutrients in addition to food. In low input agricultural systems, food-producing trees often are significant as a source of high energy (breadfruit, banana, jackfruit) and of income (apple and mango). Slow growth rate and high labor demands at harvest reduce interest in such trees, and their shade and nutrient use can reduce overall productivity of the cropping systems.

Researchers need to identify high yielding, rapidly bearing dwarf cultivars of important food trees, and to develop tree/crop systems for maximal productivity of food (root crops) or fodder under the shade of food and industrial tree crop plantings.

Develop crop production and harvest systems that maximize bioenergy as a coproduct of food and fodder. Acute fuelwood shortages occur in much of the world and accelerate rapidly as populations increase and forests disappear. Rampant deforestation has reduced tropical forests to about 1000 million hectares—a loss of 70% in the 20th century alone (10, 74). Deforestation occurs at a rate of 10 million to 20 million hectares annually, and replacement is less than 20% of that required (3 million hectares/year) to replace fuelwood needs alone (27, 83). Over half of the world's harvested wood is used for fuel, with developing countries using 80 to 90% (7). Fast-growing nitrogen-fixing trees and grasses afford the most economic sources of biofuels and can be integrated into most farming systems (59). Crops can also be grown directly as liquid fuels, or converted by fermentation to biogas.

Specific researchable areas are as follows: (a) identify short-rotation bio-fuel tree species suitable for integrated cropping systems and characterization of their fuelwood properties; (b) develop short-rotation forests of harvest systems and appropriate machinery that minimize harvest costs, losses, and hazards; and (c) search for woody species (Chinese tallow tree or tung) that provide liquid biofuels or biomass suitable for producing biogas.

Soil Considerations

Cropping practices involve the selection of particular genotypes and the cultural practices employed to grow them; all redistribute mineral nutrients and change soil physical and chemical conditions. These conditions and their interactions determine or control a plant's ability to grow and develop on any soil. Soil physical properties affect the soil's ability to provide water, oxygen, and nutrients to plant roots. Soil chemical properties affect nutrient availability and toxicity, biological processes in the soil, and plant root growth. Soil physical and chemical interactions directly affect crop productivity and the subsequent effects on surface and groundwater quality through soil erosion and loss of nutrients.

Depending on their nature, these processes, and any changes to them, either beneficially or detrimentally affect the soil as a medium for plant growth. Sound knowledge of the effects of cropping practices on soils is essential if improved production systems are to be devised.

Determine the nutrient requirements of new crops and cultivars. New crops and cultivars have a central role in the development of improved production systems on soils of low nutritional status. The need for supplemental nutrients and soil amendments should be assessed and evaluated for the most efficient time and method of placement. Genotypes should be selected or created by genetic engineering to improve the efficiency of nutrient utilization and the tolerance to soil salinity and soil acidity (18).

Phosphorus has been known as the "master key" to agriculture because it has been the nutrient often limiting crop production. This is particularly true today for tropical soils in developing countries (73). But in the United States and other developed countries heavy fertilization with phosphorus has led to soils that are high to very high in available phosphorus (24). Developing countries need genotypes that can effectively extract phosphorus that is limited in supply and tightly bonded in soils, whereas the United States needs to develop further soil analysis to identify soils that are high in phosphorus and, consequently, pose environmental problems.

Develop more effective methods for measuring the levels of available soil nutrients. Efficiency in the use of nutrients is absolutely essential in reducing the costs of crop production, in assuring the efficient utilization of other crop inputs, in maintaining reasonable farm commodity prices, and in minimizing possible deleterious effects of nutrients on the land resource itself and on the total environment, especially water bodies.

Maximum efficiency of nutrient use can be achieved by soil and plant tissue testing to assess the nutrient status of farm soils, by knowing the particular need of crop kinds and cultivars at given yield goals, by altering the soil environment by practices such as liming, and by choosing the proper form of plant nutrient and properly timing its placement.

Identifying soil fertility through a classification system using soil variables can help in selecting suitable locations for particular crops and can determine probable nutrient deficiencies. This capability enhances the producer's ability to evaluate nutrient requirements without costly testing techniques.

Practices that improve the soil for plant growth (drainage, irrigation, incorporation of organic matter, increasing soil moisture storage and retention through tillage or other cultural operations) can significantly increase the efficiency of nutrient applications. Accurate measurements of nutrient levels will help producers know what types and amounts of soil amendments/fertilizers are needed to sustain crop and soil productivity. Long-term research will be required to provide a proper basis of environmentally and economically sound recommendations in the use of plant nutrients.

Develop management strategies that will increase the efficiency of water and nutrient use, thus avoiding water pollution. An important problem in the United States is the downward leaching of nitrogen beyond the root zone. Excessive amounts of inorganic or organic sources of nitrogen may be mineralized into soluble forms that can leach out of the root zone and into the ground water. The answer to the economic problems of inefficient use of nutrients and to ground water pollution are the same. Cropping systems need to be developed which consider the science and economics of decision making by producers so that any nutrients in production systems can be most efficiently utilized (9). In addition, more stable forms of nutrients or organic residues must be used in production systems to reduce the leaching potential in crop production systems.

The efficiency of nitrogen use has an immediate and direct effect on crop production and a large though indirect effect on water quality. It is estimated that as much as 50 to 60% of the nitrogen applied is not recovered by the crop. Residual nitrogen may be recovered by succeeding crops, may be leached into surface and groundwaters, may be incorporated into soil organic matter, or may leave the soil as a gas after denitrification. Nitrogen use efficiency thus has important environmental and economic implications. Identifying the pathways of nitrogen transformations and loss mechanisms and quantifying the magnitude of nitrogen losses is essential to developing management techniques and practices that meet environmental clean-water goals as well as ensuring the economic justification for nitrogen use.

Cultural practices can influence the availability to crops of soil nutrients, the fate of fertilizers, crop growth, and the efficiency of water and nutrient use (53, 62). These are all influenced by the method and amount of water applied, and by the timing of irrigation to the water status of the crop and soil, and to the stage of crop development (67).

Select crops and management practices that help move nutrients up through soils. Throughout the world, essential nutrients are lost to agriculture through leaching beyond crop root zones. Deep-rooted crops and cultivars that can efficiently extract nutrients from depths need to be identified and incorporated into management practices. For example, deep-rooted annuals and perennials, including trees, move nutrients from lower soil depths to upper horizons. Patten (64) compared two farms in the Palouse region of eastern Washington. His studies showed that a farm using no fertilizer nutrient inputs with a winter wheat/spring pea/ Austrian winter pea or summer fallow rotation, had higher levels of extractable phosphorus and potassium than a farm using a winter wheat/ spring pea rotation and commerical nitrogen and phosphorus fertilizers. This suggests that the soils in the first farm had an upward flow and accumulation of soil nutrients in the upper part of the soil horizon, similar to natural soil-building processes.

Improve water use efficiency and quality through water delivery systems, cultural practices, and crop cultivars. Water use efficiency in both rainfed and irrigated agriculture is affected by the availability of adequate but not excessive amounts of water to support optimum plant growth, and the selection of cultural (crop selection) and soil management (tile drainage and tillage systems) practices. They also affect the utilization of intrinsic and applied nutrients.

Improved and innovative irrigation management methods can increase the efficient use of water supplies in areas of scarce supply and in areas of intermittent supply. Water resources often are not efficiently used because irrigation practices do not apply uniform quantities across entire fields. The results are areas that are either too dry to too wet for optimum plant growth. Too much water can cause leaching of nutrients into surface and subsurface water supplies and loss of usable water. It can also create high water tables that require drainage. Both extremes are detrimental to optimum plant growth. Although irrigation technology has improved (drip and subirrigation) considerable improvements are still possible. Research should be directed toward application and distribution efficiency, reduced energy requirements, timeliness of application, and reduced labor requirements.

In rain-fed areas, the distribution of rainfall is frequently not conducive to optimal crop growth. Cultural practices and soil management practices can help preserve and improve the availability of water to the crop. Such practices should conserve precipitation from periods when it is abundant and make it available to the crop during dry periods. The use of surface crop residues and furrow checks have helped, but more research is necessary. Soil structure and physical and chemical characteristics influence soil water availability. These must be monitored while cultural practices ensuring their maintenance are developed.

Research is also needed to develop crop cultivars that can sustain productivity levels in periods of drought and/or water overabundance. Development of these cultivars should take full advantage of new techniques (gene transfer as well as traditional plant breeding). Plant growth regulators potentially can influence the water use efficiency or drought tolerance of crops.

Research must seek out alternative crop species which better match rainfall patterns of the world. These crops could be used in conjunction with crops that are presently produced or in rotation with them.

Management of soil water greatly affects nutrient use efficiency and loss of nutrients, particularly nitrate-nitrogen, to surface and groundwater. Where water can be controlled, such as in irrigated agriculture, amounts and timing of fertilizer nitrogen applications can be controlled, but the consequences of this and each management action must be known (67). Where unpredictable and excessive rainfall events occur, new and improved nitrogen management options and cultural practices must be devised.

Develop reliable methods for estimating rates of nitrogen fixation in cropping systems. Biologically fixed nitrogen is an important source of nitrogen for leguminous and nonleguminous crops. Many cultures depend on the legume for providing this essential element for some crops or crop associations. Industrially fixed nitrogen supplements or substitutes for biologically fixed nitrogen in many other crop cultures. Leguminous crops and effective innoculants for specific environments should be improved to enhance their ability to fix atmospheric N_2 (36). Research is needed to quantify the biological nitrogen contribution of annual and perennial legumes in different cultural systems so that needs for supplementing industrially fixed nitrogen can be accurately specified. The economic and environmental consequences must be identified for growing legumes in different crop rotations with varying cultural practices.

Measure the different ways by which legumes increase productivity in cropping systems. It has long been known, and has been reconfirmed recently, that the yield of grain crops in limited-resource situations is significantly higher when it follows a legume crop in rotations, than when it is grown in continuous culture (20, 21, 82). For example, corn yields are usually higher the year following a soybean crop than if corn follows corn (6, 81). Symbiotic N_2 fixation by legumes represents the largest input of biologically fixed nitrogen to most cropping systems. Actinorhizal symbioses, associative N_2 fixation (79), and *Azolla* are significant under specialized environments, more often under tropical conditions. Although estimates of N_2 fixation by legumes are available (65), these are quite variable due to differences in environment, genotypes, and methodologies. Of even greater concern is the lack of data on the significance and contribution of biologically fixed nitrogen to the entire cropping system and potential environmental impact. Under intensively cultivated agriculture, residual soil nitrogen from previous crops can limit N_2 fixation. Under other environments, soil pH, aluminum toxicity, drought, salinity, and poor nodulation can reduce legume productivity.

Legumes in a cropping system contribute significantly to the input of nitrogen and offer alternatives in cropping systems and patterns. Critical to evaluating the value of nitrogen contributed are estimates of N_2 fixed and the rate at which residual nitrogen is available to subsequent crops (25). In only a few cropping systems are there accurate estimates of nitrogen input from legumes (36).

Study the interactions of soil fauna and tillage on nutrient cycling. Cycling of nutrients in cropping systems traditionally are described via plant uptake, mineralization, and immobilization and most often as microbial, chemical, and biochemical processes. Often neglected are the soil fauna contributing to the breakdown of carbonaceous materials, especially in tillage systems where organic residues accumulate on the surface. Nutrient flow via the micro-, meso-, and macrofauna and their interactions with the traditional soil microorganisms needs to be better identified.

Examine how cropping sequences affect rhizosphere activities. The rhizosphere regulates plant growth through effects of associated fauna and mycorrhiza, associative N_2 fixation, toxin-producing plants and microorganisms, growth-promoting and growth-inhibiting microorganisms, and allelopathic influences. Plant species, cropping sequences, and patterns need to be identified that promote the activities of beneficial rhizosphere inhabitants. Genetic engineering of genotypes and microorganisms has the potential to enhance N_2 fixation, promote plant growth by suppressing inhibitory microorganisms and improve the ability of

Rhizobium to nodulate legumes. Much has yet to be learned concerning the biological and physical interactions within the rhizosphere and their effects on crop growth, soil nutrient, and other processes.

Determine how alternative cropping patterns influence the proportion of soil organic matter in the labile phase. Nutrient absorption into and release from the organic fraction seems to differ depending on crop history and management. This exchange process influences retention of nutrients by the soil and their eventual release to plants.

Investigate tillage effects on soil properties. The development of tillage systems usually centers around a crop or production problem, rarely soil or water quality. Because the physical, chemical, and biological processes have not been of major concern, they have so deteriorated in many parts of the world that major efforts are necessary to stop further deterioration and to improve them (22).

Current understanding of tillage systems is extensive (8). Systems have been developed which increase surface residues or incorporate cover crops, reduce erosion and thus maintain the soil and associated nutrients (5, 55). But little is known of how these systems affect long-term productivity or the quantity and quality of added nutrients that are required to optimize crop productivity (56, 72). Tillage systems are also available that are designed to capture moisture when it is abundant and thus make needed moisture available for crop production. These systems are vitally important for increasing the soil water holding capacity in regions that have extended dry periods following an overabundance of rainfall.

Develop crop genotypes and cultural practices to counter and improve soil acidity and salinity. Soil acidity limits crop productivity in soils throughout the world. The degree of soil acidity and its location in the rooting zone of crops determines to what extent crop productivity is affected by nutrient availability. Uncorrected soil acidity causes inefficient use of resources (particularly applied nutrients), decreases productivity of most crops, and increases the potential of nutrient loss into the environment.

Although crop species can be selected and crop cultivars can be developed to grow on some acid soils, nutrient availability and biological processes are still detrimentally affected by soil acidity. Soil salinity and alkalinity (a) produce osmotic effects on plant roots which reduces water availability to the plant, (b) impede plant growth through specific ion effects (*e.g.* sodium ion is not well-tolerated), (c) restrict the type of crop to those that tolerate salts or high pH, (d) restrict water infiltration and movement through the profile, and (e) deteriorate soil structure.

Surface soil acidity can be corrected by amending the soil with carbonate materials, but subsoil acidity is difficult to correct economically. Therefore, cultural practices must be carefully chosen so that acidification of the root zone soil is avoided and further deterioration of the soil as a medium for plant growth is arrested. Mitigating the effects of salt and reclaiming salt-affected soils can greatly increase the arable land resources throughout the world. By combining the right crops and crop sequences with the use of corrective management tactics (applying gypsum and removing salts by leaching) such soils can be made far more productive.

Emerging Technologies

The ability to address the complex issues of today's agricultural production systems, and to manage these systems, requires an increased understanding of the numerous interactions among plants, their environment, and their inputs. This understanding will come from tools specifically designed to provide the requisite information. A scientist's quest for information and understanding should be limited only by the scientist's ability to comprehend the total process—not by a lack of specific tools. However, scientists often cannot obtain the information they need simply because the instruments are not available—and those that are available provide only partial information. Therefore, a research effort must be undertaken to develop tools for specific purposes. These tools will be developed using the recent advances in computer technology and sensor technology. The tools will be designed and developed through the cooperative efforts of engineers and scientists from many disciplines.

Develop sensors to improve the scientist's ability to understand and the producer's ability to manage crucial biological and physical processes. New analytical instruments are needed. The instruments presently designed for laboratory use need to be redesigned for use in the field. New instruments need to take advantage of recent developments in sensor technology (the microchip sensor). When developed, the new generation of instruments will enable scientists and producers to monitor and measure essential dynamic activities related to crop production. Thanks to the computer, the new sensors will provide instantaneous and reliable information that can be used in decision support systems. Three types of sensors are needed in this activity: sensors located in the plant and/or in the soil, sensors capable of giving composite field information, and sensors capable of giving composite region and/or continent information.

Disposable in-plant and in-soil sensors (microbiochips) will be inserted into selected plants and soil layers. The plant sensors will detect plant responses to stresses (water, chemicals, temperature) and will monitor basic biological processes (photosynthesis, respiration). The soil sensors will monitor factors such as nutrient levels, soil water capacity, soil atmosphere and compaction. This information will flow to a data collection point where it will be processed to provide basic information to scientists or be used to assist producers in making decisions (information will indicate if irrigation is necessary and how much water should be applied, or if the crop is ready for harvest and the soil will tolerate the traffic). The information will assist scientists in gaining a more comprehensive understanding of plant biology under field conditions.

Field-specific sensors will detect air temperature, solar radiation, humidity, wind speed, and other climatological information. Infrared technology is currently being used to determine plant characteristics (color, texture, water stress, and pest damage). The use of infrared photography in remote sensing to detect plant stresses still requires considerable ground truthing before it becomes a useful diagnostic or predictive tool in crop management. Infrared telemetry and sensing has been used to correlate canopy temperatures with plant response (34, 35) for a limited number of crops. The infrared technology, however, is not well correlated with biological efficiency or productivity in the crop production system. Also, the temperature sensors are not disposable, nor are they capable of long-range transmission.

Remote sensing, a current technology, uses planes or satellites to scan the earth from altitudes of 5 to 200 miles. These devices use infrared photography. Coupled with the in-plant and in-field sensing devices, remote sensing offers a way to collect information for a state, nation, or the world. Soil maps and environmental maps can be overlaid with a specific crop production system to get a precise diagnosis or prognosis. The field, plant, and soil sensors will provide immediate "ground truth" to verify remote sensing information. The result will be better decisions by producers, planners, and scientists.

The limitations to developing in-plant and in-soil sensors will depend on our (researchers') ability to understand the biological mechanisms that occur in plants. As our understanding of these basic mechanisms increases, a concurrent development is needed for converting laboratory instruments into inexpensive, disposable, minute sensors.

The limitations to developing field sensors will depend on what parameters need to be sensed. Small chips are available which sense temperature and pressure; sensors for other parameters are not available. More detailed information on plant requirements will determine which sensors are developed next.

Remote sensing suffers from imprecision. Coupled with the in-field, in-plant, and in-soil sensors, however, remote sensing will be extremely valuable. The accuracy of remote sensing depends on "ground truth" and will benefit from the development of in-plant and in-field sensors.

The development of sensors, data collection and processing systems, and control systems was given top priority by the Research Committee (A-211) of the American Society of Agricultural Engineers in 1984. At a recent (April 1985) meeting of the Sensors and Control Systems Group of Agricultural Research Service-U.S. Department of Agriculture (ARS-USDA), a comprehensive list of sensor needs was produced.

Develop "intelligent" machines to perform repetitive, hazardous, or precise tasks for scientists and producers. An intelligent machine is a compilation of sensors guiding (via computer) mechanical, electronic, or other physical components that have been assembled to perform a specific task. The task would usually require precision or it might be repetitive or hazardous. They will also collect data (such as weather information) in remote areas. The design technologies in intelligent machines would include sensors so that, for example, an intelligent machine could sense the color and texture of fruit and "decide" whether or not it is ready to be harvested. It could also take an apple and "decide" in what stage of the harvest and handling process the apple received each bruise. An intelligent machine could receive voice commands. This would be especially beneficial around machines that are a safety hazard (*i.e.* the command "stop" would shut off a machine if a person is endangered).

Biological Processing

Production systems in both developed and developing countries must become more efficient and less wasteful. One step in achieving this goal is through biological processing: the conversion of raw biological products into end products that have a specified quality and function. This definition includes all handling and processing from harvest to end use. Improved efficiency, higher quality products, and reduced waste (currently, postharvest losses account for about 30% loss in potential crop products) will be the result.

In biological processing, end product specifications dictate selection criteria of raw product materials. For example, a cereal company requires corn which exhibits a certain "milling quality." Although corn that does not meet the specifications might be processed, it could result in reduced process efficiency, lower product quality, and higher wastes. Corn plants developed for this milling quality, however, would reduce postharvest waste and increase total efficiency.

Innovative biological processes offer potential increases to total efficiency by shortening the link between the production and processing systems. For example, consider the different ration requirements for animals. Systems might be designed where part of a balanced ration or mix is grown in the field through intercropping with the rest being supplied through specific processing.

To improve our biological production and processing systems will require the development of adequate knowledge bases in several areas. Recently, three national organizations (19, 39) identified critical research needs, including: identification of appropriate raw ingredient parameters which translate to process performance and end product quality; development of analytical methods and sensors for rapid, nondestructive, and continuous analysis of ingredient and process parameters; and development of appropriate engineering analysis techniques for predicting performance of new and innovative bioprocess technologies.

Management and Decision Models

Computer models are vital tools for managing and making decisions for today's and tomorrow's production systems. They can integrate a wealth of information on the biological and physical interrelationships occurring in any crop or livestock production system. They are the tools with which researchers or producers can identify deficiencies or excesses, and thus mitigate adverse effects to production systems. To date, computer models have been used to predict how alternative management options affect productivity.

Although the worldwide demand for agricultural products will continue to increase, financial support for agricultural research and extension is declining (A Alsudery, this volume). Computer models based upon fundamental understanding, therefore, are even more important because they are tools which assist researchers in the evaluation of the interactions between plants, animals, and the environment, thus reducing costly trial-and-error research.

Computer models also are valuable for identifying gaps in information. The systematic integration of processes into a decision making model will signal areas requiring further research.

Develop management models to assist in agronomic decision making. Management models and decision support systems use information bases and are designed to help decision makers deal with real-world decision making (17). Management models can provide direct and personal support for management decisions, and can reflect the way that managers think. They can be built to be flexible and to meet changing needs, knowledge, and situations (45). There are many examples of management models and their use for decision making in large commercial enterprises (17).

A farm is similar to an industry in complexity, management needs, and economic factors. Farmers continually make planning decisions which determine the form and location of production, and they make tactical decisions in response to abiotic and biotic factors (*i.e.* weather, nutritional disorders in animals and crops, expectation or appearance of insects and diseases, and feed supplies). Each decision affects the production and the profit of the farm enterprise. Computer models support farmers' decision making and control capability, building upon their capacity to perceive and think.

Develop management models to integrate crop and animal production. Adding animals into a cropping system greatly increases the complexity of relationships determining farm production and profits. A prime concern becomes trying to match animal requirements with feed supplies (29)—a difficult task on grazed pastures which cover much of the world's agricultural land. The emphasis shifts from a single, harvested product to the continual production of vegetative material. Feed requirements continually change for animals, because their needs vary according to their physiological status (*e.g.* pregnancy and lactation) and their commercial purpose. Managers must consider these needs and must maximize profits often by allocating a field to groups of animals having the same needs or through supplementary feeding.

Field-testing the many management options would be untenable: however, models can easily and rapidly test and evaluate them. (See Christian *et al.* [15] for a model to evaluate practical grazing strategies.) Such

models result in management decisions being based on pertinent information on the entire system, rather than on intuition and personal
experiences.

*Develop models that use environmental and biological data to predict
the suitability of any crop or cropping sequence in a given environment.*
The growth and development of crops depend upon the interrelationships
between leaves and roots and the distribution of assimilates. These are
influenced by the soil and the environment, particularly temperature,
solar radiation, and rainfall. Dry matter production, time of flowering,
and grain growth are all affected by the environment in ways that have
been described for some of our main crops (42, 63, 72).

Simple models of crop production should be extended to all crops so
that their potential yields can at least be estimated, and the probability
of attaining them, for any environment in which temperature data and
rainfall probabilities are recorded. Such models could be used by farm
advisors throughout the world to provide alternative cropping opportunities whenever farmers are forced to turn from their traditional systems.

Develop and incorporate crop growth models into management models.
Crop growth models incorporated into management models will provide
predictive information such that farmers will be able to evaluate the
probable effect of any management strategy or cropping practice on the
entire production system. Crop growth simulation models allow researchers or farm advisors to examine the effect of factors such as environment,
genotype, and management on crop productivity.

Plant growth simulation models have been developed for major crop
species (3, 28, 37, 42, 63, 72). New efforts should be directed toward
deriving the biological and environmental relationships that will allow
plant growth simulation models to be developed for other crop species.

*Develop and maintain appropriate data bases to provide the information
necessary for accurate models to be developed.* The development and use
of computer models will require a corresponding development of data
bases to provide information for the models. To be widely used, each
model must be developed to a similar level of detail, each must have
similar input and output information. The most efficient way to ensure
these similarities is to develop data bases that can be used for different
plant growth and management models. Three categories of information
necessary for modeling are weather, soil characteristics, and plant genotype characteristics. Each would require a minimum set of information
(41).

Much effort has already been expended in monitoring, accumulating,
and simulating weather information for many sites throughout the world
(70, 71, 76, 77, 84). Continuing work should focus on sites where production system design and management are desired and for which the
necessary information is presently not available. Some states in the
United States are currently implementing "real time" weather monitoring
stations using automated data collection and computer interrogation of
those stations (RS Rauschkolb, personal communication). Current infor-

234   WORKING GROUP PAPERS

mation is often inadequate to fulfill the minimum set of required information. Therefore, much research is yet needed. The greatest data base
shortfall is the lack of information on plant characteristics, such as the
effect of environment on plant growth stage and biomass accumulation
for a wide range of genotypes.

Conclusion

Crop systems must be increasingly productive and efficient and must
permit long-term sustainability of production levels. Each new technology must therefore leave for its successor an improved resource base.
These criteria are common to and transcend the most probable agricultural scenarios for the coming decade.

Crop production research must move increasingly toward becoming a
more integrative science. The agricultural industry (and society) cannot
afford add-on remedies for problems nor the inefficiencies of non-inte-
grated crop systems. We must create the production systems wherein the
biotechnologies of the future will find optimum expression.

LITERATURE CITED

1. ALLEN ON, EK ALLEN 1981 The Leguminosae: A Source Book of Characteristics, Uses, and Nodulation. University of Wisconsin Press, Madison,
   WI
2. ALUJA A, RE McDOWELL 1984 Decision making by livestock/crop small
   holders in the state of Veracruz, Mexico. Cornell International Agricultural
   Mimeo 105, Cornell University, Ithaca, NY
3. ARKIN EF, RL VANDERLIP, JT RITCHIE 1976 A dynamic grain sorghum
   growth model. Trans ASAE 19: 622–630
4. AVILA M 1985 CATIE's experiences in farming systems research with emphasis on livestock. Cornell International Agricultural Mimeo. Cornell
   University, Ithaca, NY. In press
5. BAKER JL, JM LAFLEN 1983 Water quality consequences of conservation
   tillage. J Soil Water Conserv 38: 186–193
6. BALDOCK JO, RL HIGGS, WH PAULSON, JA JACKOBS, WD SHRADER 1981
   Legume and mineral effects on crop yields in several crop sequences in the
   upper Mississippi Valley. Agron J 73: 885–890
7. BARNEY G 1978 The nature of the deforestation problem: trends and policy
   implications. In Proceedings of U.S. Strategy Conference on Tropical
   Deforestation. U.S. State Department, Washington, DC
8. BLEVINS RL, MS SMITH, GW THOMAS, WW FRYE 1983 Influence of conservation tillage on soil properties. J Soil Water Conserv 38: 301–305
9. BOCK BR 1984 Efficient use of nitrogen in cropping systems. In RD Hauck,
   ed, Nitrogen in Crop Production. American Society of Agronomy, Madison,
   WI, pp 273–294
10. BREWBAKER JL 1984 Short-rotation forestry in tropical areas. In H Egneus,
    A Ellegard, eds, Bioenergy 84, Vol 1, State of the Art. Elsevier, New York,
    pp 58–78
11. BREWBAKER JL 1985 Leguminous trees and shrubs for S.E. Asia and the S.

Pacific. *In* Forages in S.E. Asia and S. Pacific Agriculture. Australian Centre for International Agricultural Research, Canberra, Australia

12. BROWN JC 1979 Genetic improvement and nutrient uptake in plants. BioScience 29: 289–292

13. BRUMBY PJ 1986 The next ten years at ILCA—a strategy paper. International Livestock Centre (ILCA), Addis Ababa, Ethiopia. In press

14. BRUMBY PJ 1984 The International Livestock Centre (ILCA) and food production in Africa. Prev Vet Med 2: 3

15. CHRISTIAN KR, M FREED, JR DONNELLY, JL DAVIDSON, JS ARMSTRONG 1978 Simulation of Grazing Systems. Pudoc, Wageningen, The Netherlands

16. CHRISTIANSEN MN, CF LEWIS, EDS, 1982 Breeding Plants for Less Favorable Environments. John Wiley & Sons, New York

17. COOK TM, RA RUSSELL 1981 Introduction to Management Science. Prentice-Hall, Englewood Cliffs, NJ

18. COUNCIL FOR AGRICULTURAL SCIENCE AND TECHNOLOGY 1984 Development of new crops: needs, procedures, strategies, and options. CAST Task Force Report No. 102 (PF Knowles, Chairman), Ames, Iowa

19. COUNCIL FOR AGRICULTURAL SCIENCE AND TECHNOLOGY 1985 (October) News from CAST 12(5): 3

20. CROOKSTON KR 1984 The rotation-effect. What causes it to boost yield? Crops Soils Mag 36(6): 12–14

21. CULICK MN, JC MCALLISTER, MC PALADA, SI RIEGER 1983 The Kutztown Farm Report. Rodale Research Center, Kutztown, PA

22. ELKINS CB, DL THURLOW, JG HENDRICK 1983 Conservation tillage for long-term amelioration of plow pan soils. J Soil Water Cons 38: 305–307

24. ELLIS BG, RA OLSEN 1985 Economic, agronomic and environmental implications of fertilizer recommendations. Publication of NC-98 Committee. In press

25. EMERICK DW, HJ EVANS 1984 Enhancing biological dinitrogen fixation in crop plants. *In* RD Hauck, ed, Nitrogen in Crop Production. American Society of Agronomy, Madison, WI, pp 133–143

26. EPSTEIN E, JD NORLYN, DW RUSH, RW KINGSBURY, DB KELLEY, GA CUNNINGHAM, AF WRONA 1980 Saline culture of crops: a genetic approach. Science 210: 399–404

27. FOOD AND AGRICULTURE ORGANIZATION (FAO) 1983 Fuelwood Supplies in the Developing Countries. FAO Forestry Paper 42, FAO/United Nations, Rome

28. FICK GW 1977 The mechanism of alfalfa regrowth: a computer simulation approach. Search: Agriculture 7(3): 1–28

29. FREED M, KR CHRISTIAN 1981 Use of simulation models in constructing grazing systems. *In* JL Wheeler, RD Mochrie, eds, Forage Evaluation: Concepts and Techniques. Commonwealth Scientific and Industrial Research Organization (CSIRO) Publ., Australia

30. GIBRAN K 1965 The Prophet. Alfred A. Knopf, New York, p 44

31. HART RD 1982 Agroecosystem Determinants. Winrock International, Morrilton, AR

32. HART R, RE MCDOWELL 1985 Crop/livestock interactions as: (1) crop determinants and (2) livestock determinants. Cornell International Agriculture Mimeo No. 107. Cornell University, Ithaca, NY

33. HARWOOD RR 1979 Small Farm Development: Understanding and Improving Farming Systems in the Humid Tropics. Westview Press, Boulder, CO

34. HATFIELD JL 1982 Future applications of evapotranspiration in agriculture. Agron Abstracts, p 14

35. HATFIELD JL, TA HOWELL, JC O'TOOLE, H YAMEDA, KR DAVIS 1982 Canopy temperatures as a method of quantifying water and salinity stress in cotton. Agron Abstracts, p 14

36. HEICHEL GH, DK BARNES 1983 Opportunities for meeting crop nitrogen needs from symbiotic nitrogen fixation. In DF Bezdicek ed, Organic Farming: Current Technology and Its Role in a Sustainable Agriculture, Special Publication No. 46. American Society of Agronomy, Madison, WI, pp 49-59

37. HOLT DA, RJ BULA, GE MILES, MM SCHREIBER, RM PEART 1975 Environmental physiology, modeling and simulation of alfalfa growth; I. Conceptual development of SIMED. Purdue Agric Exp Sta Res Bull 907

38. HORWITH B 1985 A role for intercropping in modern agriculture. BioScience 35: 286-291

39. INSTITUTE OF FOOD TECHNOLOGISTS (IFT) 1985 Proceedings of the Institute of Food Technologists Workshop on Research Needs. Food Tech 39(6): 1R-44R

40. INTERNATIONAL CENTER FOR AGRICULTURAL RESEARCH IN THE DRY AREAS (ICARDA) 1985 ICARDA annual report 1984. International Centre for Agricultural Research in the Dry Areas, Aleppo, Syria

41. JONES CA 1984 Experimental Design and Data Collection Procedures for IBSNAT, the Minimum Data Set for Systems Analysis and Crop Simulation. International Benchmark Sites Network for Agrotechnology Transfer (IBSNAT). Technical Report 01.

42. JONES CA, JT RITCHIE, DA SPANEL, DB BADGLEY, JR KINIRY, PT DYKE, DL GOODWIN 1986 CERES-Maize: a simulation model of maize growth and development. In CA Jones, JR Kiniry, eds, CERES-Maize. Texas A & M Press, College Station, TX. In press

43. JUNG GA, ED 1978 Crop Tolerance to Suboptimal Land Conditions (ASA Special Publication No. 32). American Society of Agronomy, Crop Science Society of America, and Soil Science Society of America, Madison, WI

44. KANG BT, GF WILSON, TL LAWSON 1985 Alley Cropping: A Stable Alternative to Shifting Cultivation. International Institute of Tropical Agriculture, Oyo Rd, PMB5320, Ibadan, Nigeria

45. KEEN PG, GR WAGNER 1979 DSS: an executive mind-support system. Datamation 25: 117-122

46. KESWANI CL, BJ NDUNGURU 1982 Intercropping. International Development Research Centre, Ottawa

47. LE HOUEROU HN ED 1980 Browse in Africa. International Livestock Center for Africa, Addis Ababa, Ethiopia

48. LEVITT J 1980 Responses of Plants to Environmental Stresses, Ed 2, Vol I, Chilling, Freezing and High Temperature Stresses; Vol II, Water, Radiation, Salt and Other Stresses. Academic Press, New York

49. LOCKERETZ W, G SHEARER, DH KHOL 1981 Organic farming in the corn belt. Science 211: 540-546

50. MANSFIELD TA ED 1976 Effects of Air Pollutants on Plants. Cambridge, Great Britain

51. McDOWELL RE 1978 Are we prepared to help small farmers in developing countries? J Anim Sci 47: 1184

52. McDOWELL RE, PE HILDEBRAND 1980 Integrated crop and animal produc-

tion: making the most of resources available to small farms in developing countries. Working Papers. The Rockefeller Foundation, New York

53. MEISINGER JJ 1984 Evaluating plant available nitrogen in soil-crop systems. *In* RD Huack, ed, Nitrogen in Crop Production. American Society of Agronomy, Madison, WI, pp 391–416

54. MITCHELL WH, MR TEEL 1977 Winter annual cover crops for no-tillage no-tillage corn production. Agron J 69: 569–572

55. MOLDENHAUER WC, GW LANGDALE, W FRYE, DK McCOOL, RI PAPENDICK, DE SMIKA, DW FRYREAR 1983 Conservation tillage for erosion control. J Soil Water Conserv 38: 144–151

56. MONCRIEF JF, WE FENSTER, GW REHM 1984 Effect of tillage on fertilizer management. *In* Conservation Tillage for Minnesota, AG-BU-2402, Cooperative Extension Service. University of Minnesota, St. Paul, MN, pp 45–56

57. MUDD JB, TT KOZLOWSKI, EDS 1975 Responses of Plants to Air Pollution. Academic Press, New York

58. NATIONAL RESEARCH COUNCIL 1984 Leucaena: Promising Forage and Tree Crop for the Tropics. National Academy Press, Washington DC

59. NATIONAL RESEARCH COUNCIL 1983 Firewood Crops: Shrub and Tree Species for Energy Production (2 vols). National Academy Press, Washington, DC

60. NATIONAL RESEARCH COUNCIL 1975 Tropical Plants with Promising Economic Value. National Academy Press, Washington, DC

61. NITROGEN FIXING TREE ASSOCIATION 1985 Resource documents on nitrogen-fixing trees. NFTA, Waimanalo, HI

62. OLSON RA 1984 Nitrogen use in dryland farming under semiarid conditions. *In* RD Hauck, ed, Nitrogen in Crop Production. American Society of Agronomy, Madison, WI, pp 335–347

63. ONSTAD DW, CA SHOEMAKER 1984 Management of alfalfa and the alfalfa weevil (*Hypera postica*): an example of systems analysis in forage production. Agric Systems 14: 1–30

64. PATTEN A 1982 Comparison of nitrogen and phosphorus flow on an organic and conventional farm, MS thesis (unpublished). Washington State University, Pullman, WA

65. PHILLIPS DA, TM DEJONG 1984 Dinitrogen fixation in leguminous crop plants. *In*: RD Hauck, ed, Nitrogen in Crop Production. American Society of Agronomy, Madison, WI, pp 121–132

66. POWELL JM, A WATERS-BAYER 1984 Livestock-crop interactions in West African Savanna. Proceedings of the International Savanna Symposium, Brisbane, Australia (28–31 May, 1984)

67. PRATT PF 1984 Nitrogen use and nitrate leaching in irrigated agriculture. *In* RD Hauck, ed, Nitrogen in Crop Production. American Society of Agronomy, Madison, WI, pp 319–333

68. PUTNAM AR, J DEFRANK 1983 Use of phytotoxic plant residues for selective weed control. Crop Prot 2: 173–181

69. RAMASWAMY NS 1982 *In* Expert Consultation on Appropriate Use of Animal Energy in Agriculture in Africa and in Asia. FAO, Rome

70. RICHARDSON CW 1984 WGEN: A Model for Generating Daily Weather Variables, ARS-8. U.S. Department of Agriculture, Agriculture Research Service, Washington, DC

71. RICHARDSON CW 1985 Weather Simulation for Crop Management Models.

238   WORKING GROUP PAPERS

U.S. Department of Agriculture, Agriculture Research Service, Washington, DC. In press

72. RITCHIE JT, S. OTTER 1985 Description and performance of CERES-Wheat: a user oriented wheat yield model. In WD Willis, ed, ARS Wheat Yield Project, ARS-38 U.S. Department Agriculture, Agriculture Research Service, Washington, DC, pp 159–175

73. SANCHEZ PA 1976 Properties and Management of Soils in the Tropics. John Wiley & Sons, New York

74. SIVARD RL 1981 World Energy Survey. Rockefeller Foundation, New York

75. TURNER NC, PJ KRAMER, eds 1980 Adaptation of Plants to Water and High Temperature Stress. John Wiley & Sons, New York

76. US DEPARTMENT OF COMMERCE, NATIONAL OCEANIC AND ATMOSPHERIC ADMINISTRATION. 1984 Local Climatological Data—City. National Environmental Satellite Data Information Service. National Climatic Data Center, Asheville, NC

77. US DEPARTMENT OF COMMERCE, NATIONAL OCEANIC AND ATMOSPHERIC ADMINISTRATION. 1984 Climatological Data—State. National Environmental Satellite Data Information Service. National Climatic Data Center, Asheville, NC

78. VALLEJOS CE 1979 Genetic diversity of plants for response to low temperatures and its potential use in crop plants. In JM Lyons, D Graham, JK Raison, eds, Low Temperature Stress in Crop Plants. Academic Press, New York, pp 473–489

79. VAN BERKUM P 1984 Potential for nonsymbiotic and associative dinitrogen fixation. In RD Hauck, ed, Nitrogen in Crop Production. American Society of Agronomy, Madison, WI, pp 145–163

80. VAN SOEST PJ 1982 Nutritional Ecology of the Ruminant. O & B Books, Corvallis, OR

81. VOSS RD, WD SHRADER 1979 Crop rotations—effect on yields and response to nitrogen, Pm-905, Cooperative Extension Service. Iowa State University, Ames, IA

82. VOSS RD, WD SHRADER 1984 Rotation effects and legume sources of nitrogen for corn. In DF Bezdicek, ed, Organic Farming: Current Technology and its Role in a Sustainable Agriculture. Special Publication No. 46. American Society of Agronomy, Madison, WI, pp 61–68

83. WORLD BANK 1978 Forestry Sector Policy Paper. World Bank, Washington, DC

84. WORLD METEOROLOGICAL ORGANIZATION 1981 Guide to Agricultural Meteorological Practices, Ed 2. World Meteorological Organization, Geneva

85. WRIGHT MJ, ED 1976 Plant Adaptation to Mineral Stress in Problem Soils. Cornell University Agriculture Experiment Station, Ithaca, NY

Preamble to Stage II: An Analysis of Stage I Imperatives in Light of Public Policy Needs

CHARLES M. BENBROOK AND WILLIAM L. BROWN

Stage I of the Crop Productivity—Research Imperatives Revisited conference generated 36 working group imperatives and several hundred specific research objectives under these imperatives. The following assessment attempts to highlight the public policy issues that warrant special attention during stage II and implementating strategy for the stage I imperatives. This review attempts to identify significant, new issues, and is offered to provoke thought and discussion. It also should be useful to participants in sorting out which group in stage II should address different imperatives from stage I.

Conference organizers decided upon the two-stage format for this conference for two reasons. First, research needs from the perspective of policymakers, analysts, and research administrators sometimes differ from those of scientists carrying out research. Some of these differences emerge in this review. Other views and perspectives can and no doubt will be incorporated in this review, and expressed in the overall conference report. Second, it is up to policymakers and research administrators to effectuate changes in research priorities. It is their job to create both the climate and opportunity for scientists to pursue as a relatively higher priority the research imperatives articulated in stage I. This review attempts to identify public and private policies, and related initiatives that could contribute to this goal. The task of groups 7 (Public Policies and Institutions to Enhance Crop Productivity), 8 (Development of Scientific Capabilities), and 9 (Government/Industry/University Interactions) participants (stage II) is to develop concrete recommendations involving these, and other policy instruments.

Working Group Imperatives

Group 1. Genetic Improvement

Imperative 1. Analyze the adequacy of accessions, descriptive data, and preservation technology for existing germ plasm collections. Germ plasm remains the fundamental building block for enhancing crop productivity. As in 1975, the assessment and management of germ plasm collections is a critical challenge. The methods and opportunities for preservation of germ plasm are advancing. New techniques need to be more thoroughly explored and tested. Likewise, changes in the geopolitical climate surrounding the international use and management of germ plasm have and will continue to pose critical challenges for the scientific community.

Ways must be found to communicate effectively the importance for all countries on the free exchange and preservation of germ plasm. Geopolitical aspects of germ plasm preservation and exchange need to be put into perspective, and contrasted with concerns stemming from the need to produce enough food to feed mankind.

The primary constraints for germ plasm preservation are political and budgetary. An enormous amount of germ plasm remains uncollected, unassessed, or improperly managed. Difficult technical and policy issues persist that must be overcome in order to provide a foundation for resolving both funding and political problems. Active leadership and statesmanship involving individuals from many countries will be essential to solve these problems. The United States is in a strong position, and clearly capable of offering needed support—technical, political, and financial—to multinational efforts to improve the international germ plasm system. The United States must, however, recognize the need to foster a global concensus on germ plasm issues and seize every opportunity to work constructively within established forums to reach such consensus.

Imperative 2. Enhance and refine strategies for assembling genes into optimal combinations by sexual methods. Specific research tasks under this imperative address both basic and applied plant breeding needs that are very much on the agenda of the international centers, the more research-oriented seed companies, and public sector plant breeders.

Throughout the world, plant breeding has been undertaken within a volatile institutional context. Major shifts have occurred between the public and private sector, and across and among nations. Economic incentives and opportunities have rapidly changed and promise to evolve as the patent status of various cultivars is sorted out by the international community.

Opportunities for private firms to profit from breeding activities and to enter the new markets are essential if private plant breeding research is to be sustained. Private support for progressively more basic research is particularly vulnerable to future profitability. The rather dramatic shift of plant breeding activity from the public to private sectors in many countries heightens the importance of this vulnerability. A set of global issues of profound significance to crop productivity is how public policies and private strategies will impact seed companies and plant breeding research institutions related to control and support, and sovereign *versus* multinational focus. Public initiatives and attitudes will play an integral role in determining whether current trends continue toward progressively more influence and control by private firms over germ plasm resources, and the research on how to exploit them for crop productivity. The possibility exists that geopolitical and economic tensions could impose new sorts of restrictions and conditions on germ plasm use and exchange. The scientific and pragmatic consequences of such restrictions deserve careful consideration in any effort to enhance crop productivity.

Imperative 3. Analyze the organization, stability, and instability of plant genomes.

Imperative 4. Develop, for all crops, workable and efficient technologies for the introduction of novel genetic material and regeneration of functional transformed plants.

Imperative 5. Develop the fundamental knowledge necessary for the effective genetic manipulation of desirable crop phenotypes. These imperatives encompass several of the key challenges facing plant breeders, molecular biologists, and others working with the new tools of biotechnology. The resources needed to adequately pursue opportunities already apparent within these imperatives clearly exceed available funds, and will continue to do so for sometime. Accordingly, priorities must be established, pursued, monitored, and periodically adjusted. Accomplishing this goal is an appropriate function for public policy. In the developed world, scientists tend to play an integral role by serving on panels responsible for granting public funds and defining priorities. The extent to which such mechanisms actually are followed in establishing priorities varies and is a subject sure to spark a lively debate.

Group 2. Plant and Cell Physiology

This comprehensive list of 10 imperatives covers several areas of activity. Six of the 10 imperatives identify major elements of crop growth and development as possible targets for the manipulation of crop yield and quality. These range from the regulation of DNA replication to the control of flowering and plant senescence. Three of the imperatives identify research targets that impact on the environment. The first imperative identifies a need to strengthen the support for research of plant physiology and metabolism. The imperatives of group 2 are closely tied to the major thrusts of the other five working groups of stage I.

In terms of public policy, these imperatives raise generic questions involving how to adjust funding levels, priorities, and institutional roles. In addition, progress on several of these imperatives offers considerable promise in reducing per unit production costs.

The imperatives in this group are clearly articulated and logically presented. Stage II participants may wish to consider a recommendation to the U.S. Congress and other granting agencies that these imperatives be incorporated in future competitive grant programs.

Group 3. Rhizosphere Dynamics

Imperative 1. Improve crop productivity through understanding the basic process of root growth. Specific research objectives suggest the need for new sorts of collaborative research among several disciples to study root growth.

The knowledge resulting is likely to affect on-farm management decision including cultivation methods, rotations, and water and residue

242   PREAMBLE TO STAGE II

management. Hence, our understanding of productivity will be necessary
to capture the impacts of new developments. To profit from enhanced
crop production, specialists may need new tools to monitor the status of
the root zone during the growing season so that corrective actions can be
taken. The development and applications of such tools has not traditionally been a strength of the U.S. agricultural research system. New public
incentives and initiatives may be needed to cover this problem.

*Imperative 2. Increase in the efficiency of utilization of nutrients in the
soil and plant.* Research described under this imperative ranges from
basic to applied research in the field. To pursue this work effectively,
better protocols will be needed to coordinate basic, applied, and field
activities. The sizeable and immediately positive economic consequences
of a 50% reduction in fertilizer losses—viewed by the panel as a feasible
goal—heightens the importance of pursuing this imperative as a matter
of considerable priority for the United States and in other countries that
use large quantities of fertilizer.

On-farm benefits from this area of research will come about as new
techniques become more widely adopted by individual growers and farm
support businesses. In addition, we know from past experience with
fertilizer management that the interactions of the public and private
sectors in developing and adopting such new technologies is important,
changeable, and sometimes a matter of contention. Hence, this imperative deserves scrutiny from both groups 7 and 9.

*Imperative 3. Enhance symbiotic function and control root diseases
through a better understanding of plant-microbe interactions.* This imperative discusses the need for research on diseases and microbes that
impact root growth and plant development. The discussion following
imperative 1 applies equally well to this imperative. In addition, taking
advantage of these sorts of new technologies will require new monitoring
and management support capabilities. Some of the microbial and other
production inputs likely to emerge may require regulatory approval. In
the United States, microbial pesticides must be registered for use under
the Federal Insecticide, Fungicide, and Rodenticide Act.

*Imperative 4. Improve crop productivity by altering the soil and rhizos-
phere population through (i) introduction of novel organisms, and (ii) crop
and soil management.* This imperative lists five areas of research needed
to develop genetically engineered organisms and to study their eventual
fate and effect on crop production systems. Virtually all the public policies
under review by groups 8 and 9 relate to this imperative in some way. Of
particular relevance are regulatory policies and interaction between the
public and private sector. The different prospects and hurdles facing
adoption of genetically modified organisms across nations is an interesting and significant question. Some individuals have argued that biotechnology will have a disproportionally large and swift impact on developing
nations. Others suspect otherwise. In developed nations, adoption of
advanced biotechnologies will likely proceed more deliberately than technically possible because of regulatory and economic concerns. Stage II

participants need to focus on public policies and constraints, around the world, likely to discourage the development of technologies that could make valuable contributions to meeting world food needs. Those biotechnologies that make possible a radical and sustained shift away from energy-intensive, sometimes toxic production inputs toward inputs that preserve environmental integrity deserve special encouragement.

Group 4. Biological Constraints

Imperative 1. Improve crop health through better understanding and management of crop patterns, mixtures and rotations, plant residues, and soil. This imperative involves research on indicators and determinants of cropping system performance. As such, this work needs to be undertaken mindful of the many factors shaping production systems. It will generally require multidisciplinary input, and close ties to field level production problems and realities.

A key question remains, which involves the transfer of knowledge gained under this imperative to production technologies or alterations in management practices. In the case of genetic manipulation or chemical pest control, the process of technology diffusion involves a rather predictable combination of steps. Technology ultimately is packaged in new products that can be marketed and incorporated through existing marketing and educational channels. This is not always the case, however, when research clarifies some aspect of the interactions of cropping patterns, cultivar, pest control, and fertilizer application with some broader indicator of performance such as soil erosion, water management, or profitability. It is increasingly common for greater knowledge to complicate rather than simplify management decision making. Moreover, there is no individual, or company, to effectively transfer this newly discovered knowledge to growers.

Accordingly, an important challenge for stage II is to address how progress on this and related imperatives can more readily be utilized at the farm level. This issue is of great importance because of the heavy emphasis placed by stage I participants on system-related research. The level of priority of new research boils down to the interaction of two key considerations: scientific merit and the potential to produce valuable technological innovations. Research found wanting on either score is not likely to have a high priority as limited funds are allocated.

The interpretation and use of such system-based information in regulatory programs is also becoming an increasingly important issue, especially in developed nations where urban populations exist near or around farming regions. Regulatory programs may emerge as important sources of funding for such research.

Imperative 2. Maximize the capacity of plants to resist pest attack through acquisition and application of knowledge of biochemical and physical processes and genetic determinants.

Imperative 3. Develop new or more effective biological controls of pests using classical methods and new biotechnologies. Pursuit of these imperatives will require multidisciplinary collaboration involving plant breeders, molecular biologists, entomologists, plant pathologists, and other specialists. Also, the range of important, interesting work is truly vast in contrast to available resources, so priority setting will remain a necessity. Comments made previously regarding the viability and process for practical on-farm results is sufficiently unclear in reference to this imperative to warrant early consideration in defining priorities and designing research initiatives.

Imperative 4. Develop new chemicals (pesticides) for pest control along with improved and safer methods for their sustained use compatible with crop production strategies. Research to sustain pesticide efficacy, and develop new pesticides is described under this imperative. The private sector has assumed a major role in these areas, reflecting the opportunities for financial profit from new pesticide products.

Questions remain regarding the appropriate public role in research on traditional pesticides. The stringency of standards and procedural hurdles in pesticide regulatory programs clearly contributes to the formation of research agendas in both the public and private sector. At present, between 25 and 33% of private sector research on agricultural chemicals is defensive in nature, reflecting progressively strict environmental standards. Such investments need to be weighed in light of the immense opportunities for development of new pest control technologies.

Imperative 5. Improve integrated pest management (IPM) programs by enhancing data collection and assessment, decision support, and systems design. Research under this imperative would build up the information and scientific basis for IPM systems. The fate and status of publicly funded IPM research in the United States has changed considerably since the 1975 conference, which identified IPM as a critical imperative. In the early 1970s, IPM was an exciting new concept. For several years, this approach attracted new funds and intensive interest on the part of investigators. For a host of reasons, IPM has become less fashionable, or perhaps merely obscured in recent years. Funding for IPM in the United States has declined. Remarkable progress made in some crops has not spread either as broadly or quickly as thought possible by many scientists.

The apparent hesitancy of U.S. agriculture to utilize IPM raises important questions regarding a diversity of public policies governing agricultural research, technology development, and regulatory policy. To exploit fully progress under this, and related crop protection imperatives, it may be necessary and advisable to better understand how these policies could be more strategically utilized to encourage adoption of IPM and related advanced control strategies.

Group 5. Environmental Constraints

Imperative 1. Develop a thorough understanding of the physiological effects of and responses to environmental stress on plants in order to manipulate genetically crops for greater adaptation to environmental con-

straints. Research under this imperative will track that described by several other groups, and is designed to get at genetic opportunities to overcome stress. Accordingly, comments made previously apply here as well.

The need for and complexity of priority setting, however, takes on even more immediacy in implementation of this imperative. Since virtually all crops are subject to some stress in all environments, and could be moved into new environments if certain constraints were removed, it becomes a strategic necessity to fully think through where such advances would pay the greatest dividends. In doing so, it is critical to determine how cropping systems and profitability might change if a given source of environmental stress is overcome. Secondary consequences—both positive and negative—of overcoming sources of plant stress need to be taken into account in setting priorities.

The mechanisms for the allocation of limited public funds for plant stress research have not grown at the same rate as scientific capabilities. At present in the United States, research is on-going to preserve the viability of irrigated agriculture in the west, in the face of water-pollution problems caused by salinity, selenium, and farm chemicals. Research in the east is focusing on how to expand irrigation in that region by overcoming other aspects of plant stress that constrain yields when water is no longer a limiting factor. Very little systematic consideration is given to whether one or both investments of public funds might produce greater benefits elsewhere, even when the irrigated crops are in surplus and compel sizeable treasury outlays to store.

Imperative 2. Develop a thorough understanding of how environmental modifications can minimize constraints on crop productivity.

Imperative 3. Determine the impacts of agricultural practices on the environment.

Imperative 4. Understand the impacts of anthropogenic chemicals on agroecosystems. Even though these imperatives have been repeatedly highlighted for more than a decade, systematic research on environmental degradation has been limited to a few regions and aspects of crop production. To do a better job in the next decade, it may be advisable to determine why environmental impact research tends to slip low within funding priorities even though regulatory actions, social concerns, and public activism appear to warrant greater attention.

Adverse impacts of soil erosion, fertilizer, and pesticides tend to be very localized, and highly concentrated. The vast majority of the serious problems occur in relatively few, generally known areas. Curiously, few steps have been taken to address these problems where they are most severe. Key conservation policy developments in the 1985 farm bill may initiate an important new trend by specifically targeting policy instruments (penalties and incentives) to highly erosive cropland. The same concept—targeting programs and policies to the worst areas—could and may eventually be incorporated in cases of severe water management and pest control problems.

Implementation of such policies could create considerable new impetus for research under this imperative. Moreover, scientists knowledgeable about environmental impacts need to help inform policymakers regarding how such programs might function.

Imperative 5. Develop alternative cropping and resource management strategies to minimize environmental constraints. Farm management and land use decisions are made in response to many factors. Research to design alternative schemes to minimize adverse environmental impacts should be carried out mindful of the prospects for adoption. The compatibility of other agricultural and regulatory policies with policies that might encourage use of alternative schemes also needs to be continuously evaluated.

Since many developed nations face chronic surplus production problems, the opportunity exists for changes in management schemes that achieve positive environmental/resource outcomes at the expense of some crop production. Indeed, the conservation reserve initiative in the 1985 farm bill could retire for up to 10 years some 20 to 45 million acres of highly erodible cropland. Since such policy initiatives invariably involve complex interactions among social objectives and political interests, economic considerations are bound to play an important role in determining what initiatives are perceived as fair and workable. The need for multidisciplinary collaboration is particularly great when evaluating policies that would encourage or compel changes in management schemes across broad geographic areas, or open up the possibility of substitution of crops, or the transfer of problems to other areas. As stated in reference to other imperatives, the infrastructure in support of this type of research is poorly developed in most countries, including the United States. As stated in reference to the imperative on multidisciplinary research, this need has long been widely recognized and has received much rhetorical attention. Few concrete steps have been taken, however, and are not likely to be until there are more substantial and sustained shifts in the funding priority of this type of work. Unlike other areas of research, there is not even a well conceived and proven mechanism at the national level to provide such funds.

Group 6. Productions Systems

Imperative 1. Design cropping pattern alternatives which increase productivity and optimize nutrient cycling and use, minimize soil loss, and reduce pressure from insect pests, weeds, and pathogens. Six areas of research are described. A major goal is developing improved rotations, and crops for inclusion in rotations, so that solar energy, water, and nutrients can be used more efficiently. Accordingly, the extent to which agricultural commodity programs and other policies have and could impact land use patterns is a primary concern.

The need to develop new cultivars of value in rotations raises another policy concern. Since the trends in major producing regions of the United

States are generally away from crop diversity and rotations, private companies are relatively disinterested in new crops, and other genetic research focused on rotations within multicropping systems. Accordingly, if such advances are to be made, a shift in priority within public research programs may be warranted, and steps should be considered to encourage alternative cropping systems. Alternatively, tax policies and other private sector inducements, such as patent protection for novel cultivars, might be worthy of consideration. Last, since the prospects for enhanced genetic options in any country—developed or developing—are greatest if germ plasm from around the world can be tapped, all countries stand to benefit from an open and vigorous system of germ plasm and assessment, storage, and regeneration of cultivars. (See group 1 imperatives.)

Imperative 2. Investigate and promote techniques (ranging from cropping practices and cultivars to postharvest handling and storage methods) for farms, especially in developing countries, to provide a year-round supply of nutritious feed for livestock. One obvious and critical interaction between crop productivity and livestock production—feed quality—is addressed by this imperative. On the farm with a mixed crop-livestock operation, total farm profit is determined in large part by how well the cropping system meets livestock feed needs. This imperative explicitly recognizes that crop productivity is often an interim step of less significance than the ultimate goal—a productive livestock system.

As noted in the imperative, the need for improved practices and cultivars is particularly acute in some developing countries. Forages are generally not in short supply in the United States. Indeed, chronic overproduction of grains has cut feed costs to unprecedented levels. It is worth noting that consumer preferences for lean meat may alter somewhat the mix of feeds needed for cattle production. Ultimately, beef producers may seek improved cultivars of grasses and legumes for this reason. Public sector research in this area could be a benefit in the future for both developed and developing nations.

Imperative 3. Promote the use of multipurpose trees in production systems. A wide range of research needs are described, all aimed at improving the options for including trees in integrated farm systems. To evaluate the possible benefits from particular lines of inquiry, it is necessary to develop a holistic measure of productivity that includes the interactions of the tree crop with livestock, and in terms of building soil fertility, in addition to direct contributions to human well-being through food and fuel production. Given the promising developments with multipurpose species, agroforestry may be a particularly rewarding area for an intensive, multidisciplinary research effort.

The special role of U.S.-based agricultural research in Florida, Puerto Rico, and Hawaii on these topics deserves special attention. Emerging economic opportunities arising from Latin American countries involved in the Caribbean Basin Initiative should be surveyed. A special attempt should be made to identify ways for small growers in these countries to introduce tree crops yielding cash income from export crops, but not necessitating abandonment of traditional staple crops and livestock.

The need for a new international/regional focus on agroforestry may warrant major new investments in research capacity as a logical extension of the Consultative Group for International Agricultural Research (CGIAR) system.

Imperative 4. Investigate the effects of cropping practices on changes in the physical, chemical, and biological properties of soils. The type of investigation made will be a function of the scientific sophistication of agricultural research and support infrastructure. It will be important to carefully tailor the nature of the investigation made so that research results are of practical value in devising improved production practices.

Imperative 5. Evaluate and devise innovative methods for processing and handling the biological products of the cropping systems. This is one of the only imperatives aimed at expanding the options for utilization of crop production. Results from this imperative would enhance productivity by increasing the value of the harvested product from a given system. To the extent wastes and by-products could be more effectively used, this strategy offers considerable promise. Trade-offs between alternative uses of wastes need to be assessed, such as long-term impacts on soil organic matter as a result of removing residues for ethanol production.

Like most imperatives, research initiatives to improve processing and handling methods need to be developed strategically in light of the existing infrastructure, skills, economics, and cultural preferences in a given region.

Imperative 6. Adapt emerging engineering technologies and tools that will help in measuring and understanding production systems. Initiatives under this priority would lead to new tools for monitoring biological and physical processes. Existing tools would include soil testing and feed analysis instruments. There is a need for "intelligent" machines to do repetitive, precise, and/or hazardous work.

The development of such tools has not been a high priority in either the public or private sector. In some cases, it is difficult to foresee who would pay the costs of development, purchase, and maintenance of such tools. Research applications alone may not justify the costs of development.

In advancing the state of the art in such tools, it may be necessary to demonstrate more convincingly the potential benefits so that extension specialists and private consultants can begin to determine how they could be utilized. Because of the unique hurdles such developmental work faces, an attempt by public research institutions to explore the likely path to commercial use might prove valuable. When important new capabilities are identified, public funds and special incentives may be warranted to support further development and commercialization, especially when there is no clear-cut way for any private interest to recover the development costs.

Imperative 7. Develop microcomputer-based models to improve the design and management of production systems. Five specific tasks under this initiative address a range of modeling needs. To be effective, such models must incorporate physical, biological, resource, management, and economic variables. They will require multidisciplinary collaboration.

Models can be built for almost any purpose, creating an essentially endless need for data. Progress in other sciences allows modelers to build more complex interactions into models, increasing costs for data collection, entry, computation, and interpretation. Some agricultural research and policy challenges can best be addressed through model development, which requires an integration of knowledge into a common framework. In developing priorities for investments in modeling capabilities, consideration should be given to the costs, accuracy, usefulness, and coverage of models.

Research administrators, with limited funds, face a difficult task in evaluating how much funds to devote to modeling, and in choosing which sorts of models are most likely to yield information and insights cost-effectively. Modelers need to devote more thought to providing information useful to decision makers in making such choices. The need may arise for new funding and peer review mechanisms to assist in allocation of funds for modeling.

Public Policies and Institutions to Enhance Crop Productivity

Submitted on behalf of the group by:

CHARLES M. BENBROOK   WILLIAM L. BROWN

An International Perspective for Agricultural Research

The future well-being of international agriculture requires that research and technology development be carried out in a global context. A global perspective in R&D for agriculture demands interactions and collaborative efforts between U.S. scientists and scientists in other countries. Such collaboration must include all countries of the world where future markets, exotic germ plasm, and unique ecogeographic research sites exist. Particularly rich sources of germ plasm exist in many parts of the developing world. These nations are also the primary source of food products imported by the United States and much of the developed world.

Participating in the broader international arena will further benefit domestic agricultural research by providing an opportunity for mutual discussion and exchange of research imperatives, discoveries, and applications. Moreover, such participation should help agricultural policymakers around the world identify ways to respond to shared policy and trade problems, such as surplus production capacity in some crops and areas, and food shortages in other parts of the world. While a national perspective can identify an ever evolving set of imperatives, an international perspective will provide a broader set of experiences and research problems that will expand future potential for solving national problems.

The potential is growing for a broad range of mutual benefits from technology exchange. While the humanitarian imperatives of the past remain, they no longer stand alone as the motivating force behind the need for facilitating and coordinating international research. Clearly, U.S. agriculture both contributes to and benefits from the broader context offered by international agriculture. Public policies should facilitate a global orientation of research development activities. Scientists can and must contribute to their development and implementation. Specific policies that warrant attention include: (1) development of mechanisms to assure the continued conservation of genetic resources, both plant and animal. In addition, and as a key step toward this goal, the free exchange of germ plasm resources between countries, national and international organizations, and the public and private sectors should be actively encouraged in every way possible. All countries should recognize the need to foster a global consensus on germ plasm issues, and seize every opportunity to work constructively within established forums to reach such consensus; (2) support for international agricultural research should continue to be provided by the United States, and further steps should be taken to provide opportunities for scientists to collaborate with the centers in breeding and germ plasm conservation programs; (3) the governments of developed countries are encouraged to continue positive collaborations with the World Bank, United Nations' agencies, other multinational organizations, and countries in fostering the safe and economical use of pesticides around the world; (4) better use can and should be made of routinely collected information regarding global agricultural production accomplishments and trends. Such information would be valuable throughout the research community, both within the public and private sectors, to alert scientists to emerging needs and opportunities; and (5) steps should be taken to facilitate scientific interchange, including sharing of genetic resources, with the Soviet Union, China, and other centrally planned economics.

Accommodating Changing Funding Levels and Priorities

There are no existing mechanisms that effectively involve all federal agencies in identifying and acting upon changing agricultural research needs and priorities in the United States. As budgets become constrained, this shortcoming is a weakness in our capacity to exploit emerging scientific opportunities. Adjusting priorities in an era of shrinking resources can be inefficient, costly, and disruptive. However, it also presents an opportunity to implement changes that could leave organizations stronger and more efficient.

The process of accommodating changing funding levels can become both a mandate and opportunity for administrative initiative. As steps are taken, we strongly recommend adherence to two principles: (1) cuts or increases in funding level, at both the federal and state level, should generally not be distributed across-the-board. Higher priority work should be identified and receive adequate support even in a climate of fiscal austerity; lower priority work should receive less funds even when budgets are growing; and (2) in light of the growing role of private sector research, public sector research priorities need to be continuously evaluated to assure public dollars are meeting critical and unmet needs.

Changing Priorities

Local and crop-specific research needs emerge and gain support through very different mechanisms than those affecting research direction in a federal system of laboratories. Responses to, and initiatives for changing priorities should progress through all levels of decision making and through all funding mechanisms. With scientific advance moving ahead at its current, rapid pace, there will be great need and very beneficial opportunities over the next several decades to change priorities.

Initiatives are needed to form new research teams and programs that go beyond single state or laboratory lines; and for the sharing and communication of research results among scientists and state extension personnel not directly involved with the program. Recommendations made elsewhere to foster multidisciplinary research are also relevant to the achievement of this imperative.

Both the special and competitive grants program within the United States Department of Agriculture (USDA), and other programs administered by federal agencies, are vehicles by which changing priorities can be expressed within the system: (1) competitively funded activities, open to both public and private university investigations, should remain the primary vehicle for drawing new scientific talent into basic agricultural research. Research needs, and proposals should be defined according to generic scientific challenges. Narrow and specific definitions of research areas should be avoided; (2) special grants should be authorized in instances where mission-oriented research programs can be pursued most efficiently on a regional and multidisciplinary basis. Federal grants for highly specific research programs, of primarily localized importance should be avoided since such work should remain a principal focus of state agricultural experiment stations; and (3) administrators of publicly funded agricultural research at both the state and federal level would benefit from a higher degree of flexibility and support in carrying out cost-saving administrative initiatives. Some greater degree of regional and national consolidation of certain areas of research both within the Agricultural Research Service (ARS) and state experiment stations may be advisable. Strong leadership and support in doing so from the U.S. Congress, USDA, private sector, and academia will be essential to achieve this goal.

Strategic Planning and Coordination of Research Priorities

To provide the entire federal establishment, universities, and the private sector with guidance on how to make and respond to such adjustments, including response to major new and rapidly evolving scientific opportunities, we stress the need for an improved mechanism to: (1) advise USDA and other agencies on priorities within and among broad areas of agricultural research; (2) facilitate the exchange of information and the coordination of programs across the federal establishment and with state agricultural experiment stations; and (3) compile and monitor information on federal and state agricultural research expenditures, research in the private sector, and other indicators of the health of agricultural research in the United States.

The nature of this mechanism could take any of several forms. It could be a new council or committee, a consolidation or adaptation of existing committees, or it might evolve from existing informal mechanisms of communication among federal officials responsible for administering agricultural research. Valuable principles in structuring such a mechanism include: (1) it should be independent from granting agencies, or other public or private organizations with a vested interest in some aspect of system performance; (2) it should be advisory in nature and not have policymaking or grant-making authority or responsibility; (3) it should have a source of support that ensures continuity, and permits a long-term view; and (4) it should have opportunity, and the capacity to collect appropriate data on agricultural research activities in order to assess needs and accomplishments, including information on the demand, supply, and adequacy of agricultural science personnel.

The domestic agricultural research system encompasses federal and state public institutions, public and private universities, and private sector facilities. The origins of contemporary research problems have expanded well beyond the points of application within the agricultural sector. The diversity of actors in the research arena as well as the complexity of the issues with which they deal demands effective communication across the scientific community. Institutional mechanisms can serve a useful purpose by fostering dialogue that is an essential step toward coordination. It is recognized that coordination cannot be imposed by any entity. Dialogue and information exchange can, however, contribute.

Within the context of tightening constraints on research resources, benefits will grow from any progress that can be made in the timely adjustment of research priorities.

Multidisciplinary Research

Multidisciplinary research using modern methods for data collection and analysis offers great promise in advancing crop productivity research. Unexpected yet valuable new insights will emerge as scientists trained in different disciplines design experiments, test new hypotheses, and work together.

Multidisciplinary research is a collaborative effort among scientists from various disciplines who join together to solve a problem. Possible benefits from multidisciplinary research are greater today than a decade ago. The breadth of agriculturally relevant disciplines extends across basic biological and physical sciences, engineering and applied sciences, nutrition and health, and economics and other social sciences, including the law. The emergence of specialized subdisciplines within disciplines such as biology, chemistry, genetics, and other areas has also greatly increased the combination of disciplines that can work together. In our present agricultural research system, the two primary operating scenarios for multidisciplinary research are: (1) scientist-initiated programs evolve when a group of scientists from various disciplines assemble on their own initiative through unstructured interactions to coordinate their efforts on a definable problem; and (2) institutionally initiated programs evolve when administrators identify a need for a new sort of focus, or new facilities to successfully attack a given problem. Such research programs may involve just a few individual investigators, or could entail establishment of multidisciplinary centers or institutes.

Scientist-initiated programs should be encouraged by the following mechanisms: (1) problems must have identified time frames, with clearly delineated funding sources; (2) administrators must develop mechanisms to recognize key researchers who can catalyze, and focus the activities of the group. These individuals must be given sufficient flexibility in the allocation of time to devote needed effort to the multidisciplinary project; and (3) project teams, and the administrative structures supporting them, should not generally be institutionalized into a permanent structure. Within academia, scientists in departments should be encouraged to participate in multidisciplinary projects, retaining affiliation with disciplinary units. No sacrifice should be entailed in prestige, salary, promotion, or other rewards. After completion of the project, most participating scientists would be expected to return to disciplinary departments.

Institutionally initiated programs also require a clear definition of mission-oriented research tasks, stable funds, and leadership. The size of such centers, funding needs and mechanisms, relationships to academic and other institutions, the private sector, and other considerations will clearly impact how scientists can be attracted to, and awarded for joining such multidisciplinary teams.

There should be more opportunities to carry out multidisciplinary research. Tangible support, in contrast to rhetorical encouragement is needed in the form of financial resources and professional rewards. These should be offered in appropriate ways in all segments of the agricultural research community and at all stages of career development. It is the sense of group 7 (Public Policies and Institutions to Enhance Crop Productivity) that multidisciplinary research should be encouraged, consistent with the following principles: (1) multidisciplinary research should be encouraged and supported in all ways possible, but it cannot be forced; (2) research should never be funded or otherwise encouraged solely because it is multidisciplinary; (3) competitive grants programs established by USDA, National Science Foundation (NSF), Department of Energy (DOE), other agencies, and private foundations should be encouraged to use as a selection criteria meaningful indicators of the extent and vitality of multidisciplinary collaboration as envisioned within individual research proposals; (4) multidisciplinary collaboration should be encouraged for individual investigators, whether the need is to work with another scientist on a part-time basis, or to participate in a large multidisciplinary center with hundreds of professional staff.

It is the sense of group 7 that limited progress has been made in the last decade toward providing the range of opportunities needed for multidisciplinary collaboration. Constraints to collaboration remain firmly embedded, particularly in academia. This is of concern because of the changing nature of agricultural research challenges, particularly in many areas of basic research. Multidisciplinary research is essential to research opportunities in molecular biology. We believe that this is not likely to come about without a change in attitude and a firm commitment throughout the research community. Toward this end, we recommend: (1) Research and analysis on past and present multidisciplinary research efforts should be initiated to discover the administrative and human factors that contribute, both positively and negatively, to multidisciplinary research. The goal should be to create a body of knowledge useful in designing and implementing new multidisciplinary programs. This recommendation implies a need for basic social science research. (2) A special, high-level, and concerted effort should be initiated, with leadership from the National Association of State Universities and Land Grant Colleges (NASULGC), to overcome within academia impediments to multidisciplinary research. New ways to reward, and encourage multidisciplinary activity should be appraised such as: (a) utilizing the extent of multidisciplinary accomplishments as a factor, or perhaps the key factor, in hiring and promotion decisions; (b) granting split appointments tied to demonstrable research accomplishments across departments, or even colleges, and within specialized centers; and (c) awarding research support, in part, based on viability of multidisciplinary collaboration. (3) New sources of funds for multidisciplinary research should be made available in USDA's competitive and special grants programs, particularly in areas where no support has been available. Several imperatives set out in stage I fall into this category. (4) Several new mission-oriented research centers or institutes should be funded, both with and without walls. Support for the centers should be granted competitively, and extend for several years. Sizable grants should be given serious consideration. Nontraditional public and private sources for funds to support new centers should be actively solicited, consistent with the diverse, mission-oriented focus of prospective centers.

Agriculture and Environmental Quality

The expanded knowledge base that several stage I imperatives would create has great potential to facilitate the integration of agricultural objectives with health, environmental, and conservation goals. New knowledge about crops and agricultural management practices, and their implications for the environment needs to be applied in a way that maximizes the sustainability and reliability of crop protection and minimizes environmental risks. Public policy developments that would benefit directly from such knowledge include the capability to identify water-stressed environments, highly erosive, and other fragile lands, and to assess the potential for conservation techniques to permit their sustained productivity in the United States and around the world.

Domestically the 1985 Farm Bill creates a major conservation reserve program that would remove from production several million highly erodible and other fragile lands. It would pay farmers for placing erodible lands into grass or forestry-based land uses for 10 to 15 years. This and

related programs will require consistent and defensible information about
the soil and water resources, erodibility of soils in crop production, and
the effects of alternative land uses and conservation practices.

Internationally, despite remarkable productivity gains in much of the
world, the sustainability of crop production cannot be taken for granted
without continuing attention to the quality of the soil, water, and other
natural resources. The issues pose a challenge: they arise from such
disparate actions as the destruction of tropical forests and the subsequent
cropping of tropical soils to the irrigation of arid lands. While each such
expansion of production involves unique and local aspects, each also can
benefit from assessment in light of basic scientific principles. Stage I of
the conference specified several cropping systems imperatives aimed at
creating new opportunities to enhance crop productivity in stressed and
fragile environments. New technologies embodied in novel crop production systems—sometimes incorporating trees, livestock, and multiple
crops—should be a focus of efforts.

Water Resources

With agriculture the nation's single largest consumer of water and a
major nonpoint source of water pollutants, crop production practices
have become inextricably linked to water supply and water quality issues.
Research on the environmental fate of nitrates and pesticides, on their
transport, on efficient use of irrigation water, and on the identification
of areas vulnerable to groundwater leaching is especially needed. As
regulatory and quasiregulatory programs are already being directed at
agricultural sources of pollution—e.g. in the Chesapeake Bay Basin—
information is urgently needed to ensure that actions taken are effective
while consistent with agricultural needs.

Agrichemicals

Efficient use of agrichemicals will reduce the potential for human
exposure and for their loss to the environment. For example, the Rhizosphere Dynamics working group in stage I, citing research underway in
Iowa on nitrogen fertilization, suggests that significant efficiency gains—
perhaps to 50%—may be possible through new insights into how deniti-
fication, plant uptake, and leaching processes impact the efficiency of
fertilizer use. In addition, as new tillage practices are adopted, new
practices for agrichemical management are needed, requiring research on
chemical fate and behavior under these new practices, and on new
application techniques.

Sustainable Agriculture

Alternative farming, often known as sustainable or regenerative agriculture, or organic farming, is receiving increased attention as a source
of potential insights and opportunities for lowering productivity costs
and reducing potential crop and environmental contamination risks.

Alternative farming represents a valuable practical experiment with the potential to provide insights into how farmers can reduce cash production costs. It also offers researchers valuable opportunities to carry out field level research that might otherwise not be practiced.

Environmental Impacts of Genetically Engineered Organisms

Biotechnology promises to open up new frontiers in crop productivity leading to important commercial breakthroughs. Some have already occurred, and are well along in the process leading to on-farm applications. The ultimate significance of biotechnology to agriculture is impossible to predict, although it is bound to be immense and evolve continuously for decades.

The scientific excitement of this era, however, is tempered among some by concerns regarding unforeseen problems that might arise from the release of genetically engineered organisms into the environment.

Such concerns must be responded to so that field tests necessary to determine the agricultural value of new organisms can proceed. Such tests need to be carefully designed and monitored to assure, first, that no adverse and unforeseen consequences emerge and, second, to contribute scientific insight into how the fate of genetically engineered organisms in the environment can be measured, controlled, and modified to increase either the efficacy or safety of a given product.

Important public policy decisions need to be made around the world as genetically engineered products come into widespread use. Judgments will need to be made regarding acceptable and comparative levels of risk.

In discussing public policies to advance crop productivity, and implement stage I imperatives, group 7 focused considerable attention on how to define and measure productivity. The need to recognize differences in alternative productivity concepts was highlighted.

Development of Scientific Capabilities: Human Resources and Institutions

Submitted on behalf of the group by:

VERNON W. RUTTAN   JAMES T. BONNEN
                ROGER L. MITCHELL

We are living in a constrained economic environment in which the U.S. society seems unwilling to achieve the level of public and private saving or the level of public and private investment that is needed to maintain historical rates of economic growth.

American society cannot afford to let this continue! We should base our deliberations on the assumption that, in America, society will again find it useful to expand its investment in research, including agricultural research, in order to enhance the growth of agricultural productivity and the growth of the American economy.

Human Capital for Agricultural Research

During the next decade a substantial share of the staff engaged in graduate training and in the research fields related to agriculture at the state universities, at the U.S. Department of Agriculture (USDA), and in the private sector will become eligible for retirement. A national assessment of the status of higher education faculty in agriculture, natural resources, and forestry was conducted in 1983 as part of the USDA Food and Agricultural Education Information System (FAEIS) activities (1, 2). Table I (taken from Ref. 1) lists the faculty from selected teaching specializations eligible to retire in the next decade.

While the data are not as firm, it appears that comparable rates of turnover can be expected in federal agricultural research and in private sector agricultural research.

The rapid changes in scientific staff anticipated during the next decade represents a loss of substantial research capacity. Turnover also represents an opportunity to bring new training and new perspectives into the agricultural research system. It will at the same time be a difficult challenge to the agricultural research system. Decreasing numbers of young people are entering undergraduate and graduate training in many fields related to crop production (see C. E. Hess, this volume). The opportunities to strengthen agricultural research through upgrading the human capital resources directed to research will occur only if a number of steps are taken to support the financial and professional incentives in agricultural research. We have discussed the steps that might be taken to strengthen incentives under the following leadership: (a) professional and financial incentives, (b) complementarity of graduate education and

Table I. *Retirement of Selected Faculty in the Next Decade*

Teaching Specialization	Age 55 and Over	
	Number (%)	Full-time equivalent (%)
Agricultural sciences	30	24
Agricultural business and management	24	24
Agricultural communications/journalism	30	28
Agricultural education	29	28
Agricultural engineering	26	27
Food science and nutrition	26	26
International agriculture	28	21
Plant sciences	28	26
Renewable natural resources	22	20
Soil science	32	30
Related sciences	25	23

research, (c) multidisciplinary and interdisciplinary research, (d) training and retraining of established scientists and administrators, and (e) research priorities in the area of human capital in agriculture.

Professional and Financial Incentives

An issue that is often neglected in discussions of the adequacy of professional or scientific resources is that of financial incentive. There is often an implicit assumption that choice of a career in science or in technology development should be motivated primarily by a commitment to the search for knowledge or the excitement of discovery rather than by the economic incentives that act to influence career choice in other fields. This view is not entirely misplaced. The typical research scientist is often prepared, as a result of inclination and conditioning, to accept a rather high degree of defined gratification. The satisfactions associated with the rewards of professional achievement can represent, to some degree, a substitute for economic incentives.

The mix of available professional and monetary incentives differs among the several components of the U.S. agricultural research system. The private sector sometimes offsets weak professional incentives with relatively strong monetary incentives. The USDA Agricutural Research Service (ARS) has attempted to offset eroding economic incentives by giving greater attention to professional recognition. The state system has considerable latitude in combining professional and economic incentives.

Policy Imperatives

1. *Congress should establish a Federal Scientific Research Classification System in which salary schedule would not be constrained by the level of congressional salaries. An adjustment upward of 20 to 30% at the*

upper grade levels would be necessary to bring federal salary levels to a competitive level.

We are concerned that during the last decade the salary structure in the USDA/ARS, and in the federal science agencies generally, has lagged badly relative to the salary structure in both the universities and in the private sector. The weakness in economic incentives at the federal level is most severe at the senior ranks. And these are the levels where strength in program leadership is most critical. A strong federal agricultural science cadre is an essential complement to strong science in the universities and in the private sector.

2. *Ways should be sought to give more adequate recognition, both within the university and within the science community, for outstanding professional achievement. This includes endowed chairs and programs, and professional achievement awards.*

The universities often fail to use effectively the mix of professional and financial incentives that is available to them. Ways should be sought to enhance the stature of agricultural science within the science community. Within the university the use of endowed chairs and programs could be more widely used. Within the science community a broader set of national awards could be established to recognize outstanding achievement in agricultural science and technology development.

3. *The private sector should explore, with the universities and the ARS, means of institutional methods of strengthening staff development and provide a more effective communication between public and private sector scientists.*

The private sector has not always given adequate attention to the professional development of its scientific and professional staff. Cooperative arrangements between the private sector and the university and/or the ARS could be developed that would enhance the professional capacity of mid-career staff.

Decreasing numbers of young people are expressing an interest in careers related to crop production. This could pose a serious problem as scientists presently in this area reach retirement age. Incentives should be provided both in terms of professional reward and monetary support to reverse this trend. At the same time, unrealistic expectations with regard to the number of career opportunities should be avoided. A number of possible incentives designed to make careers in areas related to crop productivity more attractive are: (a) career counseling at the high school and undergraduate level and by professional societies which provide realistic and up to date information on career opportunities available in plant sciences; (b) provision for exceptional high school students to work on research projects as a stimulus to interest and an introduction to science challenges addressed in this field; (c) Peace Corps experience to introduce those with nonagricultural, nontraditional backgrounds to the global demand for the scientific support of the food and agriculture system; and (d) fellowship support for graduate and postdoctoral students and advanced professional development. This financial support could be designed to attract general science majors to crop productivity research programs.

Complementarity between Graduate Education and Agricultural Research

The development of human capital for U.S. agriculture has been attributed to a strong institutional relationship between agricultural research and education at land grant universities (5). Schultz maintained that the steady and continued support of human resource development has been a major source of productivity growth in agriculture. While admitting that America's fertile land and ample water, political freedom, and expanding technologies were important, Schultz's theory identified the nation's investment in people and their education as a major source of the "miracle of productivity that characterizes American agriculture."

Policy Imperative

Reductions in agricultural research funding may have unforeseen impacts on graduate programs in agriculture vis-à-vis recruiting and placement. There are, however, reforms in graduate training that should be considered. Graduate student projects within a college might be intentionally clustered to promote multidisciplinary research and greater educational benefit. Such efforts are within the control of departmental leadership and cooperating faculty.

Research Imperative

Analyze alternative structures that would promote multidisciplinary research and strengthen complementarity between agricultural research and graduate education. There have been a number of examples, such as the program to place graduate students from Cornell University, at the International Center for Maize and Wheat Improvement (CIMMYT) that could be drawn on in undertaking of such studies.

It has generally been assumed that there has been substantial complementarity between graduate education and research. Questions have been raised as to whether this association continues to hold with the same force as in the past. It has been asserted that such complementarity now exists, more at the postdoctoral than at the graduate level. We have examined the arguments that might be raised regarding the complementarity or lack of complementarity between research and graduate training.

The arguments favoring complementarity include: (a) funding support that agricultural research has historically attracted is an inducement to students to enter the agricultural sciences, (b) it is difficult to imagine graduate programs without research (although research without graduate programs is possible), (c) graduate education results in greater research productivity, (d) graduate students create a beneficial environment for their research advisors and reduce their possible intellectual atrophy, (e) graduate students supported on teaching or research assistantships give the "most bang-for-the-buck," (f) agricultural scientists who teach tend to be more current and maintain broader intellectual interests, (g) involvement in graduate education contributes to improved quality of agricultural research, (h) involvement in agricultural research contributes to improved quality of graduate education, (i) graduate education involvement provides additional sources of innovation for agricultural research, and (j) the coupling of graduate education with agricultural research is a strong and long tradition. Attempts to test the strength of this tradition may be costly.

The arguments against complementarity include: (a) graduate programs need to be disciplinary and hence they interfere with the multidisciplinary needs of research. Professional societies add an additional pull away from the needs of research programs; (b) graduate students need time for course work, and other academic requirements that divert resources intended for research to graduate education; (c) graduate students, because of their level of training, tend to do less sophisticated research than would postdoctorates; (d) the coupling of graduate education to agricultural research has contributed to an overproduction of agricultural scientists; (e) graduate education causes a load on university agricultural faculty as teachers and advisors. Many faculty then become research managers who have little or no time for "hands-on" research; and (f) the need of investigators to publish has an adverse effect on graduate programs—especially at the Master's degree level where the content or duration of the research may not be suitable for publication.

The recent movement by land grant universities to charge fringe benefits, tuition remission, and direct costs (overhead) against graduate assistantships budgeted in grant proposals has caused a shift in the balance between assistantships and the choice of funding a postdoctoral researcher or a technician. More and more principal investigators budget technical appointments rather than support for graduate students. This reduces the development and support of graduate programs in the agricultural sciences.

Any trend to uncouple graduate education from research should be resisted. It may be possible to conduct research without involvement in training. But graduate education cannot be conducted without research. There is, however, a need to examine critically the appropriate mix of technicians, graduate and postdoctoral students, and senior scientific staff in both university and non-university research organizations.

Multidisciplinary and Interdisciplinary Training

Multidisciplinarity takes many forms in the agricultural research establishment (4). In its simplest form, it can consist of a new technique from a discipline looking for application opportunities in a number of other related disciplines or departments. One example is linear programmers from the discipline of economics. Another is the molecular biologist seeking applications in numerous disciplines. At a less simple level are the "institute-like" departments typically found in colleges of agriculture and agricultural experiment stations. Departments such as agronomy or horticulture involve multidisciplinary mixes that are stable enough to be parts of permanent administrative structures and useful enough to groups of practical decision makers facing important sets of practical problems to earn sustained administrative, financial, and political support. At a somewhat more complex level there are multidisciplinary subjects which arise, require attention for awhile in order to provide groups of decision makers with the required kind of multidisciplinary knowledge, and then fade in significance as the problems of concern to the decision makers are solved or lose their significance over time. Such subjects are often too ephemeral and unstable to require long-term administrative structures, but require much short-term administrative effort because of their newness and uniqueness. Long-lived administrative structures are not needed and should be avoided. At a still more complex level one finds multidisciplinary research on complex practical problems. The mixes in this instance tend to be problem specific and unstable as the mix loses its relevance as soon as the problem is solved.

It is important to pay attention to these kinds of multidisciplinarities and to the extreme of pure disciplinarity because of wide differences among research efforts involving them. Important differences exist with respect to: (a) support, mobilization, and accountability; (b) administration and conduct; (c) review and evaluation; (d) practicality; and (e) durability. These are differences encountered in the "doing" of research of varying degrees of multidisciplinarities. Only a few examples are described here. See Ref. 3 for a more extensive treatment. Disciplinary and simple forms of multidisciplinarity are much easier to administer and conduct than more multidisciplinary complex research designed to solve practical problems. The data require closely timed specific contributions from various disciples and an administrative organization which can identify, obtain, and use inputs from different disciplines when needed. At the other extreme, disciplinary and simple multidisciplinary research can be administered largely by the "discipline" of the involved disciplines through peer reviewers and evaluators. On the other hand, practical problem solving research is more appropriately reviewed and evaluated by those who faced the practical problem being researched. Support is often offered by those seeking solutions to practical problems but on the condition of greater accountability.

Many differences between the multidisciplinary subject matter investigators and problem solvers in the USDA and agricultural experiment stations, on one hand, and disciplinarians on the other, grow out of differences in the degree of multidisciplinarity of the work they do. In setting research priorities and policies, these differences should be carefully considered.

One further point remains to be made. As we proceed from rather pure disciplinary to multidisciplinary, practical, problem solving research, knowledge of values (nonmonetary as well as monetary) and of the decision makers need to decide on right solutions increase in relative importance in the required multidisciplinary mixes. A consequence of this is that the social sciences and humanities become relatively more important. A research consequence is that philosophic orientations are required to be broad enough to permit research on values and prescriptions (3) as well as on the positimistic knowledge generated by biological and physical agricultural scientists with the technique of logical positionism, as a philosophy of science.

Policy Imperative

It is important that professional, financial, and administrative incentives be restructured to facilitate the implementation of those multidisciplinary and interdisciplinary research activities which can contribute to the advancement of science and of technology development.

The complexity of biotechnology research does impose substantial constraints on efforts to achieve effectively greater capacity to conduct multidisciplinary research. Students conceivably could do a research problem and take course work that spanned two or more disciplines such as plant breeding and molecular biology, or economics, soil science, and geology. To master properly all the disciplines is a difficult task. To find professors willing to cooperate in administering such a graduate program might also be difficult and to find department heads willing to accept such a split program might be impossible. Nevertheless, students occasionally will do studies and research outside their stated speciality, often at some risk to their progress in the home department. More typically, students take sequential degrees, or go on to postdoctoral research in a discipline different from that in which they were initially trained.

It often turns out that revolutionary new developments in science are made by people who have made such discipline changes. Short of such achievements, people who have learned more than one discipline often are able to successfully do research, throughout their productive years, in an interdisciplinary atmosphere. For mature scientists to be reeducated in a different discipline is often much more difficult. Faculty appointments, granting agency expectations, and perhaps fear of losing established research status can all act to inhibit an established investigator from adding a new discipline, or from changing disciplines. Nevertheless, some have done so, usually via the relatively painless method of recruiting graduate students who will do the detailed work in the newer discipline and who will take the course work needed to master it thoroughly.

Often, such discipline additions are applied to the major goal—a problem solving one—already pursued by the researcher so that a new discipline is applied to the solution of an old problem. Such additions are often highly productive, since the investigator already has intimate knowledge of the problem—such as breeding of specific plant species and investigations of a particular insect pest.

Short of thorough training in a second or third field of research is the act of becoming familiar enough with the potentialities—and the language—of other fields that the researcher can productively work as a member of a multidisciplinary team. Each member of the team remains a specialist in a single discipline; each member contributes an essential part of the work needed to solve the research problem. Such cooperative research, especially of problem solving kinds, has been typical of agronomic research since such work was first started. Teams of plant pathologists and plant breeders, or soil scientists and plant physiologists, for example, solve problems that individually they would not be able to handle.

Team research of a multidisciplinary nature will be increasingly important in crop productivity. To incorporate biotechnology, to adjust to economic needs in agriculture, to pay due attention to sociological impacts of technological change, or to adapt crop productivity research results to global needs will all require interdisciplinary cooperation and team research.

To educate students or established scientists, to be effective members of such a team may require new approaches. Narrow specialization in course work or in dissertation problems, may permanently inhibit students from looking outside their discipline. Undue emphasis on personal success in research, on self-sufficiency may produce researchers ill-suited for team research, unable to take or give advice, or to share success.

The rule of the administrator intending to foster multidisciplinary (or interdisciplinary) research is probably best described as that of a "door-opener," staying out of the way of those researchers who have the inclination and ability to do such work. Such investigators usually are imaginative not only in ways to do research, but also in ways to finance it and to get physical facilities for it. If administrators simply fail to put department roadblocks in the way of such researchers, or if they remove some already existing impediments, the researchers often can and will do what else needed to be done (sometimes without knowledge of their administrators).

In some highly structured research units, it may be helpful to write job descriptions in ways that reward scientists for productive interdisciplinary or multidisciplinary research. In less formally structured research units, the department leader probably will need to set the tone, to make it known that productive, forward-looking interdisciplinary and/or multidisciplinary research will be encouraged and rewarded. In either situation, interdepartmental understandings at the department head level are essential; good intentions in one department can be nullified by lack of cooperation in a second department. This says, then, that at the highest level of administration there must be understanding of the benefits of interdisciplinary research and encouragement of it. But it is likely, nevertheless, that such cooperative research will most often be successful when the initiative for it starts at the researcher level and is simply facilitated by administrators.

Training and Retraining of Established Scientists and Administrators

In rapidly changing technology driven fields, there is the ever present problem of stagnation of individual scientific expertise. This is particularly true in areas which are rapidly importing technology from fields outside of their own. For example, the incorporation of molecular genetics approaches into traditional plant breeding or the importation of new approaches and instrumentation into plant physiology and biochemistry challenges the experience of established scientists. There is no segment of the scientific enterprise that is immune to this syndrome. The frequent project intensive orientation of industry and the demands of disciplinary teaching affect the industrial and university scientists in a similar fashion. While the active researcher in any setting is frequently able to monitor change, that ability is eroded as additional administrative responsibilities are acquired during career development. The inability to recognize immediately and incorporate new approaches and techniques has a high cost in lost time and research inefficiency.

Policy Imperatives

1. *Establish opportunities for short-term, 3 to 6 months, visiting investigatorships.*

These opportunities should be project-specific and be directed toward the enhancement of the skills of established and productive investigators. These should be administered as supplements to current awards and should be readily available with only minimal review. This should include an increment to support the host laboratory.

2. *Senior investigator fellowships for 1 to 2 years of study in an established laboratory for the purpose of making major adjustments in scientific activities.*

These awards should be reviewed centrally by the granting agencies, and will focus on the quality of the work at the host institution and on the potential of the fellow for future accomplishments. It should be considered that SBIR funds could be used to support industry scientists to visit university laboratories for this type of training. A subset of this program should be available for administrators to learn technical skills or additional administrative skills but should be limited to 1 year. Scientists should receive 1 year research support after returning to their home institution in order to establish their new program.

3. *A class of awards modeled on the Presidential Young Investigator awards but directed to the established investigators would assist in linking university and industry scientists for the purpose of cross fertilization.*

With a small sum award coupled to a substantial matching component a linkage between industry and university could be established in which an exchange of personnel is stimulated. The matching component should be open to the exchange of facilities and equipment.

4. *Universities and research institutes should be more active in opening their facilities to visiting industrial scientists who return for new training or research facilities.*

While the industry should offer some reward to the universities for this opportunity the universities should be prepared to relax their demands for complete ownership of the potential intellectual property. Intellectual property rules in such settings must be agreed ahead, but the host institution must be prepared to share patent rights in order to make such a system work.

Research on Human Capital Development

Considerable attention was devoted to discussion of the research that should be done to contribute to the development of human capital or employment in academic establishments, on farms, in agribusinesses, agricultural organizations, in parastatal agencies, in the legislative and administrative branches of state and in national governments, and in international agencies important for the generation of use of crop production technologies.

Research Imperative

Conduct research on the demographic characteristics of the labor force in order to adjust educational, training, recreational promotion, and retention policies.

There are several levels at which such research should be conducted. These include (a) biological, physical and social agricultural scientists in the academic, government, and private sectors; (b) administrators in academic, government, and agribusiness sector; (c) leaders in voluntary organizations, federal and state legislative bodies, and international agencies; and (d) the management workers engaged in agricultural production and the agricultural service industries.

Science Policy in Agriculture

There are multiple sources of increases in crop productivity. These include (a) advances in knowledge in the several crop science disciplines; (b) advances in biological, chemical, and mechanical technology; (c) improvements in the capacity of the human agents involved in supplying and managing agricultural technology; and (d) improvements or reforms in the design of the market and nonmarket institutions which engage in the use of the resources that contribute to agricultural production.

There is a two-way relationship between technical and institutional charge. Advances in technology may require entirely new institutions before it can be effectively utilized. And institutional changes may create demands for changes in the rate or even the direction of technical change.

Science policy imperatives were considered under four headings: (a) institutions and policy, (b) policy and ethics, (c) the United States in the global agricultural research system, and (d) the gains and losses from different rates of technical change.

Institutions and Policy

Innovations in any one factor create imbalances requiring modifications in the others before the potential productivity of an innovation can be realized by society. Different institutional configurations will have the effect in one case of facilitating the use of a technology and in another of constraining its use and value. Social science research on institutions contributes to the discovery of complementarities and the release from constraints in improving the social performance of agriculture.

Policy Imperatives

1. *The rules for allocation of federal agricultural research and education expenditures should be redesigned to compensate states for the losses of benefits from their research and development (R&D) and education investments that spill over to other states.*
2. *Reform the agricultural commodity, credit and tax policies, programs, and institutions that create incentives for periodic overinvestment of resources in crop production.*

Research on the returns to agricultural R&D shows that, in addition to lack of real dollar growth in federal R&D, the most serious deficiency is the failure to compensate states for the spillover (the gain to other states) from R&D investment. This reduces the incentive for state legislatures to invest in agricultural research and assures a total rate of investment well below the optimum for the United States.

Creation of productive capacity does not automatically lead to increased output. Economic incentives induce output and shape its mix. In periods of excess supply, it is wasteful and depresses prices and income when policy creates incentives for short-term overinvestment of resources in production.

Research Imperatives

1. *Analyze the implications of major changes in technology for the institutions of agriculture.*

Examples include: (a) evaluate alternative rules for property rights to genetic materials; (b) examine the consequences of different regulatory rules for safe development, testing, and use of the new genetic technologies; and (c) analyze the implications the information age technologies for market institutions have for research and education institutions of agriculture.

Technological change creates the need to modify institutions, if the full potential of productivity in an innovation is to be realized.

2. *Analyze the effectiveness of the articulation and coordination of research and education functions and institutions that have in the past, or might*

in the future, contribute to the productivity and social performance of agriculture.

It will be necessary to examine a number of areas: (a) how well the traditional institutions of research and education (Experiment Stations; Extension Service; Resident Instruction; USDA/ARS/FAS (Foreign Agricultural Service)/ERS (Economic Research Service) are adapted for providing educated professionals, scientists, and research in today's changing environment; and (b) the nontraditional research and educational institutions (propriatory firms, non-land grant universities) and develop designs for new public-private sector linkages that would facilitate the effective participation of these institutions in the system of agricultural R&D and education.

The historical performance of the agricultural R&D and educational institutions has depended not only on the adaptation of those institutions to their shared functions, but also to the coordination of effort through effective, interactive linkage of functions and institutions. As this system of institutions expands to include new, nontraditional institutions such as non-land grant universities and private sector research institutes and firms, it is important for productivity to maintain effective interlinkage of all elements of the system.

3. *Analyze the complementarities between different types of research and sources of productivity that need to be understood for effective R&D resource allocation and for social investments in agriculture. An inadequate understanding of these relationships continues to bias social priorities and R&D policy for agriculture.*

Among the areas that should receive attention under this imperative are: (a) the roles of different types of research and education activities in agricultural sector productivity and performance (*e.g.* basic, developmental, adaptive and maintenance research, and technology transfer and validation in use); (b) discover institutional devices for the effective allocation to and management of resources for disciplinary, subject matter, and problem solving research; and (c) examine the implications for research and education policy of the complementarities between social investments in technology, biophysical capital, human capital, and institutions.

There are a number of other important areas which we did not designate as imperatives but which in our judgment deserve serious attention. These include: (a) institutional alternatives for the control/regulation of the undesirable external effects of crop production technologies on human health and safety and on the environment; (b) the interactions of changing food preferences, improved knowledge of nutrition, and changes in relative prices of different food products for their impact on changing demand for individual crops; (c) the institutions for the allocation of rights to water and its management in use. It will be necessary to develop new institutions for dealing with water when it is simultaneously a limiting factor in crop production, industrial and urban development; (d) analyze the various agricultural policy decision processes impacting crop production and productivity. This is a moving target that is not well understood even in many of the institutions of agriculture; and (e) study the actions and behaviors in the political coalitions that attempt to sustain policies influencing crop production and productivity. This is not only a moving target but an unstable one in need of institutional innovations.

Policy and Ethics

The growing complexity of agricultural technology and its impact on people, communities, and the environment raise a large number of ethical issues that must be faced at the policy level. What can social science and humanistic research contribute to the generation and improvement of value knowledge and decision making rules and institutions to improve public policies and decisions important for crop productivity? It is important that the agricultural science community embrace a broad research agenda that will involve the moral and ethical implications of agricultural research, including both scientific research and technology development.

Policy Imperatives

1. *Systematically teach agricultural ethics for those whose work affects crop productivity. This should be taught as applicable to both private and public decision making.*
2. *Systematically expose biological and physical scientists working on crop productivity to at least the rudiments of public choice procedures and methods so that they may better deal with the public choices important for crop productivity.*
3. *Arrest the deterioration of public information systems supplying information on crop yields, acreages, input uses, expenditures incomes, quality, processing marketing, exports, and utilization.*

Research Imperatives

1. *Research the performance of public decision making institutions to improve their structures and the decision rules used in regulating input use, environmental pollution, and food chain contamination involved in crop production.*
2. *Research acquisition, storage, and retrieval systems for furnishing both value-free and -knowledge to use to improve public decisions bearing on crop productivity.*
3. *Expand basic research in the social sciences and humanities to improve the measurement of nonmonetary and monetary values involved in assessing crop production technologies.*
4. *Research on optimal public policies involving such crop production issues as (a) ground water pollution, (b) surface water pollution, (c) food chain contamination, (d) redistributive aspects of improved crop*

production activities, and (e) the employment impacts of labor saving crop production technologies

5. *Do basic research on alternative decision rules for dealing with the gains and losses which may be encountered in (a) releasing genetically engineered organisms into the environment, (b) controlling pollutants, (c) controlling food chain contaminants, particularly carcinogenic, (d) destabilization of food supplies, and (e) establishing crop production systems for climatically unstable environments.*

6. *Research alternative nonmarket programs and policies for controlling short term overcommittment of resources to crop production while assuming the substantial increases in crop production capacity needed in the long run.*

7. *Research private and public institutional and physical infrastructure changes needed to adjust to changing crop production technologies.*

8. *Develop skills in using iterative/interactive processes to clarify value and value-free knowledge and decision rules in making policy and other decisions.*

9. *Research the animal rights issue as it affects the demand for crops.*

10. *Research the ethical issues involved in alternative ways of organizing the relationship between the public sector crop productivity research organizations and the private sector agribusinesses.*

The United States in the Global Agricultural Research System

We are, in the closing years of the 20th century, completing one of the most remarkable transitions in the history of world agriculture. Prior to the beginning of this century almost all increases in crop production occurred as a result of expansion in the area cultivated. The major exceptions to this generalization were in Western Europe and East Asia. By the end of this century almost all increases in crop production will have to come from higher yields in areas that are already being used for crop or animal production. Only those areas that have been able to establish effective agricultural research capacity will be able to achieve the increases in food and fiber production needed to sustain their people.

Policy Imperatives

1. *It is essential that effective agricultural research capacity be established for each commodity and each resource of economic significance in each agroclimate region of the world by the first decade of the next century.*

The effective integration of agricultural teaching, research, and extension is essential for the effective linking of agricultural research to production. In the United States this articulating has been achieved through an agricultural research system that includes a public sector national research organization (the USDA/ARS), public sector state research organization (the land grant college-state agricultural experiment station), and the private sector institutions engaged in research and technology development.

In third world countries, teaching, research, and extension technology transfer activities are frequently not well articulated. Frequently in these countries there exists a separate government administrative agency or ministry for each teaching, research, and extension function. In such cases, the integration of these three functions into a coherent and effective program is often very difficult. This is especially true with respect to bridging the gap between research and extension. An additional problem is that of how to utilize the educational institutions to teach students (a) how to teach, (b) how to conduct research, and (c) extension education methods. In many third world countries, considerable agricultural research has been published but the findings have often not been applicable or, when applicable, have not been passed on to the producers.

In both the United States and in other countries, most of the agricultural research has been focused on the production agriculture system. Hence, support for postharvest research has been inadequate and crop productivity, when viewed from the total system perspective from the seed to the consumer, has suffered from constraints produced by the research funding structure.

Graduate education in the agricultural sciences represents a unique opportunity for U.S. colleges of agriculture to participate in graduate programs in other countries. A successful model utilized at some universities permits the graduate student to conduct research at his/her sending institution. Travel support for the students and the graduate studies advisor to travel to the students' home institution is provided. Hence, the opportunity to establish collaborative research between educational institutions in the United States and in other countries can be facilitated through graduate studies involving nonimmigrant students from other countries.

2. *The United States needs to develop an improved capacity to screen the world for the knowledge and technology that can contribute to U.S. crop productivity*

During the last two decades the capacity for agricultural research in the Organization for Economic Cooperation and Development (OECD) countries has expanded rapidly. Agricultural research capacity in a number of developing countries has also expanded rapidly, most notably in Brazil, India, Nigeria, Phillippines, Korea, and Egypt. Agricultural research has been strengthened in a number of centrally planned economies. The recent Chinese experience indicates that when the incentive structure is reformed remarkably rapid advances in production are possible.

It is clear that a share of the new knowledge and the new technology that can impact on agricultural productivity that is produced in the United States can be expected to decline. The United States must develop the capacity to screen the world for advances in knowledge and technology that can advance agricultural productivity. If the necessary exchanges of knowledge, technology, and materials are to occur, it is imperative that the agricultural science community must resist efforts on the part of national or international agencies to restrict the international transfer of knowledge, technology, and materials.

Gains and Losses from Different Rates of Technical Change

What will be losses and/or gains from slower growth in productivity and output in the agricultural sector over next several decades? What will be gains (losses) from more rapid growth? How would gains (losses) be distributed among classes (input suppliers, farm operators, landowners, consumers) and nations.

Research Imperative

Research is needed on how changes in the economic and technological environment in which they live and work that motivate farmers, consumers and governments in the United States and elsewhere in the world. A much better understanding of how the world agricultural economy operates and how individual farmers, processors, and consumers behave within it is required.

The answers to these questions will be significantly influenced by changes in demand for U.S. agricultural products. If demand shifts upward significantly (*e.g.* as in the early 1970s) slow (fast) growth in productivity will yield different results than if demand is stable or declines. It is unlikely that domestic demand will shift very much in the near future. But foreign demand can shift greatly for different reasons—production short falls (overproduction) in the rest of the world; changes in the value of the dollar, changes in the per capita income in importing countries; and international trade policy in the United States and other countries.

In a slow production growth/output situation, with level demand, the gains could include the reduction of surpluses and thus lower federal budget cost for commodity programs. However, the losses in this scenario appear to include for agriculture a continued dependence on chemicals by agriculture with increased pest/disease resistance to the chemicals, potential deteriorating quality, increased environmental pollution problems, and continued high unit cost of production.

For a fast production growth/output situation, surpluses could increase with the concomitant adverse impact on the federal budget and income of farmers. The gains or benefits might be the opposite of those elements identified in the slow productivity growth scenario provided we assume that agricultural science and technology leads by addressing the problems relating to reducing the level of inputs required per unit of product.

The distribution of gains and losses for rapid (slow) growth in productivity depends on many factors. In general, consumers tend to gain from more rapid growth in productivity relative to input suppliers, farm operators and land owners. However, food and agricultural policy as well as other policies have been and will continue to be used to modify the distribution of gains and losses.

The Physical Infrastructure and Support Facilities for Agricultural Research

Numerous research-support functions are most efficiently conducted at a central location either because individual states, or even countries, are physically or fiscally incapable of supporting them alone, or because the nature of the function requires centralization to be effective.

Policy Imperatives

1. *It is essential that centralized research-support functions be given a high priority for current or future funding.*

Frequently such functions are given low priority because they are not involved directly in the generation of research results. For example, the USDA-APHIS/ARS Plant Quarantine Program is the designated support unit for the introduction of plant material of foreign origin for plant breeders and nurseries. This unit is also responsible for the inspection and maintenance of nonresearch, noncommercial plant material apprehended at U.S. points of entry. The greatly increased workload which has developed in recent years and the severely restricted budget of this unit have resulted in its inability to meet the reasonable needs of breeders—the estimated time for release of virus-free budwood of fruit trees is 20 years, if the material can be kept alive that long.

Other USDA support functions which are essential to the programs of plant breeders include the plant introduction and germ plasm maintenance stations, the National Seed Storage Laboratory, and numerous federal programs of regional or national importance (*e.g.* the several wheat and oats support laboratories, the carrot/onion/cucumber breeding program in Wisconsin, the tomato genetics program in California, and many other programs conducted in cooperation with land grant institutions). The cooperative programs are especially significant because they comprise a major portion of the federal/state partnership.

2. *Maintain a strong federal/state research partnership.*

The federal/state partnership has been highly successful and is envied by other nations. It has been weakened by budget reductions, dilution of efforts, and long-term inflation effects. The percentage of federal contributions to state programs has been reduced greatly and should not be diluted further. Included in this federal/state partnership are: (a) regional research programs funded through Cooperative State Research Service (CSRS). These projects have been instrumental in stimulating interdisciplinary and interstate research, a large portion of which would not be conducted without the joint state/federal funding: (b) the Cooperative Research Information Service (CRIS) system for reporting and cataloging research; (c) the Competitive Research Grants Office (CRGO) which has been instrumental in the stimulation of new and fundamental research; and (d) Hatch funding, which is important for the support of long-range mission-oriented research. These functions have been highly successful and deserve increased funding.

3. *Support and encourage industry/state/federal research initiatives.*

Less institutionalized, but equally productive, have been partnerships between industry and the state/federal system. It is important to strengthen this relationship. With the development of new biotechnologies, these relationships will take on a new significance. Protocols relative to these relationships (*e.g.* with regard to patents, licenses, royalties, confidentiality) must be developed.

4. *Foster and support programs developed by individual states, countries, or institutions which have applications on an international scale.*

State, federal, private, and international support is essential for the development of regional programs of excellence which are conducted at specific research centers but which have regional, national, or international applications: (a) individual state-supported programs (perhaps also federally or privately funded) which are unique to that state but which serve other states (*e.g.* the tart cherry breeding program in Michigan, the apple rootstock breeding program in New York, the tomato genetics program in California, and many others); and (b) the international agricultural research institute system which has worldwide responsibilities for specific crops (such as the Consultant Group for International Agricultural Research (CGIAR) institutes including the International Rice Research Institute (IRRI), the International Crops Research Institute for the Semi-Arid Tropics (ICRISAT), CIMMYT, and others). The success of the above centrally supported programs points to the need for continued development of central support programs or centers to meet the needs of emerging technologies.

Research Imperatives

1. *Establish information or base centers to meet the needs of emerging technologies and high priority research areas.*

These would include: (a) nutritional data base expansion and maintenance, including nutrient composition and therapeutic characteristics; (b) development of a DNA data bank for the systematic cataloging of genetic information developed through biotechnology (Genetic Improvement, this volume); (c) development of crop and cropping system data bases for the establishment and management of cropping systems (Production Systems, this volume); (d) maintenance of a central economic time series. The current system has deteriorated; some portions have been permanently lost; and (e) the development of national/international macroscale reference data on the agricultural impacts of climatic elements. Existing, but limited, data bases are threatened by budgetary reductions, yet it is more important now with the expanded availability of computer technology to utilize such data for comparing agrometeorological research to reliable references, and development of crop models.

Such data are essential for international technology transfer in the area of agrometeorology, tracing and evaluating environmental impacts such as CO_2 increases, ground water changes, accumulation of toxins and trace elements, and acid rain.

This system could also be expanded to include a data base on the environmental limits (stress) of plant species.

2. *The independent maintenance of centralized data bases is essential to the long-range productivity of a wide range of research programs. Existing bases should not be eliminated without in-depth evaluation.*

The establishment and maintenance of these service functions should not be tied to their direct application to research by professional researchers responsible for them. Rather, they should be maintained by professional technicians or technologists.

Producer Management of New Technologies

The rapidly increasing technology available to crop producers adds a significant degree of complexity to the utilization of these technologies. A new cultivar has imbodied in it the potential yield, stress tolerance, and pest resistance factors that we aspire to add through traditional plant breeding complemented by molecular biology. But the total crop management system will require development of a capacity by the manager to integrate biological, climatic, environmental, and financial factors into his/her decision making. Most desirably, a decision making system which reviews alternatives and predicts the outcome of each alternative will enhance the quality of the decision choice for a given enterprise or may provide midcourse adjustments as needed to adapt to shifting conditions of market, weather, or pests.

Educational support as well as newly available data bases may come to the production manager from both university extension and private industry sources.

Policy Imperatives

1. *Curricula at the high school and college level need to be developed and courses offered to prepare production managers for use of computers and management science toward a systems approach to decision making.*

2. *Current production managers will need training and retraining for the utilization of such systems decision making. The rapidly expanding information technology of artificial intelligence (expert systems and natural language) approaches are just beginning to be available. We have a unique opportunity to plan together the ways in which these new approaches can be most effectively delivered to production managers.*

3. *The selection and provision of the hardware to support these more complex decision approaches will call for expanded comparative information from unbiased, nonproprietary sources. The development of software can very possibly be a joint effort between industry and universities, with appropriate understandings developed through copyright. A key dimension will be the capacity to update rapidly this material in what promises to be a very fast changing information environment.*

4. *Decisions on how the user will pay, either for stand-alone systems or those provided by input suppliers as part of a total supply package will very probably be decisions that are best made in the market place. University extension and research can play a role in developing model systems and educating production managers on the range of decision assisting systems and their characteristics that are available.*

Research Imperative

Development of expert systems and use of artificial intelligence and natural language are needed and will be a natural analog to cropping systems research: (a) design cropping pattern alternatives which increase productivity and optimize nutrient cycling and use, minimize soil loss, and reduce pressure from insect pests, weeds, and pathogens; (b) adapt emerging engineering technologies and tools that will help in measuring and understanding production systems and new-generation instruments will enable producers to monitor and measure accurately essential dynamic activities related to crop production, providing instantaneous and reliable information to be used in decision support systems; and (c) develop microcomputer-based models to improve the design and management of production systems.

LITERATURE CITED

1. COULTER K, M STANTON 1985 Higher Education Faculty in the Food and Agricultural Sciences: Agriculture, Natural Resources and Forestry. US Department of Agriculture, Office of Grants and Program Systems and Office of Higher Education Programs, Washington, DC
2. HUFFMAN WE 1985 Profile of Agricultural Doctorate Scientists. Department of Economics, Iowa State University, Ames, IA
3. JOHNSON GL 1986 Research Methodology for Economists. Macmillan, New York
4. RUSSELL MG, RJ SAUER, JM BARNES eds 1982 Enabling Multidisciplinary Research: Perspective from Agriculture, Forestry and Home Economics. Miscellaneous Publication 19. Minnesota Agricultural Experiment Station, St Paul, MN
5. SCHULTZ TW 1971 The allocation and resources to research. In WL Fishel, ed, Resource Allocation in Agricultural Research. University of Minnesota Press, Minneapolis, MN, pp 90–120

Government/Industry/University Interactions

Submitted on behalf of the working group by:

RALPH W. F. HARDY
LAWRENCE BUSCH

KENNETH R. FARRELL
RICHARD KRASNOW

Improved collaboration by government, industry, and university in both developed and developing countries will enhance science and technology generation and its use for increased crop productivity. The benefits of improved collaboration include:

1. Appropriate training, retraining, and exchange of professionals for the needs for all sectors.
2. Broad-based support including agribusiness for science and technology generation in the public sector.
3. Improved prioritization of mission-oriented public research and minimization of duplication.
4. Increased effectiveness of technology transfer.
5. Guidelines on regulation, and collaboration so that new products can be field-evaluated.
6. Integration of biological, environmental, social, and economic factors for decision making in crop productivity research.

The above benefits will increase the return on research and development (R&D) expenditures in crop productivity—an essential goal for a R&D system in which the public sector is functioning on constant or decreasing budgets.

The agricultural technologies are becoming more sophisticated and are changing more rapidly than heretofore. Such an environment will require more highly trained professionals and the rate of change will dictate the need for periodic retraining especially for the industry and government sectors where retraining has not been standard practice. The exchange of professional personnel between the sectors will facilitate understanding of the roles and needs of each sector and should be encouraged. Future professionals may spend part of their career in academe, part in government, and part in industry to the collective benefit of all sectors.

Government is the major source of R&D funds for academic and governmental research. These funds are limited. Industry provides a modest but important additional source. Academe is exploring ways to increase significantly the industry contribution to research. Industry funds represent a low percentage of total R&D support though there is hope that this may increase to upward of 10% of the total. Several significant experiments are in progress involving industrial and academic collaborations with substantial dollar input by industry. Agricultural examples include those at Cornell University, Massachusetts General Hospital, Scripps Institute, and Cold Spring Harbor, including a total input of upward of $200 million. The probability of effective technology transfer is increased by such cooperation.

Continued prioritization of mission-oriented public research is necessary. Use of a broad input from agribusiness, farmers, consumers, government, and academia should improve the quality of prioritization. Prioritization by a multisector group under the auspices of a national organization such as the Board on Agriculture of the National Research Council would be effective.

Technological transfer is most difficult across organizations and is not ideal even within organizations including industrial ones. Industry has not always been effective in transfer of government and university science and technology for useful products, processes, and services for agriculture or for other areas. The United States is much more effective in science and technology generation than in transfer to useful products. A major need is to improve the technology transfer process. Herein lies a major opportunity for the government, universities, and industry to improve its competitive position in agriculture.

Biotechnology innovations are expected to be a major source of increased crop productivity in the decades ahead. Such products, for the most part, require field-testing as have and do any other crop agricultural products. Society is concerned about the deliberate release of biotechnology products into the environment. Government, industry, and universities should work together to facilitate field-testing of biotechnology products in a manner that would ensure safety to society.

Agricultural research and development has been criticized by society for some of its innovations, such as the mechanization of the harvesting of horticultural crops. It is important that a holistic view of technology and its anticipated new products, processes, and services be provided.

The large number of studies that are being made on macro- and microeconomics and social aspects of bovine growth hormone in the dairy industry are examples of the type of evaluation that would be useful at early stages for products of crop productivity research.

University, Industry, and Government Collaboration

A number of approaches to improving collaboration between universities, industry, and government are proposed including:

1. Clarify and establish *ab initio* the roles of each actor regarding the division of responsibilities concerning the generation of new science and technology and their transfer from the research institutions to ultimate use.
2. Examine past and existing efforts at collaborative work with a view toward ascertaining factors that contribute to success or failure.
3. Allow for and encourage experimentation with a range of new and

novel organizational and institutional arrangements, recognizing that some of these experiments will be unsuccessful.

4. Develop acceptable guidelines for collaboration among the parties carrying out joint activities.
5. State explicitly and openly the rules under which collaborative enterprises are undertaken, so as to allay public fears of collusion, conflicts of interest, or other activities not in the public interest.
6. Determine existing constraints to collaborative efforts among the three parties, and take steps toward their removal. A priority at the governmental/academic interface is resolving the indirect cost problem. The problem of short-term funding should also be addressed.
7. Make a sustained, broad reaching effort at removing barriers and devising new means for personnel exchanges among the three parties.

Specific mechanisms need to be explored to foster such collaboration between actors in the respective sectors as well as joint funding. For example, models currently exist that ought to be encouraged and given greater prominence. Among them are so-called "centers of excellence," as well as exchanges of personnel such as occur between universities and government under the Inter-Governmental Personnel Act. Similar programs with industry might be explored. In addition, funding of research programs by industry consortia, direct grants to universities by industry, sponsorship of research by trade associations and commodity groups, research checkoffs, tax incentives for public research investments (for example, equipment write-offs for industry donations to universities), and matching grants each provide possibilities for collaboration.

Furthermore, investigators and research administrators from all sectors should be brought into the planning and evaluation activities of each sector, such as in curriculum planning, search committees, and evaluation panels. Innovative models for exchange of personnel should be explored. Successful examples of such exchanges include graduate and postdoctoral fellowships sponsored by industry but located at industrial laboratories, university-governmental exchange fellowships at postdoctoral as well as faculty levels, and sabbatical exchanges among government, universities, and industry.

An Integrative Approach

Imperative: Integrate biological, environmental, social, and economic factors and dimensions into decision making systems that guide crop productivity research and technology transfer. The agricultural experiment stations, government, and industry must each play a key role in establishing priorities for crop productivity research. They should do so in the context of the broadest practical view of their domain of responsibility. They should strive for a holistic view that produces a coherent and thoroughly integrated program directed to the needs of the state and the region. Station programs should provide the basis for the development of national policies by keeping national agencies and any national coordinating organizations informed. These, in turn, should develop policies and priorities on the basis of an integrated and holistic view of the national and international dimensions of crop productivity reseach.

Experiment station, state, and regional integrated plans should be developed by drawing on the expertise of research scientists (biological, social, economic, basic, and applied) as well as consumers and producers. This approach will expose individuals and groups of researchers to the integrated plan. Care must be taken to ensure that the research agenda is responsive to the needs of small as well as large farms and firms.

Within the broad context defined by the agricultural experiment station, multidisciplinary targeted programs should be fostered that will facilitate communication within the experiment station staff, attract industry collaboration, and facilitate broad-based educational programs. Research teams can provide linkages of knowledge essential in assessing potential outcomes, impacts, and constraints of proposed research initiatives.

While the experiment station-extension service collaboration has served the needs of U.S. agriculture well and with distinction, the current technological revolution coupled with the social and political changes of the past 10 years will greatly stress the present system. We urge an examination of the roles and responsibilities of these agencies with respect to education and technology transfer with a view to enhancing their effectiveness and developing methods of operation that address the new problems, both technical and socioeconomic, facing agriculture. New strategies will be needed to ensure the free flow of information among investigators, disciplines, and their constituencies.

Multidisciplinary research programs should be given a high priority in both planning and funding. At the federal level, the U.S. Department of Agriculture (USDA) competitive grants programs can provide a powerful mechanism for initiating multidisciplinary efforts. Review committees should be formed to assess multidisciplinary proposals to ensure that they are appropriately evaluated. At the state level, the experiment stations should use available funding to foster multidisciplinary initiatives, and should work with state agencies on new program development in this mode. Centers of excellence, mission-oriented interdisciplinary conferences, and opportunities for graduate and postdoctoral students, and faculty members to extend their disciplinary range can all prove effective in the creation of multidisciplinary approaches.

Of especial importance in planning, conducting, and evaluating research to enhance crop productivity is incorporation of the social and economic sciences into the multidisciplinary research process. These sciences hold the promise of providing *ex ante* forecasts of the impacts of technical change which can, in turn, aid in the development of policies that minimize undesirable externalities.

Technology Transfer: Constraints and Initiatives

Imperative: Establish new means and refine existing means for the transfer of technology among all components of the agricultural community, with due concern for the public interest. In this context, technology refers to products, processes, and accompanying organizational forms. Technology transfer includes the dynamic process of identifying needs as well as discovering, producing, evaluating, adapting, and ultimately adopting technologies to satisy those needs. For the efficient transfer of technology, it is necessary to foster a free flow of information among the various members of the agricultural and scientific communities.

Traditionally, both the public and private sectors have engaged in technology transfer. The Cooperative Extension Service and the input supply dealerships are examples of organizational forms designed to facilitate such transfer. However, changing institutional roles as well as the emergence of new actors calls for reconsideration of traditional relationships.

To achieve the goal of the above imperative, the working group recommends the following:

1. The establishment of guidelines for government/university/industry relations. Current and past models need to be evaluated for effectiveness and appropriateness. Such guidelines should be drafted so as to ensure the integrity of the various institutions involved, as well as protect against actual and potential conflicts of interest. The issues of communication of research findings, patent protection, and institutional collaboration should be addressed. Moreover, the special mission of public institutions in research on environmental protection and natural resource conservation should be recognized.
2. The establishment of mechanisms that will promote multidisciplinary research in the plant sciences for the purpose of facilitating technology transfer. Multidisciplinary research complements individual projects by ensuring that all the relevant aspects of problems are developed together, and reducing the time needed for the transfer process. In addition, a multidisciplinary environment can be used to improve linkages between mission-oriented basic research and its application and commercialization.
3. The development of further incentives for industry participation in the technology transfer process. Financial incentives are clearly significant. For example, a firm might derive a tax benefit from establishing a joint project with a university for the assessment of the environmental impacts of a proprietary product.
4. The recognition of the different needs of large and small farmers in the technology transfer process. As is well known, large farmers often communicate directly with research staff for technical information; in contrast, small to mid-size farmers use multiple information sources

including the Cooperative Extension Service and the input supply salespersons. A concern is that smaller operators may receive antiquated and/or biased information. Among possible solutions are improving extension services to small operators, better information flow to dealers and input supply cooperatives, greater use of television and audiovisual techniques, as well as field consultants (as are now used in the integrated pest management (IPM) area).

5. The recognition of the different needs of large and small input supply and output processing firms. An example concerns the differing demands placed on State Agricultural Experiment Stations by large and small seed companies.

6. The improvement of mechanisms for farmer and general public input into research and policy decision making. Such input at an early stage in the R&D process facilitates the creation of research outputs of direct relevance to specific user groups. Greater farmer and general public representation at scientific and science policy conferences should be encouraged.

7. The provision of publicly owned, professionally managed, "contained" sites for field evaluation of biotechnology products. Regulation is a subset of technology transfer. Products of the new biotechnology are expected to make significant contributions to crop productivity. Such products must be evaluated in the field to assess their usefulness and impact as is the established practice for all improved crops or microbes for crop agriculture. State agricultural experiment stations and federal agricultural laboratories have much experience in field testing. It is recommended that university, government, and industry cooperate to establish field-evaluation sites for biotechnology products. Such sites would be publicly owned using existing federal or state field testing sites. Initially a few sites (possibly five) would be identified to represent different geographic areas in the United States. Each site would be located so as to provide a significant degree of containment or isolation.

Each site will be professionally managed by a group of federal, state, and/or university scientists with a breadth of relevant skills ranging from ecology to agronomy to molecular biology. This management group would approve each field test. The proposing governmental, academic, or industrial group would conduct the experiment. The cost of the experiment would be paid for by the performing group.

The cooperation of government, academia, and industry will facilitate the development of biotechnology products for crop agriculture utilizing the professional skills already existing within the agricultural system. The public interest will be protected by the broad involvement of public institutions whose professionals have much demonstrated relevant experience in field evaluation of new agricultural products.

International Considerations

Imperative: Promote activities and policies to foster collaboration between universities, governments, and especially private industry to meet long-term security needs for food, fiber, and fuel in developing countries. Research collaboration among developed (DCs) and developing (LDCs) countries involves many facets that render it distinct from such collaboration within or between developed countries. Cultural difference among DCs and LDCs raise different goals and aspirations; geopolitical problems arise that cause different expectations and viewpoints on such issues as profits as a motivation for research, and germ plasm exchange; national economic policies on taxation, repatriation of profits, proprietariness, and employment practices may discourage private industry from investing in research in LDCs.

The development of food security in LDCs promotes political stability and foreign trade. Thus, from both a humanitarian viewpoint and for global stability and harmony among all countries, it is critical for the DCs and LDCs to collaborate to ensure adequate indigenous crop production in all countries. The DCs are especially equipped to aid the LDCs in training professionals, aiding in the establishment of research and extension infrastructures, and funding research programs. Any collaborative effort on research initiatives between DCs and LDCs should involve participation as equals. Much collaboration has occurred in the past between DC and LDC governments and public institutions, but mechanisms must be formulated that will encourage private industry to contribute to the development of adequate indigenous food, fiber, and fuel production capabilities in LDCs.

Appropriate mechanisms for cooperation between DCs and LDCs for enhancing crop productivity need to be identified. This would provide mutual benefits to both DCs and LDCs: LDCs can benefit from training opportunities, new technologies, and enhanced food security; the DCs will benefit from greater global political stability, the improvement of human welfare, and access to natural resources such as germ plasm as well as larger markets.

Several mechanisms have been tried whereby DCs promote and endow agricultural research in LDCs. For example, much U.S. Agency for International Development (USAID) research money is spent under bilateral agreements. In contrast, the Consultative Group for International Agricultural Research (CGIAR) represents a consortium that pools human resources and funding from many DC sources, and is responsible for International Agricultural Research Centers (IARCs) that have agricultural research and development responsibilities for many countries with common production problems. A comprehensive study of new and innovative methods for DC-LDC collaboration is warranted.

Means by which private industry can collaborate with DC and LDC institutions to enhance crop productivity and food security should be analyzed. To date, nearly all collaboration on agricultural research between DCs and LDCs has been sponsored by governments, universities, and foundations. In fact, in centrally planned LDCs private industry participation in research has not been permitted. However, private industry has unique expertise and capability for development and production of technologies and creating systems to deliver these technologies to the users; this expertise should be made available to the LDCs. Furthermore, private industry could well be involved in the agricultural research enterprise of LDCs just as it currently is in DCs. Encouraging private industry to collaborate in agricultural research and development will require innovation and changes in attitudes by both parties.

Many factors act as constraints on making collaborative research involving LDCs and DCs fully productive. For example the countries may have different political systems and philosophies; necessary infrastructures in LDCs may be inadequate or even nonexistent; or the number of trained personnel may be insufficient. However, past successes in collaborative research, such as that leading to the green revolution with wheat and rice, have been successful in a sufficiently diverse set of countries to show that collaborative research can succeed in a variety of settings. Therefore, there is reason to believe that, if current constraints to DC-LDC collaboration can be identified, ways can be found to mitigate or circumvent them, and thus create a setting where collaborative research could thrive.

Solicited Comments from the Participants

Comparative Land Resources. Table I reveals the disparities in agroforestry resources per capita of national population with special emphasis on the severe limitations of the poor countries (column B). The nonagricultural land available for conservation purposes, leisure, and urban and industrial development (column C) is low in most countries. A major conclusion is that, if currently nonarable land is to be protected, modern intensive agricultural practices must be adapted and improved world-wide to satisfy food needs (F. P. W. WINTERINGHAM).

Table I. *Total Land Available per Capita Compared with Presently Utilized Land and Maximum Possible Land Reserve Available for Nonagricultural Uses*

Country	Total Land (A)	Agroforestry "Resource Index" Crop Land + Permanent Pasture + Forest (B)	Maximum Possible Land Reserve for Nonagricultural Uses $(A - B) = (C)$
	hectares per head of national population		
Argentina	10.0	8.6	1.4
Australia	51.9	40.9	11.0
Bangladesh	0.16	0.13	0.03
Belgium	0.32	0.22	0.10
Brazil	6.6	6.3	0.35
Canada	40.6	16.0	24.6
China	0.94	0.50	0.44
Demark	0.84	0.66	0.18
Egypt	2.3	0.11	2.2
Ethiopia	3.7	2.65	1.1
France	1.0	0.85	0.16
Federal Republic Germany	0.41	0.32	0.09
Hungary	0.87	0.77	0.10
India	0.46	0.35	0.10
Japan	0.29	0.26	0.03
Lebanon	0.38	0.16	0.22
Mexico	2.7	2.0	0.7
Nigeria	1.1	0.80	0.26
Pakistan	0.87	0.79	0.08
Sri Lanka	0.43	0.32	0.10
United Kingdom	0.44	0.36	0.07
U.S.A.	4.0	3.1	1.0
U.S.S.R.	8.3	5.6	2.6
World	3.0	1.9	1.0

Productivity Growth. The beginning of modernization in agriculture is signaled by the emergence of sustained growth in productivity. During the initial stages of development, productivity growth is usually accounted for by improvement in a single partial productivity ratio, such as output per unit of labor or output per unit of land. In the United States and other countries of recent settlement, such as Canada, Australia, New Zealand, and Argentina, increase in labor productivity in output per worker has carried the main burden of growth in total productivity. In countries that entered the development process with relatively high population-land ratios, such as Japan, Denmark, and Germany, increases in land productivity—in output per hectare—have initially been largely responsible for growth in total productivity.

As modernization progresses, there is a tendency for growth in total productivity—output per unit of total input—to be sustained by a more balanced combination of improvement in partial productivity ratios—in output per worker, per hectare, and per unit of capital. Thus, among the countries that have the longest experience of agricultural growth, there tends to be a convergence in the patterns of productivity growth.

What is implied by the concept of productivity growth? In the above paragraphs, the term has been used in several ways. One way it was not used was as a simple indicator of growth in production! When the term "productivity" is used accurately, it always refers to a ratio—to the ratio of output to the input of a single input or to the ratio of output to an aggregation of several inputs. When the term "productivity growth" is used, it refers to changes in such ratios over time.

Crop production per acre is a traditional productivity measure used in agriculture. It is a partial productivity ratio. Output per unit of labor—labor productivity—is another commonly used partial productivity ratio. Energy yield per unit of energy applied is another partial productivity ratio that has received a good deal of attention. The major limitation of all partial productivity ratios as indicators of technical change is that improvement in one partial productivity ratio may simply reflect the effect of a decline in another partial productivity ratio. Gains in crop yield per unit area may reflect the combined effects of increases in fertilizer use per unit area and improvements in crop response to fertilizer. In this case, the partial productivity ratio, increase in output per unit area, will overstate the improvement due to technical change.

A more inclusive measure of productivity is needed to measure the gains in efficiency resulting from technical change. The closest approach to an indicator that can be used to measure differences or changes in efficiency is output per unit of total input. In this measure, the several inputs used in agricultural production—land, labor, buildings, and equipment and current inputs such as fertilizers, pesticides, and fuels—are aggregated and changes in output are related to changes in total input. When total productivity measures are constructed carefully, they can be interpreted as reasonably accurate measures of the contribution of technical change to the growth of agricultural production. A more cautious interpretation is that total productivity measures the residual growth in output that remains unexplained after the effects of the inputs included in the total input measure are accounted for.

The changes in two partial productivity measures, land productivity and labor productivity, and in total productivity are illustrated for U.S. agriculture for the period 1870 to 1982 in Table II. During the 1950s and early 1960s, all three productivity measures grew rapidly. During the late 1960s, the rate of growth of land productivity and total productivity slowed down. During the 1970s, these two productivity indexes appear to have renewed their upward trend. Note also that the labor productivity index grew more rapidly than the total productivity index throughout the entire period. Part of the growth in labor productivity is due to higher capital investment per worker. The total productivity index grew at a slower rate because the services of the capital equipment, along with labor and other inputs, are included in the input index (V. W. RUTTAN).

Table II. Average Annual Rates of Change (Percentage per Year) in Output, Inputs, and Productivity in U.S. Agriculture, 1870 to 1982

Item	1870–1900	1900–1925	1925–1950	1950–1965	1965–1982
Farm output	2.9	0.9	1.6	1.7	2.1
Total inputs	1.9	1.1	0.2	−0.4	0.2
Total productivity	1.0	−0.2	1.3	2.2	1.8
Labor inputs[a]	1.6	0.5	−1.7	−4.8	−3.4
Labor productivity	1.3	0.4	3.3	6.6	5.8
Land inputs[b]	3.1	0.8	0.1	−0.9	0.0
Land productivity	−0.2	0.0	1.4	2.6	1.8

[a] Number of workers, 1870 to 1910; worker-hour basis, 1910 to 1971.
[b] Cropland use for crops, including crop failures and cultivated summer fallow.

Comparisons of Productivity. The relative availability, cost, and extent of competing uses for production inputs varies greatly around the world, with profound consequences for international comparisons of productivity. It is often said that the U.S. agricultural system is the most productive in the world. This statement is probably true based on some measures of productivity, such as total output per country, or output per unit of on-farm labor input. But in terms of productivity per unit of capital investment, or pesticides expenditures, it may well be that the Chinese now have the most productive agricultural system in the world (C. M. BENBROOK).

Production Practices. There is a general lack of knowledge of how production practices affect plant health, the composition and balance of basic nutrients in crops, and food quality. We know that the chemical composition of plants reflects the minerals in the soil, and that plants in poor health accumulate alkaloids and other antinutritive secondary compounds, but little has been done to manipulate the nutritive content of the food produced. A major constraint is that plant breeders have little economic incentive to improve nutritive qualities of food and feed crops, and farmers have few incentives to adopt them, even though in the developed countries a significant and growing segment of the population looks for and is willing to pay more for better quality food. In developing countries the nutritive value of food is especially critical. Although this area does not fit within the structure of this conference, research is needed to determine the mechanisms by which production practices affect the nutritive value of food and feeds (E. C. CRUZE).

Some Considerations Regarding Alternative Sources of Funding for Agricultural Research and Development. Research scientists and administrators in both the United States and Canada have tended to be somewhat inward looking (myopic) when considering future sources of funding. The common refrain is "we need more resources for agricultural research!" However, little attention has been paid to the need to provide politicians with viable options in the context of resource reallocation between competing program areas.

Agricultural research funding currently commands 2 to 5% of the USDA budget. Why is this figure not 10%? The answer is simple. A sound case has not been provided for reallocation of resources from areas such as farm support programs and regulatory functions.

Given an annual average social rate of return approaching 50% on research investment, it is difficult to understand why funding for agrifood research endeavors should be static or declining. It begs the question—have we really made our case? How can we lobby more effectively for a larger piece of the pie? The answer, I believe, lies in generating visible and viable alternatives oriented to reallocation of expenditures from farm income support and regulatory programs to research endeavors.

To illustrate, the philosophy underpinning regulatory functions is "control." However, one might ask the question "Have we (the research community) done an effective job in influencing or changing this attitude from one based on the need for "control" to that focusing on "prevention." For example, it is high time that we calculated, documented and made public the administrative costs associated with the regulatory process of development, implementation and monitoring in a cost-benefit context compared to developing viable alternatives involving "preventative" research programs.

In the area of "farm income support" perhaps the benefits of a comprehensive training program on "risk management" aimed at medium to large scale producers and processors with the specific objective of making

290

them more self-reliant would far outweigh the costs. Potential savings in the farm income support area could be redirected to research.

It is highly probable that the fiscal framework over the next 5 years for agriculture programs will be static or declining. Research endeavors should not bear the brunt! The only viable alternative in this era of fiscal restraint is to develop a fiscal plan that clearly identifies the required shifts in resources from regulatory and farm income support programs to agri-food research. The support/justification for such shifts must be developed as soon as possible in a credible manner by the research community and presented in a coherent and visible manner to decision makers in the political arena (G. W. ANDREWS).

United Kingdom Research Funding in a Time of Surpluses. There is a very close parallel between today's situation in the United States and the United Kingdom's situation 6 to 7 years ago. Over this period the U.K. budget deficit has been brought down from 6 to 7% of the gross national product (GNP), to 2 to 3%. In a situation of increasing surpluses, this has led to an exceptionally severe cut of agricultural research funding, with institute closures and hundreds of jobs lost.

The cuts are being justified by the existence of surpluses, as showing that there is no need for increased production. Instead, the imperatives have become: improvement in quality, protection of the environment, decrease in inputs, added value to agricultural product via food technology. It may be advisable to give greater stress now to these or other nonproduction directed factors, to back up the case for agricultural research in the future (C. B. TINKER).

Involvement of Social Scientists. Several participants in this conference have noted that the products of agricultural research redistribute wealth and income (distributive effects). They called upon social scientists to provide some guidance on this issue. While it is undoubtedly the case that all technologies have both productivity and distributive effects, the measurement and prediction of these is in its infancy. The problem is further complicated by the fact that the products of research are always released into a market, which is itself a social creation and subject to both government and private policy.

Perhaps, in 10 more years, social scientists will have a better grasp of the technical issues in crop improvement, as well as the interactions among technical and social issues. At present, however, the best one can do is to ask technical scientists to consider distributive questions and, at a minimum, not to contribute directly to already existing social requisites (L. BUSCH).

Consequences of Changes in Weather Patterns. The agricultural research community should examine and provide information on the influence of catastrophic events such as a large-scale loss of irradiant energy, on regional, continental, and global weather patterns. The agricultural research community should also consider measures to preserve germ plasm of crops and animals in the event of continental or global disturbances and disruption of weather patterns for a prolonged period of time (S. R. RADOSEVICH, J. R. MILLER, R. L. HOUTZ, R. ROUSCH, B. S. VINSON, B. A. CROFT).

Special Concerns of Non-U.S. Participants

(Listed with a degree of priority as to frequency of expressed concern)

1. *Improved Food and Crop Utilization.* There was the general recognition that postharvest handling, preservation and utilization of food materials in the tropics was more important than crop production. Emphasis should be given to reduction of postharvest losses, better management of surpluses, preservation of root and tuber crops, and improved utilization of grain legumes and tropical fruits and vegetables.

2. *Emphasize Conventional Methods of Crop Improvement.* Continue and expand efforts in the breeding of cereal grains and seed legumes, including hybrids. A fear was expressed that much of the current effort in methods for crop improvement, management, and utilization would give way to biotechnology. The collection, preservation, and maintenance of genetic resources, especially those clonally propagated, was emphasized.

3. *Improve Local Crop Cultivars Requiring Minimal Resource Inputs.* Cultivars should be developed that will be productive on marginal soils of low fertility, require minimal pest control, and have low water requirements. Technologies should be developed that will improve the productivity of inter-, multiple-, and mixed-cropping, which are the traditional systems in much of Africa, South and Central America, Southeast Asia, and China.

4. *Management of Fragile Tropical Soils for Crop Production.* Tropical soils in many developing countries now facing the most critical crop productivity constraints are shallow, fragile, and easily erodible. Technologies of soil and crop management (conservation tillage, alley cropping, allelopathic responses) should be developed to enable continuous cropping as an alternative to the slash and burn or shifting cultivation which now exists.

5. *Emphasize Integrated Pest Management (IPM).* IPM will have significant positive impacts on costs of production, improved plant protection, human health, food safety and the environment. Special emphasis should be given for enhancing crop productivity under subsistence farming conditions, and developing evaluation procedures for resistance to biological constraints.

6. *Agroforestry.* Research in this area has been neglected, the related areas of soil fertility and nutrient cycling are especially important for perennial crops.

List of Participants

C. Eugene Allen
College of Agriculture
University of Minnesota
St. Paul, MN 55108

L. H. Allen, Jr.
U.S. Department of Agriculture
Agricultural Research Service
University of Florida
Gainesville, FL 32611

Abdelmushin Alsudery
P.O. Box 60537
Riyadh, Saudi Arabia

James H. Anderson
College of Agriculture and Natural Resources
Michigan State University
E. Lansing, MI 48824

Gerald W. Andrews
Agriculture Canada
Sir John Carling Building
Ottawa, Ontario, Canada

Charles J. Arntzen
Central Research and Development Experiment Station
E. I. DuPont and Company
Wilmington, DE 19898

Raj Bahadur
Mississippi Valley State University
Itta Bena, MS 38941

Robert Barker
300 Day Hall
Cornell University
Ithaca, NY 14853

Reah Janise Battenfield
Department of Crop and Soil Sciences
Michigan State University
E. Lansing, MI 48824

W. Dietz Bauer
Department of Agronomy
Ohio State University
Columbus, OH 43210

Anthony C. Bellotti
Center International de Agricultural Tropical
AA. 6713, Cali, Columbia

Charles M. Benbrook
Board on Agriculture
National Research Council
2101 Constitution Ave., N.W.
Washington, DC 20418

Anson R. Bertrand
U.S. Agency for International Development
320—21st St., N.W.
Washington, DC 20523

Gabor J. Bethlenfalvay
Western Regional Research Center
U.S. Department of Agriculture
Agricultural Research Service
Albany, CA 94710

David F. Bezdicek
Department of Agronomy and Soils
Washington State University
Pullman, WA 99164-6420

Taye Bezuneh
SAFGRAD Coordination Office
P.O. Box 1783
Quagadougou, Burkina Fasd
W. Africa

E. T. Bingham
Department of Agronomy
University of Wisconsin
Wisconsin, WI 53706

J. R. Black
Department of Agricultural Economics
Michigan State University
E. Lansing, MI 48824

John Blodgett
Board on Agriculture
National Research Council
2101 Constitution Ave., N.W.
Washington, DC 20418

Lawrence Bogorad
Department of Cellular and Development Biology
Harvard University
Cambridge, MA 02131

B. Ben Bohlool
Niftal Project
University of Hawaii
P.O. Box "O"
Paia, HI 96779

James T. Bonnen
Department of Agricultural Economics
Michigan State University
E. Lansing, MI 48824

James L. Brewbaker
Department of Horticulture
University of Hawaii
Honolulu, HI 96822

William L. Brown
Board on Agriculture
National Research Council
2101 Constitution Ave., N.W.
Washington, DC 20418

William A. Brun
Department of Agronomy and Plant Genetics
University of Minnesota
St. Paul, MN 55108

Orvin C. Burnside
Department of Agronomy and Plant Genetics
University of Minnesota
St. Paul, MN 55108

John E. Burris
Board on Basic Biology
National Research Council
2101 Constitution Ave., N.W.
Washington, DC 20418

Lawrence Busch
Department of Sociology
University of Kentucky
Lexington, KY 40546

L. J. Butler
Department of Agricultural Economics
University of Wisconsin
Madison, WI 53706

Frederick Buttel
Department of Rural Sociology
Cornell University
Ithaca, NY 14853

Virgilio R. Carangal
International Rice Research Institute
P.O. Box 933
Manila, Philippines

Mary E. Carter
U.S. Department of Agriculture

Agricultural Research Service
302A Administration Bldg.
Washington, DC 20250

Roy S. Chaleff
Central Research and Development Experimental Station
E.I. DuPont and Co.
Wilmington, DE 19898

Adrienne Clarke
Botany School
University of Melbourne
Parkville, Victoria 3052
Australia

Mary Clutter
National Science Foundation
1800 G. St., N.W.
Washington, DC 20550

Estel H. Cobb
U.S. Department of Agriculture
Cooperative State Research Service
Justin S. Morrill Bldg.
Washington, DC 20251

James H. Cock
Centro Internacional de Agricultura Tropical
AA67-13, Cali, Columbia

R. James Cook
U.S. Department of Agriculture
Agricultural Research Service
Washington State University
Pullman, WA 99164-6430

Anson R. Cooke
Union Carbide
P.O. Box 12014
Research Triangle Park
NC 27809

Brian A. Croft
Department of Entomology
Oregon State University
Corvallis, OR 97331

Elinor C. Cruze
Board on Agriculture
National Research Council
2101 Constitution Ave., N.W.
Washington, DC 20418

Charles R. Curtis
Department of Plant Pathology
Ohio State University
Columbus, OH 43210

James L. Davidson
Commonwealth Scientific and Industrial Research Organization
P.O. Box 1600
Canberra ACT 2601, Australia

James M. Davidson
Institute of Food and Agricultural Science
University of Florida
Gainesville, FL 32611

Peter J. Davies
Section of Plant Biology
Cornell University
Ithaca, NY 14853

Peter R. Day
Plant Breeding Institute
Maris Lane, Trumpington
Cambridge, CB2 2LY, England

Deborah Delmer
ARCO Plant Cell Research Institute
6560 Trinity Court
Dublin, CA 94568

Charles J. Delp
Congressional Science Fellow
145 Kentucky Ave., S.E.
Washington, DC 20003

David R. Dilley
Department of Horticulture
Michigan State University
E. Lansing, MI 48824

Michael J. Dover
Independent Consultant
P.O. Box 396
Peterborough, NH 03458

Stephen Dumford
Ciba-Geigy Corporation
P.O. Box 18300
Greensboro, NC 27419

Donald N. Duvick
Pioneer Hi-Bred International
P.O. Box 85
Johnston, IA 50131

Jacques P. Eckebil
Institute of Agronomic Research
B. P. 2123
Yaounde-Messa, Cameroon

Suryatna Effendi
Research Institute for Estate Crops-Sembawa
Agency of Agricultural Research and Development
P.O. Box 127
Pelambang, Indonesia

Albert H. Ellingboe
Department of Plant Pathology
and Genetics
University of Wisconsin
Madison, WI 53711

Koon-Tee Erh
Syarikat Sailcos Sdn. Bhd.
Taman Mayang
Petaling Jaya
Selangor, Malaysia

William R. Evans
Battelle-Kettering Laboratory
Yellow Springs, OH 45387

Everett H. Everson
Department of Crop and Soil Sci-
ences
Michigan State University
E. Lansing, MI 48824

Ray F. Evert
Department of Botany
University of Wisconsin
Madison, WI 53706

Kenneth R. Farrell
National Center for Food and Ag-
ricultural Policy
Resources for the Future
1616 P St., N.W.
Washington, DC 20036

James R. Fischer
Agricultural Experiment Station
Michigan State University
E. Lansing, MI 48824

James A. Flore
Department of Horticulture
Michigan State University
E. Lansing, MI 48824

Tom H. Foster
National Fertilizer Development
Center
Tennessee Valley Authority
Muscle Shoals, AL 35630

Vincent R. Franceschi
Department of Botany
Washington State University
Pullman, WA 99164

Diana W. Freckman
Department of Nematology
University of California
Riverside, CA 92521

Kenneth J. Frey
Department of Agronomy
Iowa State University
Ames, IA 50011

Raymond E. Frisbie
Department of Entomology
Texas A&M University
College Station, TX 77843

Robert G. Gast
Agricultural Experiment Station
Michigan State University
E. Lansing, MI 48824

Martin Gibbs
Institute for Photobiology
Brandeis University
Waltham, MA 02254

A. D. M. Glass
Department of Botany
University of British Columbia
Vancouver, B.C., Canada
V6R 2V3

Terrence L. Graham
Monsanto Life Sciences Center
Chesterfield, MO 63146

Peter M. Gresshoff
Botany Department
Australia National University
Canberra, A.C.T. 2600, Australia

Jake Halliday
Battelle-Kettering Laboratory
Yellow Springs, OH 45387

S.K. Hahn
International Institute of Tropi-
cal Agriculture
PMB 5320
Ibadan, Nigeria

Roger Hangarter
Department of Plant Biology
University of Illinois
Urbana, IL 61801

Andrew D. Hanson
Department of Energy-Plant Re-
search Laboratory
Michigan State University
E. Lansing, MI 48824

Ralph W. F. Hardy
Biotechnica International Inc.
85 Bolton St.
Cambridge, MA 02140

Richard R. Harwood
Winrock International
1611 N. Kent St.
Arlington, VA 22209

Roland D. Hauck
Agricultural Research Branch
National Fertilizer Development
Center
Tennessee Valley Authority
Muscle Shoals, VA 35660

Robert L. Heath
Department of Botany and Plant
Sciences
Unviersity of California
Riverside, CA 92521

Walter W. Heck
Department of Botany
U.S. Department of Agriculture
Agricultural Research Service
North Carolina State University
Raleigh, NC 27650

Gary H. Heichel
U.S. Department of Agriculture
Agricultural Research Service
411 Borlaug Hall
1991 Buford Circle
St. Paul, MN 55108

Hans W. Heldt
Institut für Biochemie der
Pflanze
Untere Karspüle 2
D 3400 Goettingen, Federal Re-
public of Germany

Charles W. Hendricks
Environmental Research Laboratory
200 S.W. 35th St.
Corvallis, OR 97333

Robert W. Herdt
Consultative Group for Interna-
tional Agricultural Research
Secretariat
The World Bank
Washington, DC 20433

Oran B. Hesterman
Department of Crop and Soil Sci-
ences
Michigan State University
E. Lansing, MI 48824

Charles E. Hess
College of Agricultural and Envi-
ronmental Sciences
University of California
Davis, CA 95616

R. James Hildreth
Farm Foundation
1211 West 22nd St.
Oak Brook, IL 60521

Nicholas E. Hollis
Agri-Energy Roundtable, Inc.
2550 M St., N.W.
Washington, DC 20037

Leland R. House
Sorghum & Millet Improvement
  Program
SADCC/ICRISAT
P.O. Box 776
Bulawayo, Zimbabwe

Robert L. Houtz
N318D Agricultural Science Cen-
  ter-North
University of Kentucky
Lexington, KY 40546

Marjorie A. Hoy
Department of Entomological
  Sciences
University of California
Berkeley, CA 94720

Wallace E. Huffman
Department of Economics
Iowa State University
Ames, IA 50011

Glenn L. Johnson
Department of Agricultural Eco-
  nomics
Michigan State University
E. Lansing, MI 48824

E. T. Kanemasu
Department of Agronomy
Kansas State University
Manhattan, KS 66506

Donald L. Keister
Nitrogen Fixation and Soybean
  Genetics Laboratory
U.S. Department of Agriculture
Agricultural Research Service
Beltsville, MD 20705

John F. Kelly
Department of Horticulture
Michigan State University
E. Lansing, MI 48824

Gurdev S. Khush
International Rice Research In-
  stitute
P.O. Box 933
Manila, Philippines

David T. Kingsbury
National Science Foundation
1800 G St., N.W.
Washington, DC 20550

Bernard D. Knezek
Department of Crop and Soil Sci-
  ences
Michigan State University
E. Lansing, MI 48824

Marcos Kogan
Illinois Natural History Survey
607 E. Peabody
University of Illinois
Champaign, IL 61820

Richard Krasnow
National Center for Food and Ag-
  ricultural Policy
Resources for the Future
1616 P St., N.W.
Washington, DC 20036

Chun-Yen Kuo
South China Institute of Botany
Academia Sinica
Guangzhou, China

Alan N. Lakso
Department of Horticulture Sci-
  ence
New York State Agricultural Ex-
  periment Station
Geneva, NY 14456

Marvin R. Lamborg
Battelle-Kettering Laboratory
Yellow Springs, OH 45387

Philip J. Larkin
Division of Plant Industry
Commonwealth Scientific and In-
  dustrial Research Organization
Canberra, A.C.T. 2601, Australia

Andre Läuchli
Department of Land, Air and
  Water Resources
University of California
Davis, CA 95616

Homer M. LeBaron
Ciba-Geigy Corporation
P.O. Box 18300
Greensboro, NC 27419

Helene Hollander Lepkowski
1783 Ivy Oak Square
Reston, VA 22090

Wil Lepkowski
Chemical and Engineering News
1155 16th St., N.W.
Washington, DC 20036

C. S. Levings III
Department of Genetics
North Carolina State University
Raleigh, NC 27695-7614

William Liebhardt
Rodale Research Center
Box 323, RD 1
Kutztown, PA 19530

Sharon R. Long
Department of Biological Sciences
Stanford University
Stanford, CA 94305

Mervyn M. Ludlow
Commonwealth Scientific and In-
    dustrial Research Organization
Tropical Crops and Pastures
St. Lucia, Queensland 4067
Australia

David R. MacKenzie
Department of Plant Pathology
Louisiana State University
Baton Rouge, LA 70803

Taichi Maki
Smikoku National Agricultural
    Experiment Station
2575, Ikano, Zentsuji
Kagawa, 765, Japan

Iris F. Martin
U.S. Department of Agriculture
Competitive Grants Office
15th & Independence Ave., S.W.
Washington, DC 20251

Philip J. McCall
Agricultural Products Depart-
    ment
Dow Chemical Company
Midland, MI 48640

Robert E. McDowell
Department of Animal Science
Cornell University
Ithaca, NY 14853

John A. Menge
Department of Plant Pathology
University of California
Riverside, CA 92521

Carole P. Meredith
Department of Viticulture and
    Enology
University of California
Davis, CA 95616

Jerome P. Miksche
U.S. Department of Agriculture
Agricultural Research Service
BARC West Bldg., 005
Beltsville, MD 20705

James R. Miller
Department of Entomology and
    Pesticide Research Center
Michigan State University
E. Lansing, MI 48824

Roger L. Mitchell
2-69 Agriculture Hall
University of Missouri
Columbia, MO 65211

Norimoto Murai
Institute of Agrobiological Re-
    sources
Tsukuba Science City
Yatabe, Ibaraki 305, Japan

C. J. Nelson
Department of Agronomy
University of Missouri
Columbia, MO 65211

Donald R. Nielson
Department of Land, Air and
    Water Resources
University of California
Davis, CA 95616

Zerubabel M. Nyiira
International Centre of Insect
    Physiology and Ecology
P.O. Box 30772
Nairobi, Kenya

Paul F. O'Connell
U.S. Forest Service
Department of Agriculture
South Bldg., Room 3116
Washington, DC 20013

Kazutoshi Okuno
Field Crops Division
Hokuriku National Agriculture
    Experiment Station
Joetsu, Nigata, Japan

Deirdre O'Leary
Department of Horticulture
Michigan State University
E. Lansing, MI 48824

Donald R. Ort
Department of Plant Biology
U.S. Department of Agriculture
Agricultural Research Service
University of Illinois
Urbana, IL 61801

John W. Patrick
Department of Biological Science
University of Newcastle
Newcastle, 2308, Australia

Richard Patterson
North Carolina Biotechnology
    Center
P.O.B. 15347
Research Triangle Park
NC 27709

Eldor A. Paul
Department of Crop and Soil Sci-
    ences
Michigan State University
E. Lansing, MI 48824

Mary M. Peet
Department of Horticultural Sci-
    ence
North Carolina State University
Raleigh, NC 27695-7609

Nicanor Perlas
Foundation of Economic Trends
1346 Connecticut Ave., N.W.
Washington, DC 20036

Donald A. Phillips
Department of Agronomy
University of California
Davis, CA 95616

Steven Price
Standard Oil of Ohio
4440 Warrensville Center Rd.
Cleveland, OH 44128

Robert Rabson
Office of Basic Energy Science,
    ER-17
Department of Energy
Washington, DC 20545

Steven R. Radosevich
Department of Forest Science/
    Crop Science
Oregon State University
Corvallis, OR 97331

Roy S. Rauschkolb
Cooperative Extension
College of Agriculture
University of Arizona
Tucson, AZ 85721

James Rawson
Standard Oil of Ohio
4440 Warrensville Center Rd.
Cleveland, OH 44128

Robert H. Rennie
Exxon Chemical Canada
c/o Agriculture Canada
Lethbridge, Alberta
Canada T1J 4B1

Minocher Reporter
Battelle-Kettering Laboratory
Yellow Springs, OH 45387

Stanley K. Ries
Department of Horticulture
Michigan State University
E. Lansing, MI 48824-1311

Jeremy Rifkin
Foundation for Economic Trends
1346 Connecticut Ave., N.W.
Washington, DC 20036

William H. Riley
The Dow Chemical Co.
1701 Building
Midland, MI 48640

Joseph T. Ritchie
College of Agriculture and Natu-
ral Resources
Michigan State University
E. Lansing, MI 48824

Thomas Rosswall
Department of Water in Environ-
ment and Society
University of Linkoping
S-58183 Linkoping, Sweden

Richard T. Roush
Department of Entomology
Mississippi State University
Mississippi State, MS 39762

Albert D. Rovira
Division of Soils
Commonwealth Scientific and In-
dustrial Research Organization
Adelaide 5064, South Australia

Charles B. Rumburg
U.S. Department of Agriculture
Cooperative State Research Serv-
ice
15th & Independence Ave., S.W.
Washington, DC 20251

Vernon W. Ruttan
Department of Agriculture and
Applied Economics
University of Minnesota
St. Paul, MN 55108

S. Sadjad
Department of Agronomy
Bogor Agricultural University
Bogor, Indonesia

K. N. Saxena
International Centre of Insect
Physiology and Ecology
P.O. Box 30772
Nairobi, Kenya

A. H. Schauer
U.S. Department of Agriculture
Competitive Grant Office
15th & Independence Ave., S.W.
Washington, DC 20251

Lawrence E. Schrader
Department of Agronomy
University of Illinois
Urbana, IL 61801

Milton N. Schroth
Department of Plant Pathology
University of California
Berkeley, CA 94720

Tim L. Setter
Department of Agronomy
Cornell University
Ithaca, NY 14853

Michael C. Shannon
U.S. Department of Agriculture
Agricultural Research Service
U.S. Salinity Laboratory
4500 Glenwood Drive
Riverside, CA 92501

Qi-quan Shao
Institute of Genetics
Academia Sinica
Beijing, China

Ken C. Sink
Department of Horticulture
Michigan State University
E. Lansing, MI 48824

David A. Sleper
Department of Agronomy
University of Missouri
Columbia, MO 65211

Sarah E. Smith
Department of Agricultural Bio-
    chemistry
Waite Agricultural Research In-
    stitute
Glen Osmond, South Australia

Scott M. Smith
Department of Agronomy
University of Kentucky
Lexington, KY 40546

Alvin J.M. Smucker
Department of Crop and Soil Sci-
    ence
Michigan State University
E. Lansing, MI 48824

Sutat Sriwatanapongse
Department of Agronomy
Kasetsart University
Bangkok, Thailand

Gary Stacey
Department of Microbiology and
    Graduate Program of Ecology
University of Tennessee
Knoxville, TN 37996

Dale Stansbury
National Association of State
    Universities and Land Grant
    Colleges
One DuPont Circle
Washington, DC 20036

B. A. Stewart
U.S. Department of Agriculture
Agricultural Research Service
P.O. Drawer 10
Bushland, TX 79012

John A. Stewart
International Mineral and Chem-
    ical Corporation
421 E. Hawley
Mundelein, IL 60060

William A. Stiles, Jr.
2256 Rayburn House Office Bldg.
Washington, DC 20515

Deborah G. Strauss
Diversity
727 8th St., S.E.
Washington, DC 20003

Michael Strauss
Food and Renewable Resources
    Program
U.S. Congress Office of Technol-
    ogy Assessment
Washington, DC 20510

Norton D. Strommen
U.S. Department of Agriculture
South Agricultural Bldg.
Washington, DC 20250

Majorie Sun
Science
1333 H St., N.W.
Washington, DC 20005

Dwayne A. Suter
College of Agriculture
Texas A & M University
College Station, TX 77843

Laura Tangley
BioScience
730 11th St., N.W.
Washington, DC 20001

Ken L. Tanji
Department of Land, Air and
    Water Resources
University of California
Davis, CA 95616

Jack W. Tanner
Department of Crop Science
University of Guelph
Guelph, Ontario, Canada
NIG2W1

James E. Tavares
Board on Agriculture
National Research Council
2101 Constitution Ave., N.W.
Washington, DC 20418

Joseph Thomas
Molecular Biology and Agriculture Division
Bhabha Atomic Research Centre
Bombay 400 085, India

Richard J. Thomas
Hill Farming Research Organization
Bush Estate, Penicuik
Midlothian, EH 26 OPY
Scotland, United Kingdom

James Tiedje
Department of Crop and Soil Sciences
Michigan State University
E. Lansing, MI 49924

P. Bernard Tinker
Rothamsted Experiment Station
Harpenden Herts, AL5-25Q, 2JQ
England

N. Edward Tolbert
Department of Biochemistry
Michigan State University
E. Lansing, MI 48824

Greg Tolla
Campbell Institute for Research and Technology
Napoleon, OH 43545

Ann Tonjes
Agri-Energy Roundtable
2550 M St., N.W.
Washington, DC 20037

Neil C. Turner
Commonwealth Scientific and Industrial Research Organization
Private Bag, P.O.
Wembly, W.A., 6014, Australia

Goro Uehara
Department of Agronomy and Soil Science
University of Hawaii
Honolulu, HI 96822

William van B. Robertson
National Science Foundation
1800 G St., N.W.
Washington, DC 20550

Edwin H. Vause
Kettering Foundation
5335 Far Hills Ave.
Dayton, OH 45429

Bradleigh S. Vinson
Department of Entomology
Texas A&M University
College Station, TX 77843

Hans von Amsberg
BASF Wyandotte Corporation
100 Cherry Hill Rd.
Parsippany, NJ 07054

Regis D. Voss
Department of Agronomy
Iowa State University
Ames, IA 50011

Virginia Walbot
Department of Biological Science
Stanford University
Stanford, CA 94305

Robert L. Wample
Department of Horticulture and Landscape Architect
Washington State University
Pullman, WA 99164-6414

Robert D. Weaver
Department of Agricultural Economics
Pennsylvania State University
University Park, PA 16802

Irvin E. Widders
Department of Horticulture
Michigan State University
E. Lansing, MI 49924

Samuel C. Wiggans
U.S. Department of Agriculture
Cooperative State Research
  Service
15th & Independence Ave., S.W.
Washington, DC 20261

John Willard
BASF Wyandotte Corporation
100 Cherry Hill Rd.
Parsippany, NJ 07054

F. P. W. Winteringham
Darbod, Harlech
Gwynedd, LL46 2RA
  England

Sylvan H. Wittwer
Agricultural Experiment Station
Michigan State University
E. Lansing, MI 48824

John F. Witty
Department of Soil Microbiology
Rothamsted Experiment Station
Harpenden Herts, AL5-2JQ,
  England

Roger Wyse
Tissue Culture and Molecular Bi-
  ology Laboratory
U.S. Department of Agriculture
Agricultural Research Service
Beltsville, MD 20705

Olen C. Yoder
Department of Plant Pathology
Cornell University
Ithaca, NY 14853

Jeff Zinn
Congressional Research Service
Library of Congress
Washington, DC 20540